The Innkeepers'
REGISTER

Country Inns of 🏮 North America
1994

INDEPENDENT INNKEEPERS' ASSOCIATION
Marshall, Michigan
Founded in 1972 by Norman T. Simpson

ENDORSED PROVIDER PROGRAM

The Independent Innkeepers Association is developing an Endorsed Provider Program to serve both our member inns and their guests. Companies selected by the Association to be Endorsed Providers offer superior products that are important to innkeepers and their guests. In many cases, guests will be able to see and enjoy these products as part of their experience at Association inns. We also envision that the special relation between the Association and the Endorsed Provider will prove advantageous to our guests in their acquisition of these products for their homes.

The first Endorsed Provider selected by the Association is Thomasville Furniture Company for its Country Inns and Back Roads furniture collection. Many of the items in this collection are reproduced from originals in Association inns. An illustration of Thomasville's CIBR collection appears inside the front cover of the *Register*. For more information, please contact Country Inns and Back Roads Home Furnishings Collection, Route 202, Box 10, Hollicong, PA 18928. Telephone: 800-500-CIBR (2427)

Photo Credits:
G. E. Arnold
  Madewood Plantation House
Patricia Brabant
  Carter House, Carter Hotel, Eureka, CA
George W. Gardner; all © copyrighted
  Boulder Inn, The, New Preston, CT
  Glasbern, Fogelsville, PA
  Orchard Inn, The, Saluda, NC
  Sea Crest by the Sea, Spring Lake, NJ
  Settlers Inn, The, Hawley, PA
  White Inn, The, Fredonia, NY
  White Oak Inn, The, Danville, OH
Denny Goodman
  LaCorsette Maison Inn, Newton, IA
Stewart Hopkins
  Johnson House, The, Florence, OR
Bruce Muncy
  Oak Bed & Breakfast Inn, The, Christianburg, VA
M. P. Myers Photography, Cape May, NJ
  Mainstay, The, Cape May, NJ
  Manor House, The, Cape May, NJ
  Queen Victoria, The, Cape May, NJ
David Schwartz
  Bell Grae Inn, The, Staunton, VA
Mort Tucker Photography, Cleveland, Ohio
  Inn at Honey Run, The, Millersburg, OH

Cover Art by Maureen Reed
Cover Design by Judy Lenz
Commentary by Virginia Rowe

For further information, call Independent Innkeepers' Association,
800-344-5244
616-789-0393

Contents

INTRODUCTION

We are exceedingly proud to present to our inn-traveling guests this full color edition of *The Innkeepers' Register*. It was only six years ago that we printed our first *Register*, an off-shoot of Norman T. Simpson's well-read *Country Inns and Back Roads* travel book. During that time it has developed into a highly respected source for country inn accommodations across America as well as in Canada and Great Britain. This year, the addition of color enhances the images of the Inns providing a more pleasant experience for the traveler who is selecting that special destination.

Charles M. Dedman, President
Beaumont Inn, Harrodsburg, Kentucky

Norman D. Kinney,
Executive Director
Independent Innkeepers'
Association
Marshall, Michigan

As you peruse the information about the 286 Inns in this directory, we encourage you to take notice of the special "offerings" at the various places. Wonderful facilities for small-group meetings have been developed at some Inns. Special barrier-free and smoke-free accommodations are noted, and frequently, mention is made of area attractions and recreational facilities. The information in this guide is updated every year; we want you to know our latest and best.

Once again, we invite you to "spend a few days" when you can. Our inns are located in beautiful and interesting villages, towns, cities, and countrysides. Many offer gastronomic adventures and delights. And, most importantly, the innkeepers at IIA Inns are delighted to welcome you and assist in every way to make your stay pleasant and memorable. We like to brag that we are ". . . the best at what we do."

" . . . the best at what we do."

from our Mission Statement
INDEPENDENT INNKEEPERS' ASSOCIATION

PREFACE

*We are an association of independent innkeepers dedicated to
providing our guests with a unique hospitality experience by
being the best at what we do . . . individually and collectively.
Through mutual involvement, we work together to educate,
promote, and support each other in our continuing efforts to set
standards for our profession.* — IIA MISSION STATEMENT

These are the goals and objectives of the Independent Innkeepers'
Association, which has evolved from the tiny group gathered together in
1966 by Norman T. Simpson. Renowned as the "father of country inns," his
book, *Country Inns and Back Roads*, was the first of its kind in contemporary
times. He held informal dinners for the innkeepers who were featured in
the first early editions. Then, as the number of inns grew, it became clear
that country innkeepers felt isolated and out of contact with like-minded
people in the hospitality industry. Hotel and motel organizations offered
little of value to keepers of country inns. Their appreciation and need for
gathering together with other innkeepers was immediately obvious.

The opportunity to discuss mutual problems and find solutions, and
the discovery that their failures and triumphs were shared by others, gave
rise to the idea of a network of fine country inns in which was implicit the
sense of responsibility to each other and their shared values and standards
in serving the public.

At first there were annual meetings, which would take place at one or
another of the inns in this book. Then, the need for smaller, more focused
sessions resulted in several regional meetings in various parts of the
country throughout the year.

By 1972, Norman formally established this loose collection of inns as the
Independent Innkeepers' Association. The innkeepers in this group came
from all walks of life, many of them having left successful careers and
lucrative opportunities to experience the joys and tribulations of innkeeping. An important quality in each of them was not only a deep sense of
commitment to their inns, but also an enthusiasm and desire to be involved
with other innkeepers who shared their goals and standards and who
wanted to work together for the common good.

The feeling of fellowship and family is a strong bond rooted in the
shared purpose of maintaining what is finest and best in the true tradition
and spirit of American innkeeping.

Today, six years after Norman Simpson's death, the board of directors
and the membership are continuing and expanding the work he began. In
this ever-increasingly competitive arena, we will hold to the standards of
personal hospitality, which he defined and which are so important to us and
our many guests who look for both professional excellence and a genuine
feeling of friendly welcome.

Accreditation Program

In accordance with our stated purpose of maintaining the highest standards of innkeeping, the Independent Innkeepers' Association requires member participation in a quality assurance program. This program provides for mandatory periodic inspection of every inn by Quality Consultants, Inc., of Greenwich, Rhode Island, specialists who have been retained to give an impartial evaluation of each inn.

Staff members of Quality Consultants are personally trained to provide thorough, unbiased and honest evaluations and do so in an unobtrusive and timely manner. The evaluation visit is for two consecutive nights, whenever possible, to permit the evaluator to get a full picture of the operation of the inn. The visits, of course, are unannounced.

The evaluation begins with the first telephone call placed by the consultants who subsequently visit the facility and report on both the highlights of their stay and any areas which may be of concern. Only upon completion of the checkout procedure do they identify themselves and go over the rough draft of their findings. A formal typed report is mailed to the innkeeper and to the IIA office within 7 days of the visit.

Following are a few of the many issues on which member inns are rated:

Basic Requirements

Warm welcome by innkeepers or staff
Architecturally attractive facility
Buildings (inside & out) well maintained
Safety of guests insured (inside & out)
Sitting room for guests only
Impeccable housekeeping throughout inn
A pleasant dining experience or fine dining available nearby
Excellent lighting in guest rooms
Bathrooms well furnished with large, quality towels and adequate shelf space, clothes hooks, etc.

Special Or Personal Touches

Fresh cut flowers or well-tended houseplants
Soft music in dining and common rooms
Quality paintings, artwork, artifacts or memorabilia
Historical references or other material of interest
Comfortable, well-maintained outdoor seating
Books, area maps, magazines, games, bulletin boards and various other materials for guests' amusement
Quality amenities, refreshments

Another important and valuable adjunct to our accreditation program involves our encouragement of guest evaluations, through card inserts in the back of our book. We are interested in hearing from our guests and will appreciate receiving evaluations of the IIA inns you have visited.

The IIA continues to work with members to support and encourage them in improving their properties and maintaining the high standards which make our members the leaders in their field.

Some Criteria For Membership In The IIA

These are a few of the criteria used in evaluating the eligibility of an inn for membership in the IIA. Other more stringent criteria are also used; however, these are the most basic requirements.

- Inn is owner-operated or the innkeeper/manager is highly committed to the spirit of personal hospitality. Staff shows genuine interest toward guests.

- The innkeeper has owned/run the inn for a minimum of three years, or, if from a background of successful innkeeping, two years.

- Inn building is architecturally interesting and attractive with appropriately groomed grounds, tasteful, comfortable and inviting interior furnishings and at least one common room for houseguests only. Guest rooms are attractively and completely furnished for comfort of guests.

- Housekeeping and maintenance is excellent, with immaculate guest rooms and bathrooms.

- Breakfast and dinner should be a pleasant eating experience. If the evening meal is not provided on the premises, fine dining must be readily available in the immediate area (preferably within walking distance).

The IIA Gift Certificate

A Lovely Gift for Someone Special

The gift of an overnight stay or a weekend at a country inn can be one of the most thoughtful and appreciated gifts you can give your parents or children, dear friends, or valued employees for Christmas, a birthday, an anniversary, or any special occasion. Innkeepers and other employers are discovering this is an excellent way of rewarding their employees, while at the same time giving them some much needed rest and relaxation.

An IIA gift certificate means that you can give the gift of a stay at any one of over 250 member inns from Kennebunkport, Maine to Southern California; from Quebec, Canada to Key West, Florida; from Martha's Vineyard, Massachusetts to Seaview, Washington. We have inns in the Blue Ridge Mountains, on ranches in the western desert, near state parks and forests and nature preserves, in restored villages in historic districts, on lakes and by the sea. Choose your pleasure.

An IIA gift certificate is good for two years and may be purchased through the IIA office by personal check or Mastercard or Visa. With each gift certificate we send along a brand new copy of the *Innkeepers' Register*. For further information call **800-344-5244**.

A five dollar ($5) postage and handling fee will be added to all gift certificate purchases.

WHAT IS A COUNTRY INN?

When Norman Simpson first began writing about country inns, he was often asked to explain the term, and at first his answer would be, "a country inn is an inn in the country." Although all country inns were not then (or now) in the country, he felt that the word "country" was still operative. He said, "country implies an escape from urban pressures and demands, and not only conjures up euphoric bucolia but a welcome innocence associated with the American past. In many ways country inns are personified by some 19th-century attitudes concerning reliability, sincerity, warmheartedness, and a genuine desire to be of service. Each inn is original and unique, reflecting not only the old-time American ideal of rugged individualism, but also the personalities and tastes of the innkeeper-owners, who are more than likely on hand to make their guests feel personally welcome, comfortable, and at ease."

Although there were a number of specifics Norman looked for in an inn, his "bottom line" was always the people who ran it. One of his favorite expressions in referring to country inns was "personal hospitality," meaning the strong feeling of involvement and commitment on the part of the innkeeper, and a hospitable friendliness that came out of a genuine liking for people.

Among his personal set of requirements, beyond cleanliness, good housekeeping, maintenance, attractive furnishings with individuality, excellent service, and good food, were the little indications that the comfort and needs of the guests were being met: adequate lighting and an extra pillow for reading in bed, interesting reading material in guest rooms, generous-sized, thick towels, adequate shelf space in the bathroom, and all the special and personal touches, such as plantings, fresh flowers, music, paintings and artwork, and various and sundry articles of interest, that create the feeling of a "home away from home." He approved of the quiet afforded by the absence of television and telephones in guest rooms. He expected an inn to have at least one hospitable parlor or sitting room where guests could meet and talk in a convivial atmosphere.

He had a strong conviction that anything of a business or commercial nature should be kept to a bare minimum, and above all, the real thing, as opposed to the ersatz, should be used in furnishings as well as foods. If reproductions of antique furniture were used, they should be excellent reproductions, and if, God forbid, anything plastic was discovered, it had better be virtually invisible and of superior quality. Food should be fresh and made from scratch.

He felt that country inns should reflect their regions, and he was particularly happy when he found an inn that was rooted in its community with all the local color and flavor of the area.

A convivial place to meet new people, to have good conversation, to make friends, to relax or to be active — ultimately, to feel "at home." For Norman Simpson, these were the attributes of a good country inn.

by Virginia Rowe

HOSTING YOUR SMALL GROUP

Meeting planners responsible for arranging and hosting small meetings and conferences have found that many country inns offer a new and exciting opportunity. The traditional impersonal and somewhat sterile atmosphere of many larger Conference Centers has forced the astute planner to turn to the many pleasantries found at country inns. Usually, the size of the facility ensures privacy and personal hospitality. Many larger Conference Centers must book several groups at a time to efficiently utilize their facility. Small group meetings, on the other hand, are frequently the only guests enjoying the comfortable, nicely appointed ambiance of a country inn facility.

State of the art audio-visual and facsimile equipment is now commonplace in meeting rooms at IIA inns. The only thing missing is the often exorbitant surcharge assessed for this equipment by larger establishments. Innkeepers happily work with meeting planners to arrange local entertainment and visits to special area attractions as well as fitness and exercising opportunities for their conferee-guests. A small group meeting and personalized hospitality are a natural combination at country inns.

Food service for small group meetings is another natural for innkeepers and their chefs. The usual non-commercial orientation of inn kitchens ensures specialized menus and many "from scratch" dishes to please the appetites of business people after a full schedule of meetings. Innkeepers often tell of conferees who make arrangements to return to the inn with friends for a non-meeting visit because they wanted to share their special gastronomic discoveries.

This *1994 Innkeepers' Register* includes information about the conference facilities available at each inn. A phone call to the inn can quickly provide answers to your specific questions and access to brochures and conference information packets. As astute meeting planners have found, personal contact with an IIA innkeeper can take the work and worry out of planning meetings.

KEY TO SYMBOLS

	ENGLISH	FRENCH	GERMAN	JAPANESE	SPANISH
	number of rooms; rates and rate plan for 2 people number of suites; rates and rate plan for 2 people credit cards accepted	nombre de chambres, les prix pour deux personnes, plan de repas; nombre d'apparte-ments, les prix pour deux personnes, plan de repas les cartes de crédit acceptées	Anzahl der Zimmers; Tarif-und Tarifplan Anzahl der Zimmerflüchte; Tarif-und Tarifplan Kreditkarten angenommen	部屋数：宿泊料金と料金別プラン スイート数：宿泊料金と料金別プラン クレジットカード通用	número de habitaciones; tarifas y tablas de tarifas para dos personas número de apartamentos; tarifas y tablas de tarifas para dos personas tarjetas de crédito que aceptamos
	baths—private/shared	salle de bains et WC privés ou communs	Bäder privat/geteilt	バス付／共同バス	habitaciones con baño / sin baño
	open/close	période de fermeture ou ouverture	offen: geschlossen	営業中／休業ーシーズン	temporado—fecha en que se abre / fecha en que se cierra
	children and pets acceptability, inquire for rates	les enfants admis? chiens admis? renseignez-vous sur les tarifs	Kinder und Haustiere erlaubt; nach Tarifen erkundigen	子供とペット可、別料金	reglamentos para niños y animales domésticos (pídase tarifas)
	recreation and attractions on premises or in area	les sports et les divertissements à l'hôtel ou l'environs	Erhohlung und Sehenswürdigkeiten; an Ort und Stelle oder in der Gegend	当地のレクレーション・催し物	atracciones y diversiones / en los terrenos o cercanos
	meals available; wine & liquor available	repas offerts et bar sur place	Speise und Spirituosen erhältlich	食事と飲食可	comida y licores en venta / no se venden
	smoking acceptability	zone fumeur ou non fumeur	Rauchen erlaubt/ begrenzt/verboten	喫煙可	se puede fumar / no se puede fumar
	special features, i.e., wheelchair access; conference facilities	accés pour fauteuil roulant; capacité pour séminaires	Sondermerkungen; Rollstuhl Zugang, z.B. Konferenzräume	特別施設　会議室車イス出入口	a notar: acceso para sillas de ruedas, facilidades para conferencias
MAP	Modified American Plan	Breakfast & dinner included in rate demi-pension Frühstück und Abendessen im Preis einbegriffen 特別アメリカプランー朝・夕食付 la tarifa incluye cena y desayuno			
AP	American Plan	3 meals included in rate pension complète (3) drei Mahlzeiten im Preis inbegriffen アメリカプランー3食付 la tarifa comprende desayuno, almuerzo y cena			
EP	European Plan	no meals included in rate les repas ne sont pas compris Keine Mahlzeiten im Preis inbegriffen ヨーロッパプランー食事なし la tarifa no incluye comida alguna			
B&B	Bed & Breakfast	Breakfast included in rate le petit déjeuner est compris Frühstück einbegriffen 朝食付 la tarifa incluye el desayuno			

RESERVATION AND RATE INFORMATION

Rates listed herein represent a general range of rates for two people for one night at each inn, and should not be considered firm quotations. The rates cover both high and low seasons; tax and gratuities are usually not included. It is well to inquire as to the availability of various special plans and packages. Please be aware that reservation and cancellation policies vary from inn to inn. Listed recreation and attractions are either on the premises or nearby. For more detailed information, ask for inn brochure.

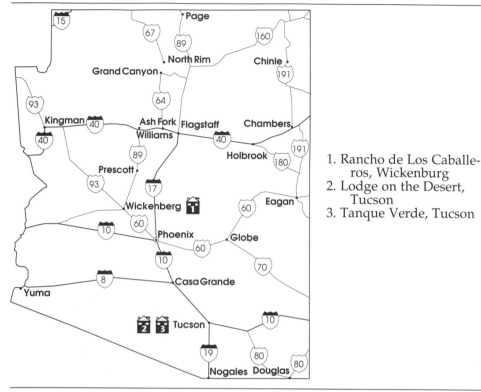

1. Rancho de Los Caballe-
   ros, Wickenburg
2. Lodge on the Desert,
   Tucson
3. Tanque Verde, Tucson

THE LODGE ON THE DESERT

33 Rooms, $56/$131 B&B
7 Suites $70/$175 B&B

Visa, MC, Amex, Diners,
CB, Discov.

All Private Baths

Open year-round
Children Welcome
Pets by prior arrange-
ment

Heated Swimming Pool,
Croquet, Golf, Tennis,
Racquet ball, Shuffle-
board, Ping-pong

Continental Breakfast,
Lunch, Dinner; AP &
MAP available 11/1-6/1
Wine & Liquor available
Smoking accepted

Conference Facilities (40)
Wheelchair Access
(7 Rooms)

The feeling of old Mexico and of the Southwest is everywhere in the adobe-colored casas grouped around intimate patios at this Mexican hacienda-style resort-inn. Magnificent mountain and desert views, spacious lawns, and colorful gardens belie the proximity of fine residences and nearby downtown Tucson, with all its cultural and recreational attractions.

From I-10 take Speedway exit, 5 mi.
(E) to R. turn (S) at Alvernon Way. .8
mi. to Lodge on L. bet. 5th & Broad-
way.
**TEL 602-325-3366 or 800-
456-5634; FAX 602-327-5834**
306 N. Alvernon Way,
P.O. Box 42500
Tucson, AZ 85733
Schuyler & Helen
Lininger, Innkeepers

RANCHO DE LOS CABALLEROS

🛏	73 Rooms, $228/$264 AP 12 Suites, $276/$336 AP
💳	No Credit Cards
🛁	All Private Baths
🏨	Open 1 Oct. to 30 May
🐎	Children Welcome No Pets
🏇	18 Hole Golf, Riding, Tennis, Heated Pool, Skeet & Trap Shooting, Cookouts, Sq. Dancing
🍽	All Meals AP Wine & Liquor Available
🚭	No smoking in dining room
🏛	Conference Facilities (275)
♿	Wheelchair Access

From Phoenix take I-17 north 29 m. to 74 (Carefree Hwy). Take 74 west 30 m. to 60. Turn right on 60 and go northwest 12 m. through Wickenburg to 2nd stop light (Vulture Mine Rd.). Go south 1 1/2 miles.

TEL. 602-684-5484
FAX. 602-684-2267
1551 S. Vulture Mine Rd.
Wickenburg, AZ 85390

D. C. Gant, Jr., Innkeeper

A green jewel in the desert, with an 18-hole championship golf course, tennis courts, trail rides and other planned activities for adults and children, this rambling ranch-resort has been run by the same family since its inception in 1948. Individual bungalows and terraces, poolside buffet lunches, and evening cookouts brighten winter vacations.

TANQUE VERDE RANCH

🛏	50 Rooms, $200/$320 AP 15 Suites, $250/$360 AP
💳	Visa, MC, Amex, Discov
🛁	All Private Baths
🏨	Open Year-round
🐎	Children Welcome; No Pets
🏇	Horseback Riding, Tennis, Spa, Hiking; all programs and activities in American Plan rates
🍽	All Meals AP (including activities) Wine & Liquor Available
🚬	Smoking Accepted
🏛	Conference Facilities (120)
♿	Wheelchair Access (56 Rooms)

In Tucson, take Speedway Blvd. (E) to dead end at ranch.

TEL. 602-296-6275
14301 E. Speedway Blvd.,
Tucson, AZ 85748

Robert Cote, Innkeeper

In a spectacular setting of desert and mountains, this 125-year-old ranch evokes the spirit of the Old West. Horseback riding, guided nature hikes, bird study programs, as well as a modern health spa, tennis, indoor and outdoor pools, selective menus, and a casual, relaxed atmosphere mean good times for lucky guests. It has a 4-star rating by Mobil.

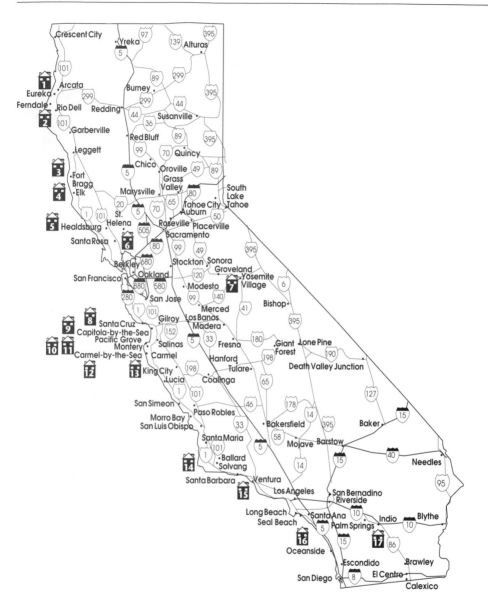

1. Carter House, Eureka
2. The Gingerbread Mansion, Ferndale
3. Grey Whale Inn, Fort Bragg
4. Harbor House Inn by the Sea, Elk
5. Madrona Manor, Healdsburg
6. Wine Country Inn, St. Helena
7. Groveland Hotel, Groveland
8. The Babbling Brook, Santa Cruz
9. The Inn at Depot Hill, Capitola-by-the-Sea
10. The Martine Inn, Pacific Grove
11. Old Monterey Inn, Monterey
12. Sandpiper Inn at-the-Beach, Carmel-by-the-Sea
13. Vagabond's House, Carmel
14. Ballard Inn, Ballard
15. Simpson House, Santa Barbara
16. Seal Beach Inn and Gardens, Seal Beach
17. Villa Royale Inn, Palm Springs

THE BABBLING BROOK

12 Rooms, $85/$150 B&B
Visa, MC, Amex, Carte Bl, Discov, Diners

All Private Baths; 4 Jet Baths (2 are enlarged baths for 2)

Open Year-round

Children, with restrictions; No Pets in rooms

Golf, Tennis, Jogging, Beaches, Hiking, Bike Trails, Surfing, Sailing, Boardwalk, Fishing, Antiques, Artist's Studios, Theater, Narrow-gauge Railroad

Full Breakfast, Afternoon Tea, Mrs King's Cookies, Wine & Cheese Evenings

Smoking Outside

Conf. Facilities (12-15)

Wheelchair Access

From Hwy. 17 take Half Moon Bay exit to Hwy. 1 (N). Continue on Mission St. to L. on Laurel at signal, 1 1/2 blks. down hill on R. From (S) on Hwy 1, turn L. on Laurel, 1 1/2 blks. on R. From (N) on Hwy. 1 turn R. on Laurel St.

TEL. 408-427-2437; 800-866-1131; FAX 408-427-2457

1025 Laurel St
Santa Cruz, CA 95060
Helen King, Innkeeper

Historic waterwheel, falls and brook in an acre of redwoods and pines surround this secluded inn. Built in 1909 on the foundation of a 1790 gristmill and 2000-year-old Indian fishing village, it's on the National Register of Historic Places. Rooms in French decor with four jet bathtubs, private entrances, decks overlooking the gardens, most have fireplaces. Gazebo is popular for weddings. Top Inn Award, *Country-Inn Magazine*, 1994.

BALLARD INN

15 Rooms, $160/$195 B&B

Visa, MC, Amex

All private baths

All Year except Christmas

No Pets, Well-behaved Parents with Children

Wineries, Golf, Art Galleries, Biking, Hiking, Shopping, Antiques, Glider Rides, Horseback Riding, Horse Ranches

Full cooked to order breakfast; Evening of world class local wines and hors d' ouevres

No Smoking

Conference Facilities (30)

Wheelchair Access (1 rm., dining rm. & conf. fac.)

From Highway 101, take Solvang Exit. Follow Route 246 E. through Solvang to Alamo Pintado Road; turn left. Drive 3 miles to Baseline Ave., turn right and Inn is 50 yards on the right.

TEL. 805-688-7770,
1-800-638-2466

FAX 805-688-9560

2436 Baseline Ave
Ballard, CA 93463
Kelly Robinson, Innkeeper

Comfortably elegant accommodations in the heart of the Santa Barbara wine country. Just 40 minutes from Santa Barbara, yet nestled in a country neighborhood of orchards and vineyards, the Ballard Inn offers an intimate retreat. Each of the 15 guest rooms possesses its own special charm and character reflecting local history. All feature individual controlled heating and air conditioning, as well as private baths.

CALIFORNIA
CARTER HOUSE/HOTEL CARTER

🛏	20 Rooms, $95/$155 B&B 11 Suites $145/$255 B&B
💳	Visa, MC, Amex, Discover
🛁	All Private Baths; 16 Jacuzzis
🏮	Open Year-round
🐾	No Pets/Children Appropriate
☀	Redwood Forests, Isolated Beaches, Unique Shopping, Galleries, Theater
☕	4-course Breakfast; Dinner Wine & Cordials available
🚬	Smoking in Restricted Areas
🏨	Conference Facilities (20)
♿	Wheelchair Access (24 Rms., dining rm. & conf. fac.))

🏠 A remarkably detailed re-creation of an 1884 San Francisco mansion, the inn sits at the gateway to Eureka's historic district. It offers guests exquisite decor, unrivaled hospitality, and what has been called "the best breakfast in California." Hotel Carter next door, another marvelous replica, offers more rooms, a fine restaurant, and conference facilities. The recently restored "Belle House" next to the Inn has three suites with jacuzzi and fireplaces, cable TV, VCRs, and a large common kitchen perfect for groups.

From Hwy. 101 (N) (5th St.) turn L. on "L" St. From Hwy. 101 (S) (4th St.) turn R. on "L" St. Inn is at 3rd & "L" Sts.

TEL. 707-444-8062
800-404-1390
FAX. 707-444-8062
301 L. Street
Eureka, CA 95501

Mark & Christi Carter,
Innkeepers

THE GINGERBREAD MANSION

🛏	5 Rooms, $90/$145 B&B 4 Suites, $120/$185 B&B
💳	Visa, MC, Amex
🛁	All Private Baths
🏮	Open Year-round
🐾	Appropriate for Children over 10; No Pets
☀	Games, Library, Bicycles, English Garden, Redwood Parks, Beach, Fishing, Galleries, Unique Shops
☕	Breakfast, Afternoon Tea with homemade cookies, cakes, candies, and bars
🚬	No Smoking
🏨	
♿	

🏠 Exquisitely turreted and gabled, the Gingerbread Mansion Inn is truly a visual masterpiece. Located in the Victorian village of Ferndale, the inn is surrounded by lush English gardens. The nine romantic guest rooms all offer private baths; some have old-fashioned tubs and fireplaces, for fireside bubble baths. Amenities include a morning tray service, full breakfast, afternoon tea, turn-down service with bedside chocolates, bathrobes, and use of the garden and bicycles.

Hwy. 101, 15 mi. south of Eureka, take Ferndale exit. Continue over bridge 5 mi. to Main St. Turn L. at Bank of America bldg. Go 1 block.

TEL. 707-786-4000
400 Berding St.,
P.O. Box 40
Ferndale, CA 95536-0040

Ken Torbert, Innkeeper

GREY WHALE INN

14 Rooms $80/$160 B&B
Off seas. 20% less Su.-Th.

Visa, MC, Discov,
Enroute, Amex, JCB

All Private Baths; 1 Jacuzzi

Open Year-round

Appropriate for Children
over 12; No Pets

TV theater with VCR, rec.
room with pool table,
fishing, hiking, whale-
watching. Phones in rms.

Buffet Breakfast
Complimentary spar-
kling beverages for spe-
cial occasions

Non-smoking inn

Conference Facilities (34)

Hwy. 101 to Cloverdale, then Hwy.
128 W. to Hwy. 1. Continue (N) to
Fort Bragg (3 1/2 hrs. from S.F.). Or
Hwy. 1 along the coast (5 hrs. from
S.F.)
TEL. 707-964-0640
FAX 707-964-4408
Res. 800-382-7244
615 No. Main Street
Fort Bragg, CA 95437
John & Colette Bailey, Innkps.

Mendocino Coast landmark since 1915, and Fort Bragg's premier Bed & Breakfast Inn. Classic revival architecture. Spacious comfort and the utmost in privacy. Ocean, garden or hill views; fireplaces, decks, Jacuzzi. Decor varies: French floral countryside, Traditional elegance, American country comfort, Romantic hideaway. Lavish breakfast buffet includes hot entree, prize-winning coffee cake, fresh fruit. Stroll to ocean, restaurants, shops, galleries, theatre, and Skunk Train. AAA and Mobil approved accommodations.

GROVELAND HOTEL

14 Rooms, $75/$95 B&B
3 Suites, $155 B&B

Visa, MC, Amex, CB, DC,
DISC

All Private Baths

Year-round

Children OK; Pets by
Arrangement
Yosemite National Park (23
m.), Golf, Tennis, Hiking,
Fishing, Swimming, (Lake
w/ 3 beaches), Pool,
World-class White Water
Rafting
Full Breakfast, Afternoon
Tea, Wine, Gourmet Res-
taurant
No Smoking

Conference Facilities (25)

Wheelchair Access (6 rms
and dining rm)

From Bay Area 3 hours, 680 to 580 to
120 at Tracy. From Sacramento 2
hours, 99 to 120 at Manteca. Hotel is
located on 120 (Main St. in Groveland).
TEL 209-962-4000;
800-273-3314
FAX 209-962-6674
18767 Main Street
PO Box 481
Groveland, California 95321
Peggy A. Mosley, Innkeeper

The 1849 Adobe and 1914 Queen Anne buildings offer 14 rooms and 3 suites with European antiques, terry robes, down comforters, upscale linens and private baths. Some have private entrances to the verandas where white wicker abounds. Suites have separate sitting rooms, fireplaces, and spa tubs. The parlour has books, games, a fireplace, and television.

21

CALIFORNIA
HARBOR HOUSE INN BY THE SEA

	10 Rooms, 4 of which are cottages, $140/$255 MAP
	No Credit Cards
	All Private Baths
	Open Year-round
	Children over 12 No Pets
R	Private beach, Kayaking, Wineries, Galleries, Golf, Riding
	Breakfast & Dinner Wine & Beer available
	Smoking in garden and decks only

Harbor House, on the outskirts of the quiet, rural village of Elk on the spectacular Mendocino Coast, is a unique sanctuary—a memorable lodging and dining experience. Dramatic ocean views, where massive rocks jut from the sea, benches along a winding wildflower-edged path down to a private beach, quiet moments for solitude and reflection—all of this and more at this gracious inn, built entirely of virgin redwood.

From S.F., 3 hrs. (N) on Hwy. 101. In Cloverdale take Hwy. 128 (W) to Hwy. 1 (S) 5 mi. to Elk.

TEL. 707-877-3203
Box 369
5600 S. Highway One
Elk, CA 95432

Dean & Helen Turner,
Innkeepers

THE INN AT DEPOT HILL

	4 Rooms, $165/$195 B&B 4 Suites, $195/$250 B&B
	Visa, MC, Amex
	All Private Baths, 4 Hot Tubs
	Open Year-round No Pets
	Walk to Beach, Esplanade, Wharf, Water Sports, 14 Restaurants, Shops, World-famous
R	Golf. Wineries, Tennis, Redwoods, S. Cruz Boardwalk, Steam R.R.
	Full Breakfast, Afternoon Tea or Wine, & Hors d'oeuvres, After Dinner Dessert
	Smoking On Private Patios Only
	Conference Facilities (16)
	Wheelchair Access (1 rm., dining rm. & conf. fac.)

Near a sandy beach in a quaint, Mediterranean-style resort, this award-winning inn was named 1 of top 10 inns in the country. A decorator's delight, upscale rooms resemble different parts of the world. All rooms have fireplaces, TV/VCR, stereo systems, phones, modems, robes, featherbeds, and flowers. Most have private hot tubs in private garden patios. Mobil 4 Stars!

From 1 take Park Ave. exit turning towards the ocean for 1 mile. Left on Monterey Ave. and immediately left into our driveway. Look for white columns and international flags.

TEL. (408) 462-3376
800-572-2632
FAX (408) 462-3697
250 Monterey Ave.
Capitola-by-the-Sea, CA 95010
Suzie Lankes, Innkeeper

MADRONA MANOR

	18 Rooms, $135/$185 B&B 3 Suites, $185/$225 B&B
	Visa, MC, Amex, Discov
	All Private Baths
	Open Year-round
	Children accepted Leashed Dogs, outer bldgs.
	Swimming pool on site, Tennis, Golf, Wine tast- ing, Canoeing, Balloon Rides nearby
	B&B Sun.-Thurs., Full Breakfast; Dinner & Sun. brunch; Wine & Beer available
	Smoking in restricted areas
	Conference Facilities (40)
	Wheelchair Access (1 rm., dining rm. & conf. fac.)

Rte. 101 (N) to Central Healdsburg
exit. At 3-way light, sharp L. on Mill
St., 3/4 mi. to arch.
TEL. 707-433-4231
FAX 707-433-0703
800-258-4003
101 Westside Rd.
Healdsburg, CA 95448
John & Carol Muir
Innkeepers

This majestic Victorian manor, on the National Register of Historic Places, conveys a sense of homey elegance and gracious hospitality. Guests enjoy thick terry robes, unique and tantalizing cuisine, beautiful mountain views and surrounding Sonoma wine country. Beautiful grounds, eight acres. A new suite, with fireplace & sitting room, boasts a king bed, deck, marble bath and jacuzzi. Internationally acclaimed restaurant serves superb dinners by candlelight. Gold medal wine list. We keep getting better!

THE WONDERFUL WORLD OF COUNTRY INN COOKERY

Just as every country inn has its own individual style in furnishings and decoration, so, too, is its cuisine different and distinctive from every other inn. There are those who adhere to the principle that simple, wholesome, home-cooked, family-style meals, probably with a definite regional flavor, are the best. Others offer more sophisticated French, European, or even exotic ethnic cuisine choices. Nowhere will you find standardized hotel food.

The cook might be the innkeeper himself or herself, who also might be a graduate of the Cordon Bleu or the Culinary Institute of America—or just a naturally great cook. Some innkeepers are master chefs. Some inns hire well-known chefs, who give a special patina to their culinary presentations.

Dining rooms are usually arranged restaurant-style with small tables, but there are still a few places where meals are served family-style and guests sit together at a large table where everyone joins in the conversation. Sometimes meals are served on porches or terraces with lovely views, or in courtyards, patios, and gardens.

With the growing interest in wines, more inns are widening their selection and can boast extensive cellars of fine wines. Bed and breakfast inns often offer complimentary before-dinner wines and other refreshments, while some full-service inns follow the custom of having a get-acquainted cocktail hour before serving dinner.

Afternoon teas and Sunday brunches are opportunities to display all sorts of marvelous pastries and wonderful specialties and are usually served to the public as well as houseguests.

Vegetable and herb gardens are an integral part of a number of inns, which take great pride in the freshness and flavor of their produce. And nothing could be fresher for a guest than the fish he caught that afternoon and had cooked for his dinner that night—which is possible to do at a few inns.

(For a sampling of the kind of food you might find at a country inn, see page 55.)
— **by Virginia Rowe**

CALIFORNIA
THE MARTINE INN

	19 Rooms, $125/$230 B&B 3 Suites, $250/$280 B&B
	Visa, MC, Amex
	All Private Baths
	Open Year-round
	Children OK; No Pets
	Spa, Pool Table, Vintage Art Collection, Fishing, Hiking, Bike Riding, Bird & Otter Watching, Roller Blading, Shopping, Sightseeing, Monterey Bay Aquarium
	Breakfast, Wine available, Lunch & Dinner for groups only
	Smoking Restrictions
	Conference Facilities (20)
	Wheelchair Access (1 rm., dining rm. & conf. rm.)

Come relax & enjoy breathtaking views of the Monterey Bay where seals, otters, and whales can be seen while staying at this romantic cliffside mansion. Your room may have a view of the crashing surf or a woodburning fireplace to snuggle up to that special person. Awake to a sumptuous breakfast awaiting you in the parlor.

Hwy. 1 to Hwy. 68 (Forest Ave.) to Pacific Grove. R on Ocean View Blvd. (15 blocks). Inn On right.
TEL. 408-373-3388
or 800-852-5588
FAX: 408-373-3896
255 Oceanview Blvd.
Pacific Grove, CA 93950
Marion & Don Martine & Tracy Harris, Innkeepers

OLD MONTEREY INN

	8 Rooms, $170/$240 B&B 2 Suites, $240 B&B
	Visa, MC
	All Private Baths
	Closed Dec. 24-25
	No Pets; not suitable for small children
	Golf, Tennis, Horseback Riding, Beach Activities, Bicycling, Monterey Bay Aquarium, Carmel, Big Sur coast near by
	Breakfast, Champagne
	Smoking Restrictions

Surrounded by over an acre of English gardens, Old Monterey Inn offers an exclusive retreat hidden among the trees in the heart of Monterey. This award winning 1929 Tudor mansion, furnished with antiques, has all the modern comforts—private baths with amenities, comfortable sitting areas, wood burning fireplaces, jacuzzi, gourmet breakfasts and hors d'oeuvres, full concierge service for restaurant reservations, golf, tennis, bay cruises, historical tours and tickets to the Monterey Bay Aquarium.

From Hwy 1 take Munras Ave. exit. Make an immediate left to Soledad Dr. then right on Pacific St. Proceed 1/2 a mile to Martin St. on your left.
408-375-8284
1-800-350-2344
FAX 408-375-6730
500 Martin St.
Monterey, CA 93940
Ann & Gene Swett, Innkeepers

24

SANDPIPER INN AT-THE-BEACH

16 Rooms, $79/$180 B&B

Visa, MC, Amex

All Private Baths

Open Year-around

Appropriate for Children Over 12; No Pets

Pebble Beach golf, Tennis, Point Lobos St. Park, 17-Mile Drive, Fine Dining, Boutiques, Galleries, Big Sur, Monterey Bay Aquarium Packages.

Breakfast, Complimentary beverage, Continental Breakfast, Buffet, Afternoon Refreshments

Smoking in restricted areas

Conference Facilities (15)

Hwy. 1, R. at Ocean Ave. (W) thru Carmel 1 mi. L. at Scenic Rd. (S) .8 mi. to end of beach at Martin Way (S).

**TEL. 408-624-6433;
800-633-6433**
FAX 408-624-5964
2408 Bay View Ave.
Carmel by-the-sea, CA 93923

Graeme & Irene Mackenzie
Innkeepers

Only 60 yds. from Carmel's white beach, with unique ocean views across the bay to Pebble Beach. Early California architecture is complemented by country antiques, gardens & patio. Comfortable lounge has a cathedral ceiling & fireplace. Rooms are individually decorated, some with fireplaces. A romantic getaway in a beautiful, quiet residential area with warm, restful ambiance.

THE SEAL BEACH INN AND GARDENS

10 Rooms, $118/$155 B&B
13 Suites, $185/$255 B&B

Visa, MC, Amex, Diners, Discovery, JCB

All Private Baths, Jacuzzis, Fireplaces

Open Year-round

No Pets, Well-behaved children accepted

Beach, Beach Sports, Sailing, Surfing, Wind Surfing, Scuba, Jet Ski, Water Ski, Boating, Onsite Swimming Pool, Golf, Tennis, Racquetball, Handball Nearby

Breakfast, Evening Social Hour, Catered Meals by request, Liquor nearby

No Smoking Inside

Conference Facilities (24)

Wheelchair Access (dining rm and conf fac.)

Hwy. 405 Fwy., Seal Beach Blvd. exit, turn L. for 2.7 mi. R. on Pacific Coast Hwy. for .7 mi. L. on 5th St.

TEL. 310-493-2416; 800-HIDE-AWAY (Reservations only)
FAX 310-799-0483
212 5th Street
Seal Beach, CA 90740

Marjorie Bettenhausen Schmaehl & Harty Schmaehl, Innkeepers

The Seal Beach Inn and Gardens is an elegant, historic inn one block from the Pacific Ocean. The Inn sits in lavish colorful flowering gardens in a charming urban seaside village setting. Exquisitely detailed rooms and suites, library, tea room, pool, and accommodations artfully provide a soothing welcome and capture this area's culture and history. Our caring staff look forward to serving you in the Old World tradition of warmth and hospitality.

CALIFORNIA
SIMPSON HOUSE

🛏	7 Rooms, $90/$175 B&B 4 Suites, 3 Cottages, $150/$275 B&B
💳	Visa, MC, Amex, Disc
🛁	All Private Baths
🌳	Open Year-round
🐩	No pets and no facilities for children
🎯	Lawn Croquet, Bicycles, Picnic Baskets, Beach Equipment
🍷	Breakfast, Wine & Liquor Available
🚭	Smoking Restrictions
⊢⊞⊣	Conference Facilities (20–25)
♿	Wheelchair Access (1 rm., dining rm. and conf. fac.)

🏠 Awarded Grand Hotels Award by travel writers and editors—best bed and breakfast in Southern California. The 1874 Victorian, historic landmark estate, secluded in an acre of beautiful English gardens, is elegantly decorated with European antiques, oriental carpets, and fine art. Guest rooms with handprinted Victorian reproduction papers, luxurious suites, and private cottages. Seclusion and luxury within walking distance to downtown.

From north on 101, exit on Mission St, go left, at Anacapa St right and at Arrellaga St left. From south on 101, exit Laguna-Garden St. Right on Garden St., at Gutierrez St. left, then right on S. Barbara St. At Arrellaga St. left.
TEL 805-963-7067; 1-800-676-1280; FAX 805-564-4811
121 East Arrellaga St.
Santa Barbara, CA 93101
Linda Davies, Glyn Davies,
Gillean Wilson, Innkps.

VAGABOND'S HOUSE INN

🛏	11 Rooms, $79/$145 B&B Suites, $204 B&B
💳	Visa, MC, Amex
🛁	All Private Baths
🌳	Open Year-round
🐩	Appropriate for Children over 11; Pets accepted
🎯	Carmel Beach, 17-Mile Drive, Golf, Tennis, Big Sur, Monterey Bay Aquarium
🍷	Breakfast; Cream Sherry
🚭	
⊢⊞⊣	
♿	

🏠 The stone courtyard here is an almost magical experience, with the great oak and cascading waterfalls, surrounded by vines, ferns, and gorgeous flowers. Tuffy, the watch cat, suns on a doorstep. Around the courtyard are unique rooms with fireplaces. All the natural beauty and fascinating shops of Carmel are just around the corner.

Turn off Hwy. 1 to Ocean Ave., (W) to town center. R. onto Dolores for 2.5 blocks to inn.
TEL. 408-624-7738 or 800-262-1262
FAX 408-626-1243
P.O. Box 2747
Dolores & 4th
Carmel, CA 93921

Honey Spence, Innkeeper

VILLA ROYALE INN

33 Rooms, $59-75/
$169-200 B&B
Suites, $120-150/
$225-270 B&B
Visa, MC, Amex
All Private Baths

Open Year-round

Adults preferred, no pets

Two pools, jacuzzi

Breakfast, Lunch, and
Dinner; Wine & Liquor
Available

Smoking Permitted

Wheelchair Access, 5 rms
& dining rm

From I-10 follow 111 to Palm Springs;
111 becomes Palm Canyon Dr. Follow Palm Canyon Dr. to East Palm
Canyon. Go 1/4 miles on East Palm
Canyon to Indian Trails.
TEL. 619-327-2314
FAX 619-322-3794
1620 Indian Trails
Palm Springs, CA 92264

Bob Lee, Innkeeper

Situated on 3 1/2 acres, the Villa Royale is a full service country inn with a decided European ambiance. With softly splashing fountains, draping bougainvillea, brick courtyards, column arcades, and tile-roofed buildings, one could easily be in the south of France. There are 33 accommodations, each representing a different country. Many have wood burning fireplaces and private spas. Europa Restaurant, with its fireplace & terra-cotta walls, could be considered the most romantic dining in the desert.

THE WINE COUNTRY INN

20 Rooms, $95/$160 B&B
4 Suites, $180/205 B&B

Visa, MC

All Private Baths

Closed the two weeks
prior to Christmas

Children and Pets not
encouraged

Pool & Jacuzzi, Wineries,
Tennis, Golf, Hiking

Breakfast; Wine & Liquor
Soon

Smoking Permitted

Wheelchair Access (dining room)

From S.F. take I-80 (N) to Napa exit.
Follow Hwy. 29 (N) 18 mi. to St. Helena & 2 mi. beyond to Lodi Lane.
Turn R. for 1/3 mi. to inn.
TEL. 707-963-7077
FAX 707-963-9018

1152 Lodi Lane,
St. Helena, CA 94574

Jim Smith, Innkeeper

Perched on a small hill, overlooking the manicured vineyards and nearby hills of the Napa Valley, this inn is known for its casual and quiet atmosphere. The intimate rooms boast family-made quilts, private balconies, fireplaces and pine antiques. Famous restaurants and wineries tours round out the Napa Valley experience.

COLORADO

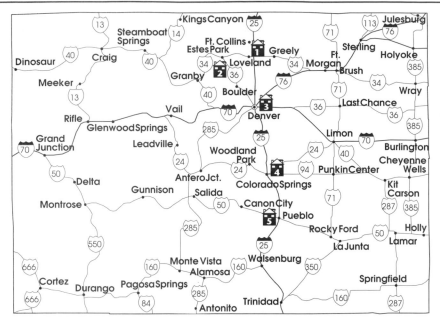

1. River Song, Estes Park
2. The Lovelander Bed &
   Breakfast Inn, Loveland
3. Castle Marne, Denver
4. Hearthstone Inn, Colorado Springs
5. Abriendo Inn, Pueblo

ABRIENDO INN

6 Rooms, $54/$89 B&B
1 Suite, $83 B&B

Visa, MC, Amex, Diners

All Private Baths

Open Year-round

Children over 7
Welcome; No Pets

Museums, Nature, Bike
Trails, Historic Walking
Tour, Rafting, Fishing,
Boutiques, Galleries,
Shops

Breakfast, afternoon
Cheese & Crackers, and
Beverages; BYOB

Smoking permitted on
veranda and grounds

Make this classic mansion your home while visiting Pueblo. Experience the comfortable elegance of the beautiful Foursquare architecture.   Feel like you belong here at the Abriendo Inn as you stroll the park-like grounds, view the surrounding neighborhood, and walk through nearby Historic Union Ave. district. From the spiral staircase to the curved stained glass windows and parquet floors, the Inn provides an enchanting ambiance. For your convenience all rooms have the privacy of in-room phones and TV.

I-25 to Exit 97-B Abriendo Ave. 1 Mile
from exit on left side of street

TEL. (719) 544-2703
FAX (719) 542-1806
300 West Abriendo Avenue
Pueblo, CO 81004

Kerrelyn M. Trent,
Innkeeper

CASTLE MARNE

7 Rooms, $85/$120 B&B
2 Suites, $145/$175 B&B

Visa, MC, Amex, Discov, Diners

All Private Baths

Open Year-round

Unsuitable for Children Under 10; No Pets

Game Room, City Park w/ Tennis, Running Paths, Golf, Zoo, Museum, Botanic Gardens, Shopping, Historic Sites

Full Breakfast
Afternoon Tea

Smoke-Free Inn

Conference Facility (12)

Wheelchair Access (1 rm., dining rm. & conf. fac.)

From Denver International Airport, take Peña Blvd. to I-70 (W) to Quebec (S) to 17th Ave., right (W) to Esplanade, left (S) one block to 16th Ave., right (W) 4 blocks to Race St.

TEL. 303-331-0621;
800-92-MARNE;
FAX 303-331-0623

1572 Race St.,
Denver, CO 80206
Peiker Family, Innkeepers

 Denver's grandest historic mansion B&B (National and Local Register). Close to Museum of Natural History, Zoo, Botanic Gardens, Cherry Creek Business and Shopping district. Near downtown's 16th Street Mall, Larimer Square, Art Museum, US Mint and Molly Brown's House. Hand rubbed woods, stained glass "Peacock Window," ornate fireplaces blend with period antiques and family heirlooms to create a charming Victorian atmosphere. Game Room and English Garden. Full gourmet breakfast and Afternoon Tea.

HEARTHSTONE INN

20 Rooms, $80/$125 B&B
3 Suites, $110/$140 B&B

Visa, MC, Amex

All Private Baths

Open Year-round
Children Accepted; No Pets

On property—Croquet, Puzzles, Games. Nearby— Walking, Jogging Trail, Golf, Tennis, Pikes Peak, Museums, Rafting, Air Force Academy, Olympic Training Center, Colorado College

Full Gourmet Breakfast Daily; Luncheons can be arranged for 20-48 persons

No Smoking

Conference Facilities (40)

Wheelchair Access (1 rm., dining rm. & conf. fac.)

From I-25, Exit 143 (Uintah St.) (E) away from mountains 3 blocks to Cascade. Turn R. (S) 7 blocks to corner of Cascade & St. Vrain.

TEL. 719-473-4413, 800-521-1885; FAX 719-473-1322

506 No. Cascade Ave.
Colorado Sprgs, CO 80903
Dot Williams, Ruth Williams, Mark Mitchell, Innkeepers

 Bright Victorian colors of plum, bittersweet, and lilac accent this stunning inn. Antiques throughout, color-coordinated linens, gourmet breakfasts, and friendly, helpful people make this in-town inn a comfortable change of pace. Rooms with working fireplaces are especially popular in the winter while those with open air porches are sought after in the spring and summer. With all the activities of the Pikes Peak Region, you'll find exciting things to see and do for several days!

COLORADO
THE LOVELANDER B&B INN

🛏	11 Rooms, $84/$125 B&B
💳	Visa, MC, Amex, Discov
🛁	All Private Baths
🛋	Open Year-round
🐕	Children over 10 welcome; No Pets
R	Rocky Mountain Natl. Park, Big Thompson Canyon, Benson Sculpture Park, Galleries
🍷	Breakfast; Beverages & Snacks Available
🚭	No Smoking
🎪	Conference Fac. (15-30)
♿	Limited Wheelchair Access

Combining the essence of Victorian style with contemporary convenience, the Lovelander lies nestled in the Rocky Mountain foothills, a short drive from breathtaking Rocky Mountain National Park. Beautifully appointed rooms, peaceful surroundings, gourmet breakfasts, and old-fashioned hospitality from the heart create a haven for recreational and business travelers alike.

I-25, Exit 257B, to U.S. Hwy. 34 (W) for 5 mi. to Garfield Ave. Turn L. 10 blks. to 4th St., then R. to 2nd house on R.

TEL. 303-669-0798
217 W. 4th St.
Loveland, CO 80537

Marilyn & Bob Wiltgen,
Innkeepers

ROMANTIC RIVER SONG

🛏	3 Rooms, $95/$125 B&B 6 Suites, $130/$180 B&B
💳	Visa, MC
🛁	All Private Baths
🛋	Open Year-round
🐕	Not Suitable for Pets or Small Children
R	Fishing on our Trout Stream, Hiking Trails on Property, , Snowshoeing, XC Skiing, Fabulous Wildlife Viewing (deer, elk, etc.), Horseback Riding, Rock Climbing
🍷	Breakfast; Gourmet Candlelight Dinner by advance res. BYOB
🚭	No Smoking
🎪	Conference Facilities (16)
♿	Wheelchair Access, 2 suites

Imagine lying in a magnificent antique bed with the glaciers of the Rocky Mountain National Park looming just over the tops of your toes, or seeing the stars through the skylights above your brass bed, or thrill to feeding a gentle fawn outside your door, or being lulled to sleep by a melodious mountain stream. After snow shoeing in the Park, come home to your own romantic fireside jacuzzi. Ahhhh, at River Song, Time seems to stand still.

Please call for directions
TEL. 303-586-4666
P.O. Box 1910
Estes Park, CO 80517

Sue & Gary Mansfield,
Innkeepers

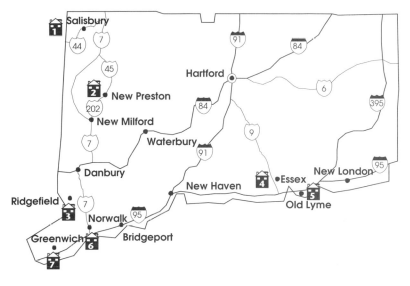

1. Under Mountain Inn, Salisbury
2. Boulders Inn, New Preston
3. West Lane Inn, Ridgefield
4. Griswold Inn, Essex
5. Bee and Thistle Inn, Old Lyme
6. Silvermine Tavern, Norwalk
7. Homestead Inn, Greenwich

BEE AND THISTLE INN

11 Rooms, $69/$125 EP
1 Cottage, $195/$195 EP

Visa, MC, Amex, Diners

10 Private, 1 Shared Baths

Closed Jan. 5 to Jan. 24

Appropriate for Children Over 12; No Pets

Gardens, River, Golf, Museums, Art, Beach, Mystic

Breakfast, Lunch, Dinner; Sun. Brunch, English tea
Wine & Liquor available

Smoking in Restricted Areas

Conference Facilities (20)

I-95 (S) Exit 70, turn R. off ramp to inn, 3rd bldg. on L. I-95 (N) Exit 70, turn L. off ramp to 1st light, R. to T in road, then L. to inn. 3rd bldg. on L.

TEL. 203-434-1667; 800-622-4946; FAX 203-434-3402

100 Lyme Street
Old Lyme, CT 06371

Bob & Penny Nelson, Innkeepers

In an unspoiled historic village on the Lieutenant River, sits this lovely 1756 inn. Its English gardens, sunlit porches, fireplaces, beautiful, carved staircase, canopied and 4-poster beds, antique quilts and furnishings reflect a gracious lifestyle. Widely commended for its cuisine, it has been voted the most romantic place to dine in Connecticut.

CONNECTICUT
THE BOULDERS INN

🛏	17 Rooms, Suites, Guesthouses, \$125/\$215 B&B; \$175/\$265 MAP
💳	Visa, MC, Amex
🛁	Some Private Baths, 1 Jacuzzi
🕯	Open Year-round
🐕	Children Under 12 by special arrangement; No Pets
R	Tennis, Beach, Boating, Hiking, Bicycles, Downhill & XC Skiing, Antiquing, Golf, Music Festival
🍷	Breakfast, Dinner, Sun. Brunch; Wine & Liquor Available
🚭	Non-smoking Dining Room
⌷	Conference Facilities (20)
♿	Wheelchair Access (guesthouse only)

🏠 This 1895 Victorian mansion is located in a spectacular setting at the foot of Pinnacle Mountain, where breathtaking sunsets over Lake Waramaug are enjoyed from the elegantly appointed living room, the glass-enclosed dining room, and most of the guest rooms and guest houses, many of which have fireplaces. The widely-renowned cuisine is also served on the outside terrace in summer.

Rte. 84(E) Exit 7 to Rte. 7(N) to New Milford. Take Rte. 202 to New Preston. L. on E. Shore Rd. (Rte. 45) to Lake Waramaug.

TEL. 203-868-0541
East Shore Rd. (Rte. 45)
New Preston, Ct 06777

Ulla & Kees Adema,
Innkeepers

THE GRISWOLD INN

🛏	14 Rooms, \$80/\$165 11 Suites, Petit/\$95; Suite/\$105; Luxury/\$135; Garden/\$175
💳	Visa, MC, Amex
🛁	All Private Baths
🕯	Dining Room Closed Christmas Eve/Day
🐕	Children Accepted Pets Accepted
R	Tennis, Golf, Swimming, Goodspeed Opera, Mystic Seaport
🍷	Free Continental Breakfast, Lunch, Dinner; Famous Sunday Hunt Breakfast; Wine & Liquor Available
🚭	Non-smoking rooms available
⌷	Conference facilities (25)
♿	Wheelchair Access (dining rm. & conf. fac.)

🏠 A kaleidoscope of nostalgic images delights the eye here: myriad Currier & Ives steamboat prints and Antonio Jacobsen marine art, ship models, firearms, potbellied stove, to name a few. The superb New England cuisine features seafood, prime rib, meat pies, and the Inn's own 1776© sausages. Lucius Beebe considered the Taproom the most handsome bar in America.

I-91 (S) to Exit 22 (S). Rte. 9 (S) to Exit 3 Essex. I-95 (N&S) to Exit 69 to Rte. 9 (N) to Exit 3 Essex.

TEL. 203-767-1776
FAX 203-767-0481
36 Main St.
Essex, CT 06426

Victoria & William Winterer,
Innkeepers

THE HOMESTEAD INN

17 Rooms, $137 D&B
6 Suites, $160/$185 B&B

All Major Credit Cards

All Private Baths

Open Year-round

Children Accepted
No Pets

Walking, Running Trails,
Parks, Beaches,
Shopping, Movies,
Theater—all nearby

Breakfast, Lunch, Dinner,
Sun. Brunch
Wine & Liquor Available

Smoking Permitted

Conference Facilities (24)
I-95 to Greenwich, Exit 3.

From NYC: turn L. off ramp; from New Haven: turn R. off ramp, then L. at light onto Horseneck Ln. (just before RR overpass), to L. at Field Point Rd. Continue 1/4 mi. to inn on R.
TEL. & FAX 203-869-7500
420 Field Point Rd.
Greenwich, CT 06830
Lessie Davison & Nancy Smith, Innkeepers; Dorothy Jenkins, Hotel & Conf. Mgr.

Gracious, historic elegance with a convivial atmosphere. Exquisitely decorated. Three-star French restaurant under the talented guidance of Parisian chef, Jacques Thiebeult. Described by Fodor's as, ". . . one of the finest lodgings in America." Only 45 minutes from New York City. Corporate travelers find The Homestead a "home away from home." Unique meeting facilities bring meeting-goers from all over.

THE SILVERMINE TAVERN

10 Rooms, $80/$99 B&B

Visa, MC, Amex, Diners

All Private Baths

Closed Tuesday

Children Accepted
No Pets

Golf, Boating, Beach,
Tennis

Complimentary Breakfast; Lunch, Dinner, Sun.
Brunch
Wine & Liquor Available

Non-Smoking Dining
Area

Conference Facilities (16)

I-95, Exit 15 or Merritt Pkwy., Exit 40A. Call for directions.
TEL. 203-847-4558
FAX 203-847-9171
Perry Ave.
Norwalk, CT 06850

Frank Whitman, Jr.,
Innkeeper

A 1785 inn beside a millpond with swans and a waterfall: what could be more romantic? The inn features Early American guest rooms, a treasure house of Early Americana and primitive paintings, and country dining at its best. New England dishes such as lobster pie and Indian pudding are just a few of the inducements here. From its creaky wooden floors and venerable ancestor paintings to its New England cuisine and antique canopy beds, the Silvermine Tavern is all a country inn should be: warm, friendly, and inviting.

33

CONNECTICUT
UNDER MOUNTAIN INN

7 Rooms, $150-170/$160-180 MAP; Special package rates

Visa, MC

All Private Baths

Open Year-round

Appropriate for Children over 6; No Pets

Boating, Hiking, Alpine/Nordic Skiing, Rafting, Antiquing, Music & Theater, Golf, Tennis, Fishing, Horsebk. Riding

Breakfast, Dinner, Afternoon Tea; Liquor & Wine available

Limited Smoking; No Pipes or Cigars

Conference Facilities (15) Wheelchair Access (dining rm.)

Enjoy British-flavored hospitality in an 18th century farmhouse, with a proper cup of tea, *The Manchester Guardian*, and a full English breakfast. Dinners could be bangers & mash, steak & kidney pie, or other English specialties cooked up by Manchester-born owner-chef Peter Higginson. A well-stocked library and cozy fireplaces vie with the lure of outdoors and many cultural attractions. *Travel and Leisure* raved, "This is the country getaway we all wish we had."

From Boston: Mass. Turnpike, Exit 2, (W) on 102, (S) on 7, (W) on 23 in Gt. Barrington, MA, S on 41. Inn is .7 mi. (S) of CT border. From NYC: (N) on Taconic Pkwy., (E) on 44, (N) on 41 for 4 mi. to inn.

TEL.203-435-0242
FAX 203-435-2379
482 Undermountain Road
Salisbury, CT 06068
Peter & Marged Higginson,
Innkeepers

WEST LANE INN

20 rooms, $100/$165 B&B With Fireplaces st. at $145

Visa, MC, Amex, Diners

All Private Baths

Open Year-round

Children Accepted No Pets

Golf, Tennis, XC Skiing, Swimming, Antiques, Shopping

Continental Breakfast

Smoking Permitted

Conference Facilities (20) Wheelchair Access (1 rm, dining & conf. fac.)

Rich oak paneling, deep pile carpeting, and a cheery fire crackling on the hearth sets the tone of polished refinement at this luxurious inn. Framed by a stand of majestic old maples, a broad lawn, and flowering shrubs, it offers gracious hospitality and a quiet retreat from worldly cares, about an hour north of New York City.

From NYC & Westside Hwy. (N) to Sawmill River Pkwy. & Exit 43 (Katonah). Turn R. on Rte. 35 (E) 10 mi. to Ridgefield. Inn is on L. From Rte 90 & I-84, Exit 3 to Rte. 7 (S) to Rte. 35 and Ridgefield.

TEL. 203-438-7325
FAX 203-438-7325
22 West Lane
Ridgefield, CT 06877
Maureen Mayer, Innkeeper

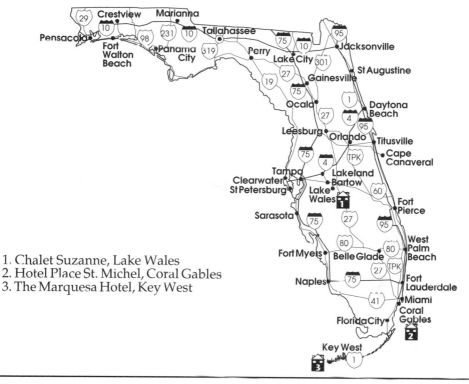

1. Chalet Suzanne, Lake Wales
2. Hotel Place St. Michel, Coral Gables
3. The Marquesa Hotel, Key West

CHALET SUZANNE

26 Rooms, $125/$145 B&B
4 Suites, $145/$195 B&B

Visa, MC, Amex, Discov.
DC, Personal Checks

All Private Baths

Open Daily except Monday in Summer

Children Welcome
$20 Per Pet

Swimming, Lawn Games, Jogging, Antiquing, Fishing, Airstrip, Baseball, Winter Passion Play, Golf, Tennis and Lake Cruises nearby.

Breakfast, Lunch, Dinner; Special Packages

Intimate Lounge, Extensive Wine Collection

Non-Smoking in most Dining Rooms

Conference Facilities (50)

Wheelchair Access (2 rms.)

I-4 (W) from Orlando or I-4 (E) from Tampa to U.S. 27 (S), Exit 23 (Cypress Gardens) 18 mi. (S). Turn L. on County Rd. 17A for 1.5 mi. to inn on R.

TEL. 813-676-6011 or 800-433-6011
FAX 813-676-1814
U.S. Hwy 27 & Co. Rd. 17A
3800 Chalet Suzanne Dr.
Lake Wales, FL 33853-7060
Hinshaw family, Innkeepers

 "Fairy tales can come true…" This is a storybook inn with an around-the-world look to its cottages grouped at odd angles, its fountain courtyards, and fascinating furnishings. Awarded Uncle Ben's National Award — Ten Best Country Inns of 1991–1992, the Mobil 4-star restaurant is famous for superb fare and caring attention. Chalet Suzanne is on the National Register of Historic Places.

FLORIDA
HOTEL PLACE ST. MICHEL

🛏	27 Rooms, $109/$125 B&B 3 suites, $165 B&B
💳	Visa, MC, Amex, Diners
🛁	All Private Baths
🛋	Open Year-round
👫	Children—Yes Pets Not Accepted
Ⓡ	Beaches, Golf, Tennis, Coral Rock Swimming Pool, Theaters, Galleries, Shopping, Jogging, Bike Trails, Fitness Ctr. Nearby
🍷	Restaurant, French Deli, Sun. Brunch; Bar-Lounge, Wine & Liquor Available
🚭	Non-Smoking Dining Area
🏛	Conference Facilities (30)
♿	Wheelchair Access (dining rm.)

🏨 Filled with antiques, this intimate European-style hotel (ca. 1926) in the heart of Coral Gables, offers superb service and comfort. Welcome baskets of fruit and cheese, complimentary continental breakfast, & the morning paper at your door. One of Florida's "top 10" small hotels, with award-winning restaurant. Major renovations in 1993.

I-95 (S), becoming U.S. 1 (S. Dixie Hwy.), continue (S) to Ponce de Leon Blvd., R. to corner of Alcazar Ave. & hotel.

TEL 305-444-1666
800-848-HOTEL
FAX 305-529-0074
162 Alcazar Ave.
Coral Gables, (Miami) FL 33134
Stuart N. Bornstein, Alan H.
Potamkin, Innkeepers

THE MARQUESA HOTEL

🛏	11 Rooms, $115/$215 EP 4 Suites, $150/$260 EP
💳	Visa, MC, Amex, Diners
🛁	All Private Baths
🛋	Open Year-round
🐕	Children – Yes Pets not Accepted
Ⓡ	Heated Pool, nearby Snorkeling, Fishing, Sailing, Historic attractions and homes
🍷	Restaurant or Room service for Breakfast, Dinner; Poolside beverage service; Wine & Liquor available
🚬	Smoking permitted
🏛	Conference Facilities (25)
♿	Wheelchair Access

🏨 In the heart of Key West's historic district, the Marquesa Hotel and Cafe is a landmark 110-year-old home, restored to 4-Diamond status in 1988. Floor-to-ceiling windows, large bouquests of flowers, a shimmering heated pool and lush gardens are Marquesa trademarks. Rooms and suites are luxurious, all with private marble baths. Located within walking distance to Duval Street for galleries, shops, and nightlife. The *Miami Herald* rated it as one of Florida's 10 top inns.

U.S. 1, R. on No. Roosevelt Blvd., becomes Truman Ave. Continue to R. on Simonton for 5 blks. to Fleming. Turn R. to front of hotel.

TEL. 305-292-1919; 800-
869-4631; FAX 305-294-
2121
600 Fleming St.
Key West, FL 33040
Richard Manley,
Erik de Boer, Owners;
Carol Wightman, Manager

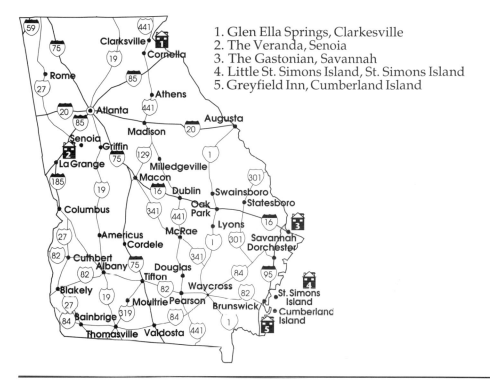

1. Glen Ella Springs, Clarkesville
2. The Veranda, Senoia
3. The Gastonian, Savannah
4. Little St. Simons Island, St. Simons Island
5. Greyfield Inn, Cumberland Island

THE GASTONIAN

10 Rooms, $115/$200 B&B
3 Suites, $165/$275 B&B

Visa, MC, Amex

All Private Baths, 6 Jacuzzis

Open Year-round

Appropriate for Children over 12; No Pets

Antiquing, Guided tours, Beaches, Biking, Fine Dining, Galleries, Museums, River Cruise & nearby Golf, Sea Fishing, Tennis

Full Breakfast
Wine Available

No Smoking

Conference Facilities (25)

Wheelchair Access (1 rm.)

From I-16 exit at W. Martin Luther King Blvd. straight ahead with no turns, which becomes Gaston St. Continue to inn at 220 East Gaston St.

**TEL. 912-232-2869;
800-322-6603;
FAX. 912-232-0710**
220 E. Gaston St.
Savannah, GA 31401
Hugh & Roberta Lineberger,
Innkeepers

In the largest Historical Landmark District in the U.S., this 1868 inn is furnished with English antiques, offers beautiful gardens and sundeck with hot tub. Rooms have fireplaces, heat and A/C, Jacuzzi baths, showers, cable TV, fruit and wine — plus nightly turndown with sweets and cordials. Guests feast on a full, hot, sitdown Southern breakfast. Mobil ★★★★, AAA◆◆◆◆.

GEORGIA
GLEN-ELLA SPRINGS

	14 Rooms $85/$150 B&B 2 Suites $150 B&B
	Visa, MC, Amex
	All Private Baths
	Open Year-round
	Children in some rms. No Pets
	Gardens, Gift Shop, Pool, Nearby Hiking, Boating, Horseback, Antiquing
	Breakfast (guests only), Lunch (Sum. & Fall) Dinner (by reservation, days limited in Winter), BYOB
	Smoking in some areas
	Conference Facility
	Wheelchair Access (5 Rms., dining rm. & conf. fac.)

Down a country lane at the edge of the Chattahoochee National Forest, this 100-year-old inn on the National Register combines charm of the past with modern comfort. All of the pine paneled guest rooms open onto proches with rocking chairs and lovely views. The 17 acres of grounds contain beautiful perennial, herb, and vegetable gardens, a creek, and a swimming pool. Located just a short 90 miles north of Atlanta, the inn has a 3 diamond AAA rating and was selected in 1992 as one of Travel and Leisure's top ten resorts.

About 3 1/2 miles off US 441 north of Clarksville and Clayton; 70 miles north of Atlanta: I-85 to I-985, which becomes US 441, L. on G Hardeman Rd. at Turnerville, R. on Old 441 & follow signs.
TEL. 800-552-3479 (except GA); 706-754-7295
FAX 706-754-1560
Bear Gap Rd, Rt 3, Box 3304
Clarkesville GA 30523
Bobby and Barrie Aycock, Innkps.

GREYFIELD INN

	7 Rooms, 4 Suites, $275/$315 AP
	Visa, MC, Pers. Checks
	3 Private, 3 Shared Baths
	Open Year-round except August
	Children 6 years & up No Pets
	Birdwatching, Hiking, Swimming, Shelling, Biking, Fishing, Photography
	Breakfast, Picnic Lunches, Dinner, Wine & Liquor Available
	Smoking only in Bar & Porches
	Conference Facilities (22)

This turn-of-the-century mansion is on Cumberland Island, Georgia's largest and southernmost island. Miles of hiking trails traverse the island's unique ecosystems along with a beautiful, endless beach for shelling, swimming, sunning and birdwatching. Fine food, lovely original furnishings, and a peaceful, relaxing environment provide guests with a step back into another era. Overnight rate includes an island outing with our naturalist, bicycles for exploring the island, and roundtrip boat passage on our private ferry.

Cumberland Island is accessible only by boat; our ferry service provides transportation to island from Fernandina Beach, FL.
TEL. 904-261-6408
Cumberland Island, GA
P.O. Box 900
Fernandina Beach, FL 32035-0900
Mitty & Mary Jo Ferguson,
Innkeepers

LITTLE ST. SIMONS ISLAND INN

11 Rooms, $250/$390
1 Suite, $350/$440

Visa, MC

All Private Baths

Feb.–Nov.

No Pets; Children 6 years & up; all ages June–Aug. 15

Canoeing, Hiking, Beach-combing, Fishing, Motor-boating, Birding, Naturalist Tours, Horse-back Riding, Golf

Breakfast, Lunch, Dinner; Early Light Breakfast, Snacks, Cocktails;Wine & Liquor Available

Smoking Restricted

Conference Facility (3 rms., 24)

Meet our boat for a short ride over to the island. Boat leaves from north end of St. Simons Island. Map on back of reservation confirmation.

TEL. 912-638-7472
FAX 912-634-1811
PO Box 21078
St. Simons Island, GA 31522

Debbie McIntyre, Innkeeper

Comfortable country inn on 10,000 acre privately-owned island. A visit to this island is a step back in time. Seven miles of beaches, acres of pristine forests and marshes offer the opportunity to explore, hike, birdwatch, canoe, motorboat, and fish. Take a driving tour with a naturalist; enjoy the swimming pool and rocking chairs. Rates include accommodations, meals, and all activities except horseback riding.

THE VERANDA

9 Rooms, $85/$105 B&B

Visa, MC, Amex

All Private Baths, 1 Whirlpool

Open Year-round; Reservations necessary

Children Accepted (inquire); No Pets

Rare Player Piano/Organ, Extensive Library; nearby: Tennis, Golf, Fishing, Callaway Gardens, Warm Springs, NASCAR Races, Braves Baseball

Full Breakfast; Dinner & Lunch by reservation only

Smoking only on verandah

Conference Facilities (20)

Wheelchair Access (downstairs)

From Atlanta I-85 (S), Exit 12; L.(SE) on Hwy. 74 for 16.7 mi. R.(S) on Rockaway Rd. for 3.3 mi. At light turn L.(E) for 1 block to inn. Ask for brochure/map.

TEL. 404-599-3905
FAX 404-599-0806
252 Seavy St., Box 177
Senoia, GA 30276
Jan & Bobby Boal, Innkeepers

With wrap-around porch and rocking chairs, this elegant turn-of-the century inn on the National Register offers a quiet, relaxed Southern lifestyle just 37 miles south of bustling downtown Atlanta. Guests enjoy fresh flowers, kaleidoscopes, books, games, puzzles, walking canes, and historic memorabilia, plus The Veranda's acclaimed gourmet meals and lavish breakfasts. Local attractions include antiques, historic tours, Riverwood Studios (where movies such as *Fried Green Tomatoes*, *The War*, etc. were filmed) and The Veranda's unique gift shop. 1990 INN OF THE YEAR.

1. The Checkerberry Inn, Goshen

THE CHECKERBERRY INN

	11 Rooms, $104/$130 B&B
	3 Suites, $152/$300 B&B
	Visa, MC, Amex
	All Private Baths
	Closed January
	Well-behaved Children welcome; No Pets
R	Tennis, Outdoor Pool, Croquet Green; Golf, Lakes nearby
	Breakfast; Lunch, (Wed. only); Dinner, Tues.-Sat.; Beer & Wine Available
	Smoking in Library Only
	Conference Facilities (28)
	Wheelchair Access (3 rms., dining rm. & conf. fac.)

Watch for Amish horses and buggies in this pastoral farmland. On a 100-acre wooded estate, the inn offers breathtaking views of unspoiled rolling countryside from individually decorated rooms. While away the hours enjoying fields of wildflowers, massive Beech trees, miles of country roads, and grazing horses in a nearby pasture. Imaginative meals and fine wines provide memorable dining.

Exit 107, Ind. toll road, (S) on State
Rte. 13 to R. on State Rte. 4 to L. on
County Rd. 37; 1 mi. to inn on R.
TEL. 219-642-4445
FAX 219-642-4445
62644 CR 37
Goshen, IN 46526
John & Susan Graff,
Innkeepers
Shawna Koehler & Kelly Graff,
Asst. Innkeepers

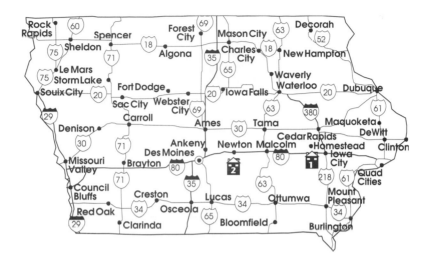

1. Die Heimat Inn, Homestead
2. LaCorsette Maison Inn, Newton

DIE HEIMAT COUNTRY INN

19 Rooms, $36.95/$62.95

Visa, MC, Discov.

All Private Baths

Open Year-around

Children Welcome; Well-behaved Pets Accepted

Historic Amana Colonies, Nature trail, Hiking, Golf, Woolen Mills, Family-style Dining, Furniture Factories, Wineries

Breakfast

Smoking restricted

Conference facilities (20-40)

I-80, Exit 225, (N) on Hwy. 151; (E) on Hwy. 6 to Homestead and inn at end of street. From Cedar Rapids: Hwy. 151(S) 20 mi. to Homestead.

TEL. 319-622-3937

Amana Colonies, Main St.
Homestead, IA 52236

Warren & Jacki Lock, Innkeepers

Die Heimat means "the homeplace" in German and is the oldest and largest B&B in the colonies. This inn was once a communal kitchen of the Amana Colonies, which were originally settled by German immigrants who established their own religious and communal way of life. Walnut and cherry furniture made by Amana craftsmen, German heirloom antiques, and beautiful quilts offer a glimpse into the past.

IOWA
LACORSETTE MAISON INN

Erected in 1909, LaCorsette Maison Inn is a mission-style mansion. The Inn is elegant, yet comfortable, with cozy rooks and alcoves. It is on the National Historic Register. Kay Owen, the innkeeper, is also a gourmet chef and specializes in Continental food with a French flair. The Inn offers deluxe accommodations and exquisite meals to travelers.

Just north of I-80 east of Des Moines.
TEL. 515-792-6833
629 1st Ave. East
Newton, IA 50208

Kay Owen, Innkeeper

COUNTRY INN ARCHITECTURE

Country inns are probably more often found in Victorian buildings than in any one other style of architecture; however, that includes such a variation in styles as Queen Anne, Edwardian, Carpenter Gothic, and Italianate. Showy and flamboyant, these buildings have great eye-catching appeal with their cupolas, chimneys, gables, shingles, widow's walks, and capacious wraparound porches. The sometimes rather unusual combinations of exterior paint colors can be a little shocking to the modern eye, but were *de rigueur* for the Victorians. Understandably, as the country expanded westward in the 19th century, building followed the current architectural styles, and consequently there are more inns in Victorian buildings in the Midwest and Far West than in the East and South.

In New England will be found the more pristine and classic pre-Revolutionary, Federalist, and Georgian Colonial buildings. White clapboard or red brick, black shutters, two or more chimneys, "6 over 6" or "12 over 12" double-hung windows (infrequently with the original hand-blown wavy glass), and a fanlight over the door most often characterize the exterior of Colonial buildings. The very earliest have low, beamed ceilings and great fireplaces, sometimes with a blackened crane, that provide a cozy, welcoming setting for guests.

Beyond those two predominant styles, country inn architecture takes off in all directions. Rustic log houses with bark still covering the beams, 19th-century red brick mansions or brick factory buildings and small Midwestern hotels reflecting opulent early days, Greek Revival, English Tudor, Bavarian hip-roofed buildings with balconies, French Mediterranean, Spanish haciendas with flower-laden courtyards, classic, simple Shaker buildings — country inns offer hospitality in these and many other kinds of buildings. Many of them are listed on the National Register of Historic Places.

In the South, there are inns in "shotgun" or "single" houses, built sideways to the street with open piazzas along the side, for privacy, allowing cool breezes to blow through the house. Imposing Southern Colonial mansions with graceful 2-story Grecian pillars house several inns, although there are a few of these transplanted to other parts of the country, too. Some inns have been built in more contemporary styles, and these are usually found in very natural forest or mountain settings, utilizing local woods and stone and other materials.

A few buildings have been designed by famous architects, such as Cass Gilbert, Charles Bulfinch, and Walter Martens. Many American country inns are reminiscent of the country house hotels of Britain.
— **by Virginia Rowe**

1. Beaumont Inn, Harrodsburg
2. Inn at Pleasant Hill,
      Harrodsburg
3. Boone Tavern Hotel, Berea

BEAUMONT INN

33 Rooms $75/$95 EP

Visa, MC, Amex, Discov

All Private Baths

Open Late Feb.–Mid-Dec.

Children Accepted; No Pets

Swimming Pool, Tennis, Shuffle-board, Golf, Fishing, Historic attractions

Breakfast, Dinner Daily Lunch, Tues.–Sun.

Non-smoking rms. available, non-smoking dining rm.

Conference Facilities (25)

In Harrodsburg at intersection with U.S. 68, take U.S. 127 (S) to inn, at south end of town on east side of U.S. 127.
TEL. 606-734-3381
800-352-3992
FAX 606-734-6897
638 Beaumont Dr.
Harrodsburg, KY 40330
The Dedman Family, Innkeepers

Owned and operated by 4 generations of the Dedman family, this country inn, on the National Register of Historic Places, was built in 1845 as a school for young ladies. In the heart of Bluegrass country, it is redolent of Southern history, brimming with beautiful antiques, fascinating memorabilia, and the food is traditional Kentucky fare. Over 30 varieties of trees grace the grounds. The town of Harrodsburg, founded in 1774, is the first permanent English settlement west of the Allegheny Mountains. Located amid numerous historic sites and attractions.

43

BOONE TAVERN HOTEL

🛏	59 Rooms, $57/$87 est.
💳	Visa, MC, Amex, Discov, Diners
🛁	All Private Baths
🛋	Open Year-round
👪	Children Welcome; No Pets
☀	Campus Tours, Appalachian Museum, Craft & Antique Shops, Danforth Chapel, and Planetarium
🍽	Breakfast, Lunch & Dinner served daily; Dress code for Dinner and Sunday Lunch
🚭	We Kindly Request No Smoking
🏨	Conference Facility
♿	Wheelchair Access (2 rms., dining rm. & conf. fac.)

Historic Boone Tavern Hotel is nestled within and owned by Berea College, which provides tours and attractions to guests. Berea proudly bears the title of "Arts and Crafts Capital of Kentucky" because of its many crafts and antique shops. The Hotel dining and meeting rooms offer superb southern cuisine, charming atmosphere, and friendly student service. Come to Boone Tavern Hotel and experience the true southern hospitality that is always waiting for you.

I-75 S. Lexington approx. 45 mi, Exit 76, L off ramp, follow U.S. 25 to 4th stop light, R. 1 block to Boone Tavern Hotel, or I-75 N. Knoxville, TN to Exit 76, R off ramp, follow U.S. 25 to 4th stop light, R 1 block to Boone Tavern Hotel

TEL. 800-366-9358;
606-986-9358
Main and Prospect Street
Berea, KY 40403
Robert A. Stewart, Innkeeper

INN AT PLEASANT HILL

🛏	75 Rooms, $55/$100 EP 5 Suites, $100/$150 EP
💳	Visa, MC
🛁	All Private Baths
🛋	Closed Dec. 24 & 25
👪	Children Accepted No Pets
☀	Village Touring, Riverboat
🍽	Breakfast, Lunch, Dinner
🚭	Non-Smoking Dining Rm.
🏨	Conference Facilities (75)
♿	

Part of a restored Shaker community, originally established in 1805, the inn's rooms are located in 15 of the 33 original buildings clustered along a country road on 2,700 acres in Bluegrass country. Rooms are simply and beautifully furnished with examples of Shaker crafts. Meals are hearty and homemade, and tours, demonstrations, and cultural events abound.

From Lexington, U.S. 68 (W) 25 mi. and R. to village. From Harrodsburg, U.S. 68 (E) 7 mi. Turn L. to village.

TEL. 606-734-5411
3500 Lexington Rd.
Harrodsburg, KY 40330

Christopher Brassfield, Innkeeper

1. Madewood Plantation House,
Napoleonville

MADEWOOD PLANTATION HOUSE

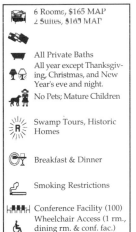

6 Rooms, $165 MAP
2 Suites, $185 MAP

All Private Baths

All year except Thanksgiving, Christmas, and New Year's eve and night.

No Pets; Mature Children

Swamp Tours, Historic Homes

Breakfast & Dinner

Smoking Restrictions

Conference Facility (100)
Wheelchair Access (1 rm., dining rm. & conf. fac.)

75 mi. NW of New Orleans. From New Orleans, I-10 W to Exit 182 (Donaldsonville/Sorrento). Follow "Bayou Plantations" signs. Cross Sunshine Bridge to 70 to Spur 70 to L. onto 308, through Napoleonville, 2 mi. farther on 308.
TEL 504-569-7151
FAX 504-369-9848
4250 Hwy 308
Napoleonville, LA 70390
Keith & Millie Marshall, Innkeepers; David D'Aunoy, Res. Mgr.

The "Queen of the Bayou," Madewood Plantation House offers elegant accommodations in a homelike atmosphere. This National Historic Landmark is lovingly maintained by its long-time staff, who provide the relaxed atmosphere for which Madewood is noted. Guests enjoy antique-filled rooms and canopied beds along with a wine and cheese hour prior to a family style candlelight dinner prepared by Madewood's cooks. One of the top 12 inns of '93 by *Country Inns* magazine.

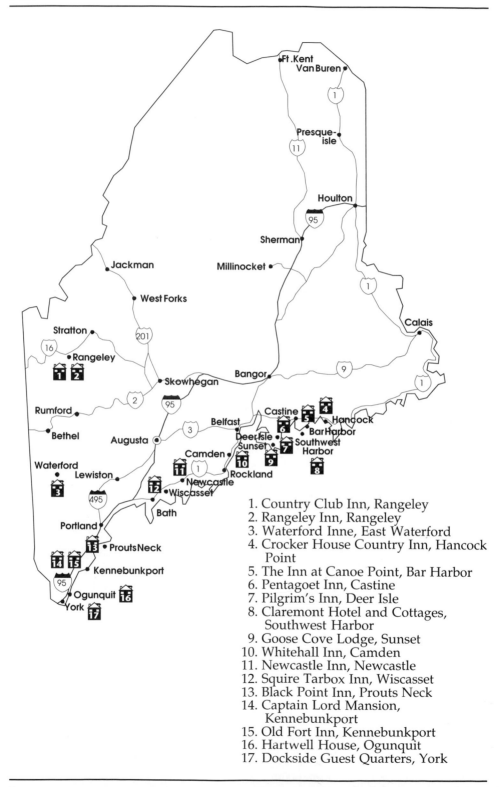

1. Country Club Inn, Rangeley
2. Rangeley Inn, Rangeley
3. Waterford Inne, East Waterford
4. Crocker House Country Inn, Hancock Point
5. The Inn at Canoe Point, Bar Harbor
6. Pentagoet Inn, Castine
7. Pilgrim's Inn, Deer Isle
8. Claremont Hotel and Cottages, Southwest Harbor
9. Goose Cove Lodge, Sunset
10. Whitehall Inn, Camden
11. Newcastle Inn, Newcastle
12. Squire Tarbox Inn, Wiscasset
13. Black Point Inn, Prouts Neck
14. Captain Lord Mansion, Kennebunkport
15. Old Fort Inn, Kennebunkport
16. Hartwell House, Ogunquit
17. Dockside Guest Quarters, York

BLACK POINT INN

	75 Rooms, $180/$320 MAP 5 Suites, $300/$350 MAP
	Visa, MC, Amex
	All Private Baths
	Open April 15–Dec. 15
	No Children or Pets Golf, Tennis, 2 Beaches, 2 Pools (1 indoor), 2 Hot Tubs, 1 Sauna, Bird Sanctuary, Fishing, Sailing, Bicycles, Croquet, Volleyball
	Breakfast, Lunch, Dinner AP rates available Wine & Liquor Available
	No Smoking
	Conference Facilities (200) Wheelchair Access (3 rms, dining rm. & conf. fac.)

I-95 (Maine Turnpike) to Exit 6, turn left at first light onto Payne Rd., turn right at next light onto Rt. 114, drive thru next light. Rt. 114 becomes Rt. 207. Drive 4.8 mi. to Inn.
TEL. 207-883-4126
Reserv. 800-258-0003
510 Black Point Rd.
Prouts Neck, ME 04074
Normand H. Dugas,
Innkeeper

Quintessentially New England is this seaside resort inn, the favored retreat of generations of guests since the late 1800s. Easy, gracious hospitality and understated, genteel elegance, along with the vast ocean views, bracing salt air, hearty meals, beachcombing, sailing, and more, make this a world-class seaside resort-inn.

CAPTAIN LORD MANSION

	16 Rooms, $125/199 B&B
	Visa, MC, Discov
	All Private Baths
	Open Year-round
	Appropriate for Children over 6; No Pets
	Antiquing, Shopping, Beaches, Sailing, Whale watching, Tennis, Golf, Fishing, Bicycling
	Full Breakfast; BYOB
	Smoking in Guest Rooms Only
	Conference Facilities (14)

ME Tpke., Exit 3. L. onto Rte. 35 for 5.5 mi. to Rte. 9 (E). Turn L., go over bridge. R. onto Ocean Ave.; after 3/10 mi., turn L. onto Green St.
TEL. 207-967-3141, 800-522-3141, FAX 207-967-3172
P.O. Box 800
Kennebunkport, ME 04046-0800
Bev Davis & Rick Litchfield,
Innkeepers

The beautifully appointed, spacious rooms of this stately 1812 mansion, with its elliptical staircase and imposing cupola, feature period wallpapers, crystal chandeliers, fireplaces and many objects d'art. Superb comfort and gracious hospitality have been rewarded for many years with four diamonds by AAA. Many year-round activities are offered in this charming seacoast village.

CLAREMONT HOTEL & COTTAGES

🛏	25 Rooms, $125/$200 MAP 2 Suites, $170/$190 MAP 12 Cotts., $85/$190 EP
🛁	All Private Baths
🎋🍸	Cottages Open 5/20–10/ 14; Hotel 6/17–10/24
🐕	Children Accepted; No Pets
☀R	Tennis, Croquet, Rowboats, Bikes, Golf, Sailing, Swim- ming, Acadia Nat'l. Park
🍽	Breakfast and Dinner; Lunch mid-July and Aug. only. EP off-season; Wine & Liquor Available
🚭	No Smoking in Guest Rooms
⊢▦⊣	Conference Facilities (125)
♿	Wheelchair Access (5 rms.; dining rm. & conf. fac.)

🏠 The dock and the Boathouse on Somes Sound are the center of much activity at this 110-year-old summer hotel, although croquet and the annual Claremont Classic run them a close second. On the National Register of Historic Places, the Claremont, with its panoramic views of mountains and ocean, offers serene and happy sojourns to its many returning guests.

ME Tpke., Exit 15 (Augusta), Rte. 3 (E) thru Ellsworth to Mt. Desert Is. Take Rte. 102 to SW Harbor, Follow signs.

TEL. 207-244-5036
FAX 207-244-3512
Box 137,
Southwest Harbor, ME 04679

John Madeira, Jr., Manager

COUNTRY CLUB INN

🛏	19 Rooms & 1 Cottage, $68/$77 MAP
💳	Visa, MC, Amex
🛁	All Private Baths
🎋🍸	Open mid-May.–mid- Oct.; late Dec. – late Mar.
🐕	Children Welcome; Pets Allowed, $10 daily
☀R	Golf, Swimming Pool, Hik- ing, Fishing, Lake Swim- ming, Boating, Lawn Games, Canoeing, Antiqu- ing, X-country & Downhill Skiing, and Snowmobiling
🍽	Breakfast & Dinner; Box lunch available; Wine, Beer & Liquor available
🚭	No smoking in Dining Room
⊢▦⊣	Conference facilities (100)
♿	

🏠 AN INN FOR ALL SEASONS . . . A sophisticated little resort catering to only 40 guests desiring casual luxury, tranquility, sumptuous meals, and warm hospitality. Few locations offer such beauty and grandeur in all seasons as Rangeley with its wide skies, vast mountain ranges and sparkling lakes. Magnificent scenery can be enjoyed from all guest rooms, dining room, and lounge at nearly 2000 feet in elevation. Public 18-hole golf course adjacent to Inn (golf packages available), Hiking, Boating, Fishing, X-country skiing, downhill skiing, and over 100 miles of snowmobile trails.

ME Tpke., Exit 12 to Rte. 4. I-91 in VT & NH to St. Johnsbury; (E) on Rte. 2 to Gorham & Rte. 16(N) to Rangeley.

TEL. 207-864-3831
P.O. Box 680
Rangeley, ME 04970

Sue Crory, Margie & Steve
Jamison, Innkeepers

CROCKER HOUSE COUNTRY INN

11 Rooms, $75/$90 in season, B&B
$60/$75 off season, B&B
Visa, MC, Amex, Discov

All Private Baths

Closed Jan.1 — Apr. 20;
Restaurant open Th., Fri., Sat., in Nov. & Dec.

Well mannered Children Accepted; Pets with prior permission

Spa, Croquet, Library, Clay Tennis courts, Antiquing, Golf, Acadia Nat'l Park region

Breakfast & Dinner; Sunday brunch Memorial-Labor Day

Smoking & Non-smoking Dining Rooms

Conference Facilities (36)

From Ellsworth on U.S. Rt. 1 go 79 miles (N) to R. on Hancock Pt. Rd. Continue 5 mi. to inn on R. Mooring available with advance notification.

TEL. 207-422-6806
Hancock, ME 04640

Richard Malaby, Innkeeper

Sequestered on Hancock Point, this restored 109-year-old inn is a three minute walk from Frenchman Bay. The carriage house, converted in 1992, adds two spacious guestrooms, an additional common room and a spa. The restaurant, open to the public, continues to draw guests from distant places for its extraordinary cuisine and live jazz piano on Friday and Saturday nights.

DOCKSIDE GUEST QUARTERS

15 Rooms, $58/$100 EP
6 Suites, $98/$142 EP
Off season rates and packages available
Visa, MC, Personal Chks.
19 Private, 2 Shared Baths

Open year-round
Winter apts. available
Children welcome
No Pets

Beaches, Boats, Bicycles, Fishing, Shuffleboard, Badminton, Croquet, Swimming, Golf Tennis, Outlet shopping, Historic sites

Breakfast, Lunch, Dinner; Lounge; Weddings, Group functions
Wine & Liquor available
Non-smoking Rooms

Conference Facilities (30)

From I-95 exit to U.S. 1 South. Rte. 1-A thru Old York to Rte. 103. Cross bridge & watch for signs to inn.

TEL. 207-363-2868
1-800-270-1977
Harris Island Rd.
P.O. Box 205
York, ME 03909

The David Lusty Family, Innkeepers

A small family run resort uniquely situated on a private peninsula in York Harbor. A seacoast inn and multi-unit cottages offer comfortable and attractive guest rooms, most with private decks and water views. Spacious grounds offer privacy and classic Maine scenery, The restaurant is renowned for creative presentations of fresh Maine seafood. Rated 3 diamonds by AAA.

GOOSE COVE LODGE

🛏	10 Rooms, $140/$176 MAP 11 Cotts, $160/$208 MAP
💳	MC, Visa, Personal Checks
🛁	All Private Baths
🛋	Open mid-May to mid-Oct
🐕	Children Welcome; No Pets
☀R	Sea Kayaking, Sailing, Beach, Nature Trails, Golf, Tennis, Sailing, Bicycling, Acadia Nat'l. Park
🍷	Breakfast & Dinner, May-Oct.; B&B Option in off-season; Wine & Liquor Available
🚭	No Smoking in Main Lodge
🏨	Conference Facility
♿	Wheelchair Access (1 Rm)

🏠 Secluded lodging, sand beaches, moss-covered trails, and magnificent ocean vistas. Cottages have fireplaces, sundecks, kitchenettes and ocean views. Many artists and craftspersons nearby. Pleasant daytrips on land and water. Outstanding cuisine in rustic "Down East" lodge with lobster cookouts on the beach. A Family resort.

I-95 to Augusta, Rte. 3 to Belfast. Rte. 1 (N), 4 mi. past Bucksport. R. on Rte. 15, in town of Deer Isle R. on Sunset Rd., 3 mi. to inn sign & R. 1.5 mi. to inn.

TEL. 207-348- 2508

Deer Isle,
Sunset, ME 04683

Joanne & Dom Parisi,
Innkeepers

HARTWELL HOUSE

🛏	11 Rooms, $80/$135 B&B 3 Suites, $125/$175 B&B
💳	Visa, MC, Amex, Disc.
🛁	All Private Baths
🛋	Open Year-round
🐕	Appropriate for Children over 14; No Pets
☀R	Atlantic Ocean, Beach, Fishing, Swimming, Boating, Golf, Tennis, XC Skiing, Biking
🍷	Breakfast Wine available
🚭	No Smoking
🏨	Conference facilities (5–65)
♿	

🏠 View the sculpted lawn and gardens from your balcony filled with flowers. Unwind with a walk along the breathtaking and nearby marginal way. Early American and English antiques, stunning fabrics, and a delicious gourmet breakfast all add to the ambiance of this elegant country inn. Walking distance to beaches and Perkin's Cove. Seasonal lodging and dining packages available.

I-95 (N) & York/Ogunquit Exit. L. on Rte. 1 for 4.4 mi. to R. at Pine Hill Rd. L. at Shore Rd. for .2 mi. to inn.

TEL. 207-646-7210
FAX 207-646-6032
118 Shore Rd., P.O. Box 393
Ogunquit, ME 03907

Trish & Jim Hartwell, Renee & Alec Adams, Innkeepers

THE INN AT CANOE POINT

	3 Rooms, $75–115/$90––135 B&B; 2 Suites, $110–160/$140–210 B&B Personal Checks accepted
	All Private Baths
	Open Year-round
	Not Appropriate for younger Children; No Pets
	Acadia Natl. Pk. adjacent, Hiking, Biking, Sailing, Mtn. Climbing, XC Skiing
	Full Breakfast, Afternoon Refreshments; Port Wine in Rooms; BYOB
	Non-Smokers Preferred
	Conference Facilities (20)

From Ellsworth, Rte. 3 (NE) approx. 15 mil. toward Bar Harbor, through Hulls Cove Village. Continue past Acadia Natl. Pk. entrance 1/4 mi. to inn on L.

TEL. 207-288-9511
Box 216, Hulls Cove
(Bar Harbor), ME 04644

Don Johnson & Esther Cavagnaro, Innkeepers

This secluded waterside inn among the pines is only moments away from lively Bar Harbor and next door to the unspoiled natural attractions of Acadia National Park. With views of Frenchman's Bay, mountains, trees, flowers, rocky coast and the ocean, guests will be tempted to laze by the fieldstone fireplace in the ocean room or out on the deck, listening to the rolling surf.

THE NEWCASTLE INN

	15 Rooms, $55/$130 B&B $120/$190 MAP
	Visa, MC
	All Private Baths
	Open Year-around
	Older, well behaved Children; No Pets
	Walking trails, Beaches, Bicycling, Antiquing, Birding, Boating, Touring, XC Skiing
	Breakfast – Guests only Dinner by Reservation Wine & Liquor available
	No Smoking
	Conference Facilities (20)

Maine Tpke. to Exit 9; I-95 (N) to Brunswick Exit 22, Rte. 1(N); 6 mi.(N) of Wiscasset. Take R. on River Rd. Continue 1/2 mi. to inn on R.

TEL. 207-563-5685
800-832-8669
River Road
Newcastle, ME 04553

Ted and Chris Sprague, Innkeepers

At the end of your day's travels, a warm greeting, exceptional dining with national acclaim, and a pampering atmosphere await you, overlooking the harbor and lovely flower gardens here by the broad and salty Damariscotta River. Individualized attention is reflected in the details you will find in each of our bedchambers. In one of the midcoast Maine's quintessential villages, with easy access to numerous attractions, the feeling of warmth, friendship, and seclusion make this a retreat where guests may relax and unwind.

OLD FORT INN

🛏	16 Rooms $120/$240 B&B
💳	Visa, MC, Amex, Discov. Enroute
🛁	All Private Baths; 4 Jacuzzis
🌳🛋	Closed Dec. 10 — April
🐕	Appropriate for Children over 12; No Pets
⟨R⟩	Tennis Court, Pool, Bikes, Ocean, Golf, Walking, Jogging
🍽	Breakfast
🚭	Non-smoking
⊢▦▦⊣	Conference Facilities (32)
♿	

🏠 A short walk from the ocean along a country road, this secluded inn in an old seaport town offers rooms with antiques, canopied and 4-poster beds, color TV and phones. Guests find new friends over a buffet breakfast of fresh fruit and homemade breads; a charming antiques shop, fresh-water pool, and private tennis court provide pleasant diversion. The unique combination of yesterday's charm and today's conveniences entice many guests to return to the Inn year after year and recommend it to their friends. AAA Four Diamond Award.

I-95 Exit 3, turn L. on Rte. 35 for 5 1/2 mi. L. at light at Rte. 9 for 3/10 mi. to Ocean Ave. Go 9/10 mi. to Colony Hotel, then L. & follow signs 3/10 mi. to inn.

**TEL. 207-967-5353;
800-828-3678
FAX 207-967-4547**
Old Fort Ave., P.O. Box M
Kennebunkport, ME 04046
Sheila & David Aldrich, Innkps.

THE PENTAGOET INN

🛏	16 Rms., $154/$174 MAP 1 Suite, $195 MAP
💳	Visa, MC; Personal checks preferred
🛁	All Private Baths
🌳🛋	Open May–October
🐕	Appropriate for Children over 12; No Pets
⟨R⟩	Boating, Hiking, Biking, Tennis, Golf
🍽	Breakfast & Dinner; to the public by reservation Wine & Liquor available
🚭	No Smoking
⊢▦▦⊣	Conference Facility (20)
♿	

🏠 Capacious porches, fresh flowers and nightly room freshening are just a few of the "perks" at this lovely old Victorian inn. With its feeling of a private country home, the Pentagoet offers excellent food and an extensive wine list. After a day of exploring or relaxing, join others for cocktails and special chamber music or storytelling preceding dinnerTiny, historic Castine in Penobscot Bay provides fresh sea air, harbor activities in a tranquil setting.

I-95 to Augusta & Rte. 3 (E) to Belfast, turn L. (N) on Rte. 1 past Bucksport 3 mi. to R. (S) on Rte. 175. Turn (S) on Rte. 166 to Castine. Inn is on Main St.

**TEL. 207-326-8616
800-845-1701**
Main St., P.O. Box 4
Castine, ME 04421

Lindsey & Virginia Miller,
Innkeepers

PILGRIM'S INN

🛏	13 Rms., $130/$170 MAP 1 Cottage, $180 MAP
💳	No Credit Cards
🛁	Private & Shared Baths
🧺	Open mid-May to mid-Oct.
👫	Appropriate for Children over 10; No Pets
🚴	Touring, Hiking, Bicycling, Sailing, Golf, Tennis
🍷	Breakfast & Dinner Wine & Liquor available
🚭	Smoking in common Rooms only
👥	Conference Facilities (35)
♿	

I-95 (N) to Augusta. Rte. 3 (N) to Belfast, thru Bucksport to Rte. 15 (S), thru Blue Hill. Over bridge to Deer Isle Village. Turn R., 1 block to inn on left.

TEL. 207-348-6615
Deer Isle, ME 04627

Dud & Jean Hendrick,
Innkeepers

🛡 Overlooking Northwest Harbor and a picturesque millpond, this 1793 Colonial home is surrounded by the unspoiled beauty of remote Deer Isle in Penobscot Bay. Glowing hearths, soft Colonial colors, pumpkin pine floors, antique furnishings, combined with warm hospitality and gourmet meals in the charming barn dining room, have pleased many happy and contented guests.

RANGELEY INN

🛏	50 Rooms, 1 Suite $57-–$67/$97–$107EP
💳	Visa, MC, Amex, Discov
🛁	All Private Baths; Several Whirlpools
🧺	Open Year-round
👫	Children Accepted; Pets Discouraged
🚴	Skiing at Saddleback & Sugarloaf; x-country & snowmobiling from our backdoor; swimming, sailing, canoeing, hiking near
🍷	Breakfast & Dinner, MAP optional; Dining Open Mem. Day–Col. Day & Wint.; Wknds. and for Group Business anytime; Wine & Liquor Available
🚭	Smoking Restrictions
👥	Conference Facilities (150)
♿	Wheelchair Access (2 rms., dining rm.)

On Rte. 4 past Farmington 40 mi.to Rangeley. From west take Rte. 16. Inn is on Main St.

TEL. 207-864-3341
1-800-666-3687
FAX 207-864-3634
Box 160, Main St.
Rangeley, ME 04970

Fay & Ed Carpenter,
Innkeepers

🛡 The big blue clapboard building with the long veranda across the front has that grand old summer hotel look and the homelike, roomy lobby has a bit of an old-fashioned feeling. The elegant dining room is up to the minute with creative, interesting menus. Several acres of lawns and gardens border a bird sanctuary, and the area is a nature-lover's and sportsman's paradise. So return with us now to yesteryear—and visit our mountain & lake resort from our 1907 Inn. We look forward to serving you.

MAINE
THE SQUIRE TARBOX INN

11 Rooms, $75/$160 B&B
$125/$210 MAP

Visa, MC, Amex, Discov

All Private Baths

Closed late Oct. to Mid-May

Appropriate for Older Children; No Pets

Walking path, Rowboat and Bikes on premises, Beaches, Harbors, Antiques nearby

Breakfast for guests only; Dinner to public by reservation; Wine & Liquor available

Smoking in weather protected area

12 This comfortable colonial farmhouse on a wooded hillside by a small inlet, is a respected full-service inn offering historical significance, a natural country setting, relaxed comfort, and a diversity of Maine Coast interests. Quiet rural privacy is here for guests who seek moments of personal solitude. Known for its savory fireside dinners and goat cheese from its purebred dairy herd. Built 1763–1820, the Inn is pleasantly removed from tourist crowds, but still near to beaches, harbors, antique shops, museums, lobster shacks, and L. L. Bean.

I-95 to Brunswick, Exit 22, follow Rte. 1 (N) past Bath bridge 7 mi. to Rte. 144. Continue 8.5 mi. on Westport Island.

TEL. 207-882-7693
R.R.2, Box 620, Route 144
Wiscasset, ME 04578

Bill & Karen Mitman,
Innkeepers

THE WATERFORD INNE

9 Rooms, $75/$100 B&B
1 Suite, $100 B&B

Amex

7 Private Baths; 1 Shared Bath

Closed March 15—April 30

Children Accepted; Pets with $10 fee

Library, Parlor Games, Down-hill & XC Skiing, Swimming, Boating, Hiking, Antiquing

Breakfast & Dinner; BYOB

Smoking Discouraged

Conference Facilities (15)

Some Wheelchair Access

3 A 19th-century farmhouse situated on a country lane midst 25 acres of fields and woods, Distinctively different, a *true* country inn offering uniquely decorated guest rooms, a charming blend of two centuries—the warmth of early pine furnishings combined with contemporary comforts. Outside—rolling terrain, a farm pond, an old red barn. Inside—an air of quiet simple elegance, antiques and art, barnboard and brass, pewter and primitives. Country chic cuisine to pamper your palate.

From Maine Tpke.: Use Exit 11, follow Rte. 26 N. approx. 28 mi. into Norway, then on Rte. 118 W. for 8 mi. to Rte. 37 S. (left). Go 1/2 mi., R. at Springer's Gen. St., up the hill 1/2 mi.
TEL 207-583-4037
FAX 207-583-4037
Box 149 Chadbourne Rd.
Waterford, ME 04088

Rosalie & Barbara
Vanderzanden, Innkeepers

WHITEHALL INN

	50 Rooms, $130/$165 MAP
	Off Season $80/$110 B&B Visa, MC, Amex
	Private & Shared Baths
	Open May 27–Oct. 20
	Children Accepted; No Pets
	Tennis, Shuffleboard, Gardens, Library, Games, Rocking Chairs, Golf, State Park, Lakes, Sailing
	Breakfast, Summer Sunday Brunch, Dinner; Wine & Liquor Available
	No Smoking in Dining Room
	Conference Facility (85)
	Wheelchair Access (4 rms, dining rm. & conf. fac.)

Camden is 2 hrs. north of Portland on Rte. 1. Inn is .5 mi. north of village.

TEL. 207 236-3391
1-800-789-6565
FAX 207-236-4427
52 High St., P.O.Box 558
Camden, ME 04843

The Dewing Family, Innkeepers

If ever an inn and a setting were made for each other, this is it—Camden, Maine and the Whitehall Inn. Tree-lined streets, comfortable old homes echo the feeling of old-fashioned friendliness and hospitality in this rambling, homey inn, originally built in 1834, and operating as an inn since 1901. The inn has been run by the Dewing family for 23 years. One of the few remaining authentic coastal summer hotels preserving not only its history and grandness, but the commitment to comfortable accomodations, fine service, and dining excellence.

COUNTRY INN FOOD SAMPLER

Colonial corn and mussel chowder, cured salmon, rabbit in puff pastry, half duckling in apple and peppercorn sauce, baked grapefruit with a sautéed chicken liver, romaine soup, local fish baked in wine, leg of lamb with fresh rosemary, lobster pie, double-thick lamb chops, baked ham with peach glaze.

Homemade Georgia crackers with fresh fruit salad, Louisiana chicken with artichoke hearts and almonds, roast duckling with orange-cranberry sauce, sautéed mountain trout, vegetable strudel, steak and kidney pie, roast squab with fresh peaches, veal with pomegranate wine, crayfish fritters.

Carolina quail with savory cabbage, fillet of beef on fried eggplant, tomato cups with fresh corn, low country squash pie, local channel bass in puff pastry, smoked ham, grits, and cornbread, stuffed pork chops, Midwestern fish boils, cooked outside in huge iron cauldrons over a roaring fire and served with coleslaw, fresh-baked bread and cherry pie.

Desserts might be fudge walnut cake, pistachio cake, pecan pie, hot gingerbread with lemon sauce, triple mousse cake with whipped cream, deep dish apple pie, fruit cobbler, Indian pudding, sour cream apple pie, fresh figs filled with white chocolate mousse, homemade angel food cake with strawberries and whipped cream.

Some breakfast possibilities: Crepes Suzette, blueberry pancakes, herbed eggs with cheese and mushrooms, fresh fruit, sausage or ham biscuits, German apple pancakes, eggs Benedict, French toast with strawberries and whipped cream, cheddar egg bake with Dijon mustard and broccoli, fresh-baked muffins with quince jelly, poached pear in caramel sauce, kiwi with pureed raspberries. — **by Virginia Rowe**

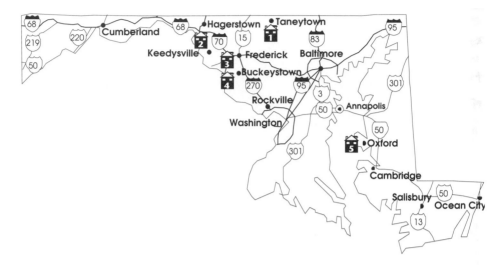

1. Antrim 1844, Taneytown
2. Antietam Overlook Farm, Keedysville
3. Tyler Spite House, Frederick
4. Inn at Buckeystown, Buckeystown
5. Robert Morris Inn, Oxford

ANTIETAM OVERLOOK FARM

6 Rooms, $103/$148 B&B

Visa, MC, Amex, Diners

All Private Baths

Open Year-around

Teenage Children Welcome: No Pets

Antietam National Battlefield, Hiking Trails, Game & Birdwatching, Antiquing in Quaint Villages

Memorable Country Breakfast, Comp. Wine, Soda, & After-dinner drinks; Wine available, BYOB
No Smoking

Our 95-acre mountaintop farm overlooking Antietam National Battlefield has extraordinary views of four states. The hand-hewn timber framing, rough-sawn walls, and stone fireplaces juxtaposed to the softly flowered furnishings and fine crystal create a warm, comfortable atmosphere. Spacious suites include fireplaces, queen beds, sumptuous bubble baths, and private screened porches. While our seclusion and tranquility are unparalleled, many guests also enjoy visiting the neighboring Civil War battlefields at Gettysburg, Bull Run/Manassas, and Harpers Ferry.

Located in the Western Maryland mountains just over one hour west of Baltimore and Washington D.C.— Call for directions and availability

TEL. (800) 878-4241
P.O. Box 30
Keedysville, MD 21756
Barbara & John Dreisch,
Innkeepers

ANTRIM 1844

8 Rooms, $150/$175 B&B
5 Suites, $250/300 B&B

Visa, MC, Amex, Discov

All Private Baths

Open Year-round

Some Restrictions

Swimming, Tennis, Croquet, Touring Gettysburg and Countryside Wineries, and Antiquing

Breakfast & Dinner; Wine & Liquor

Smoking Restrictions

Conference Facility (30)
Wheelchair Access (1 rm., dining rm. & conf. fac.)

From Wash., D.C. , 495 to I-270 N; then 15 N and 140 E to Taneytown. Through light and over tracks and then bear right on Trevanion Rd.
TEL. 800-858-1844;
410-756-6812;
FAX 410-756-2744
30 Trevanion Rd
Taneytown, MD 21787
Dort & Richard Mollett, Innkeepers

 One of Maryland's most renowned country inn resorts. Antebellum ambience together with genuine hospitality and acclaimed cuisine has earned Antrim 1844 a place in country inn connoisseurs' hearts. Guestrooms are appointed with elegant decor, roaring fireplaces, and jacuzzis. Relax by the fire in the Pickwick Tavern, Library, Smokehouse, or Drawing Rooms. Turn-down service, tea, cocktail party, and endless amenities spoil even the most discriminating traveler. "A must see" if your are near Washington, D.C. or Baltimore.

THE INN AT BUCKEYSTOWN

3 Rooms, $167/$209 MAP
4 Suites, $188/$272 MAP
(Tax & Service Incl.)
Visa, MC, Amex

All Private Baths

Open Year-round
By Reservation Only

Appropriate for Children over 16; Pets by permission in 1 cottage

Lawn games on premises, Hiking, Antiquing, Civil War sites

Breakfast & Dinner
Complimentary Wine

Smoking only in parlors

Conference facilities (20)

From I-70 or I-270, take Rte. 85(s) to Buckeystown. Inn is on left. (35 mi. from Dulles Airport.)
TEL. 301-874-5755
RES. 800-272-1190
c/o General Delivery
3521 Buckeystown Pike
Buckeystown, MD 21717
Daniel R. Pelz, Chase Barnett, Rebecca Shipman-Smith, Innkeepers

 Lovingly restored, this impressive 1897 mansion and 1884 church are in a nostalgic village, on the National Register of Historic Places. Rooms are luxuriously furnished with outstanding antiques and collectibles. A wraparound porch with rockers looks out on park-like grounds. Gourmet dining and the friendly ambiance bring guests back to this award-winning Inn. The changing seasons and all holidays are reasons to celebrate here. In fact, all stays are considered celebrations—a celebration of life!

THE ROBERT MORRIS INN

🛏	35 Rooms, $70/$185 EP
💳	Visa, MC
🛁	All Private Baths
🏡	Lodging Year-round B&B Dec.-Mid Mar.; Rest. open Mid Mar.-Nov.
🐕	Appropriate for Children over 10; No Pets
⚡	Tennis, Biking, Golf, Antiquing, Sailing, His- toric Car Ferry, Goose Hunting
🍽	Full Service Wed.-Mon.; Cont. Bkfst. only Tues.; Wine & Liquor available
🚭	All Rooms Non-Smoking
🪑	Executive Conference Facilities (10-20)
♿	Wheelchair Access, 2 rms.

Chesapeake Bay and the Tred Avon River play a big part in the life of this Eastern Shore country-romantic 1710 inn. Delicacies from the bay are featured in the nationally acclaimed seafood restaurant and the Tred Avon offers lovely views from many of the rooms and porches. Country furnishings add to the friendly feeling here in the historic waterside village of Oxford. James A. Michener, author of "Chesapeake," rated the Robert Morris Inn's crab cakes the highest of any restaurant on the Eastern Shore."

Hwy. 301 to Rte. 50 (E). Turn R. on Rte. 322 for 3.4 mi. Turn R. on Rte. 333 for 9.6 mi. to inn

TEL. 410-226-5111
312 No. Morris St.
P.O. Box 70
Oxford, MD 21654

Wendy & Ken Gibson, Owners
Jay Gibson, Innkeeper

TYLER SPITE HOUSE

🛏	5 Room, $120/$180 B&B 5 Suites, $150/180
💳	Visa, MC, Amex
🛁	All Private Baths
🏡	Open Year-round
🐕	No Children or Pets
⚡	Swimming Pool on pre- mises; Tennis, Biking, Boat- ing nearby; Civil War Museum and Performing Arts Theater 3 blocks away
🍽	Breakfast, High Tea at 4:00 P.M., Complimen- tary Wine & Sherry
🚭	No Smoking
🪑	Conference Facility (5–15)

A romantic 1814 Inn located in the heart of Frederick's historic district. Spacious, beautifully appointed rooms with 13 1/2 foot ceilings, marble fireplaces, oriental carpets, comfortable antique furnishings and paintings captivate our guests who are looking for the ultimate in romanticism. Walled gardens replete with color entice guests for a leisurely stroll. A stay is complete once you ascend from the carriage block located at the front door for a horse drawn carriage tour through Frederick's quaint city.

Route 70 to Market St., left on 2nd St., 2 blocks and left on Record St, 2 blocks and at corner of Church St.

TEL. 301-831-4455
800-417-3264
112 W. Church St
Frederick, MD 21701

Bill & Andrea Myer,
Innkeepers

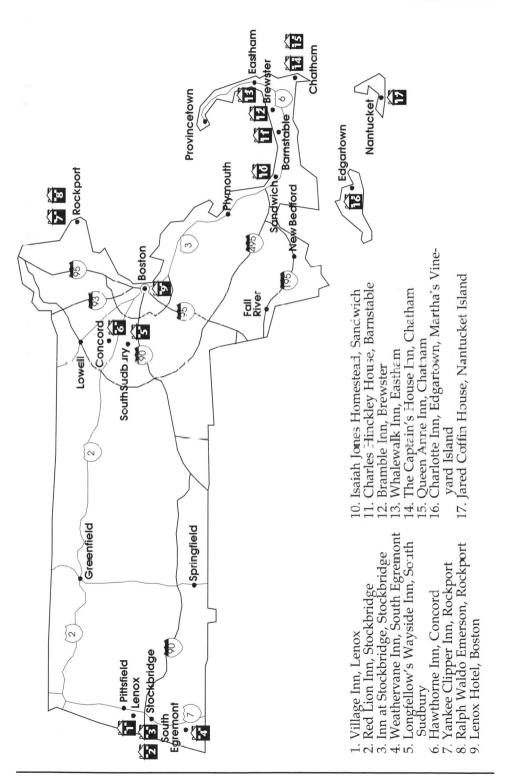

1. Village Inn, Lenox
2. Red Lion Inn, Stockbridge
3. Inn at Stockbridge, Stockbridge
4. Weathervane Inn, South Egremont
5. Longfellow's Wayside Inn, South Sudbury
6. Hawthorne Inn, Concord
7. Yankee Clipper Inn, Rockport
8. Ralph Waldo Emerson, Rockport
9. Lenox Hotel, Boston

10. Isaiah Jones Homestead, Sandwich
11. Charles Hinckley House, Barnstable
12. Bramble Inn, Brewster
13. Whalewalk Inn, Eastham
14. The Captain's House Inn, Chatham
15. Queen Anne Inn, Chatham
16. Charlotte Inn, Edgartown, Martha's Vineyard Island
17. Jared Coffin House, Nantucket Island

MASSACHUSETTS
THE BRAMBLE INN AND RESTAURANT

	12 Rooms, $78/$130 B&B 1 Suite, $130/$170 B&B
	Visa, MC, Amex
	All Private Baths
	Open April 15–Dec. 31
	Appropriate for Children over 8; No Pets
	Tennis, Swimming, Fishing, Bicycling, Horseback, Riding, Whale-watching, Antiquing
	Breakfast, Price-fix Dinner by reservation, Wine & Liquor available
	Smoking restricted
	Wheelchair access (3 Rooms)

Dine superbly at one of Cape Cod's top three restaurants, where Ruth Manchester creates dishes sought after by *Bon Appetit* and *Gourmet*. Wide pine floors, antiques, and flowered wallpapers adorn the guest rooms in the three 18th and 19th century buildings of this family-owned and operated intimate inn on the historic north side.

Rte. 6, Exit 10 & bear L. on Rte. 124 to R. on Rte. 6A for 1/8 mi. to inn on left.

TEL. 508-896-7644
2019 Main St.
Route 6A, Box 807
Brewster, MA 02631

Cliff & Ruth Manchester, Innkeepers

THE CAPTAIN'S HOUSE INN OF CHATHAM

	15 Rooms, $125/$200 B&B 1 Suite, $150/$175 B&B
	Visa, MC, Amex
	All Private Baths
	Open Year-round
	Doesn't meet needs of Children; No Pets
	Beaches, Tennis, Golf, Boating, Theater, Fishing, Bicycling, Lawn Croquet
	Breakfast, Afternoon Tea
	Non-Smoking Inn
	Conference Facilities (16)

A quiet getaway, without television, and cheerful, caring attention are here for guests who choose to stay at this historic, elegant 1839 inn set on two acres, a half-mile from Cape Cod's south shore beaches. The decor is reminiscent of Williamsburg with fine antiques, canopied beds, and fireplaces in warm, inviting guest rooms. This lovely inn has rated the AAA 4-diamond award.

Rte. 6 (Mid-Cape Hwy.) to Rte. 137, Exit 11 (S) to Rte. 28; left on Rte. 28 to Chatham Center. Continue around rotary on Rte. 28 toward Orleans 1/2 mi. to inn on left.
TEL. 508-945-0127
FAX 508-945-0866
369-377 Old Harbor Rd.
Chatham, Cape Cod, MA 02633
Jan & David McMaster, Innkeepers

CHARLES HINCKLEY HOUSE

2 rooms, \$119/\$139 B&B
2 suites, \$149 B&B

Personal Checks accepted

All Private Baths

Open Year-round except
Dec. 22–27

Appropriate for Children
10 & over; No Pets

Antiquing, Beaches, Golf,
Tennis, Sailing, Fishing,
Museums, Historic Sites

Complimentary Breakfast, Lunch upon request,
Dinner on weekends
only, Complimentary
Sherry
No Smoking

Wheelchair Access (1
room)

Rte. 6 to exit 6, end of ramp stop sign
go left onto Rte. 132 to stop sign, turn
right onto 6A, 1 1/2 miles on left
TEL. 508-362-9924
FAX 508-362-8861
Olde Kings Hwy., (Rte. 6-A),
P.O. Box 723
Barnstable, MA 02630

Les & Miya Patrick,
Innkeepers

An architectural gem listed on the National Register of Historic Places on the Olde Kings Highway is this 1809 Colonial home of an early shipwright. The young innkeepers have lovingly restored and furnished it, polishing the wide pumpkin pine floors, refurbishing the fireplaces, and putting in 4-poster beds. Where no detail is overlooked. The Charles Hinckley House defines elegant simplicity. A small intimate country inn where great expectations are quietly met. The unspoiled natural beauty of Cape Cod Bay is just a stroll away.

THE CHARLOTTE INN

22 Rooms, \$95–195/
\$215–295 B&B
2 Suites, \$295–350/\$400
550 B&B
Visa, MC, Amex
All Private Baths

Open Year-round

Appropriate for Children
14 & over; No Pets

Boating, Golfing, Tennis,
Fishing, Swimming,
Bicycling

Comp. Continental
Breakfast, Sunday
Brunch, Dinner (weekends off-season). Wine &
Liquor available
Smoking discouraged

Woods Hole/Martha's Vineyard
ferry (res. needed for car). In
Edgartown, take first R. off Main St.
to Summer St., continue 1/2 block to
inn.
TEL. 508-627-4751
South Summer St.
Edgartown, MA 02539

Gery & Paula Conover,
Innkeepers

Art, aesthetics, and exquisite attention to detail are the hallmarks of this beautifully restored inn, surrounded by lovely gardens and brick pathways. Original oils and watercolors and beautiful wallpapers adorn luxuriously furnished rooms, some with fireplaces. Cuisine at the French restaurant pleases the most sophisticated palates.

MASSACHUSETTS
HAWTHORNE INN

🛏	7 Rooms, $85/$160 B&B
💳	Visa, MC, Amex, Discov
🛁	All Private Baths
💡	Open Year-round
🐑	Children Welcome; No Pets
☀	Swimming (Walden Pond), Museums, Wooded trails for Hiking & XC Skiing, Canoeing on Concord River
🍷	Breakfast
🚭	No Smoking
⌗	Conference Facility (10)

On land where Emerson, Alcott, and Hawthorne lived, and among trees planted by these illustrious men, the Hawthorne Inn follows their lead in the cultivation of art and appreciation of the spiritual in life. Friendly, caring innkeepers and nature walks, where land, sky, and water refresh the senses, imbue this winsome, intimate inn with a very special feeling.

Rte. 128-95, Exit 30-B (W) (Rte. 2A) for 2.8 mi. Bear R. at fork toward Concord for 1.2 mi. Inn across from Hawthorne's home.

TEL. 508-369-5610
462 Lexington Rd.
Concord, MA 01742

Gregory Burch & Marilyn Mudry, Innkeepers

THE INN AT STOCKBRIDGE

🛏	6 Rooms, $85/$215 B&B 2 Suites, $125/$235 B&B
💳	Visa, MC, Amex
🛁	All Private Baths, 1 Whirlpool
💡	Open Year-round
🐑	Appropriate for Children over 12; No Pets
☀	Pool on premises, golf & tennis privileges at local club, hiking, horseback riding, downhill & crosscountry skiing nearby
🍷	Breakfast, Dinners for groups can be arranged Complimentary Wine
🚭	No Smoking
⌗	Conference Facilities (20)
♿	

Consummate hospitality and outstanding breakfasts distinguish a visit at this turn-of-the-century Georgian Colonial estate on 12 secluded acres in the heart of the Berkshires. Close to the Norman Rockwell Museum, Tanglewood, Hancock Shaker Village, summer theaters, and four-season recreation. The inn has a gracious, English country house feeling, with two well-appointed living rooms, a formal dining room, and a baby grand piano.

Mass. Tpke. Exit 2 & (W) on Rte. 102 to Rte. 7 (N) 1.2 mi. to inn on R. From NYC, Taconic Pkwy. to Rte. 23 (E) & Rte. 7 (N) past Stockbridge 1.2 mi.

TEL 413-298-3337
FAX 413-298-3406
Rte. 7 (North), Box 618
Stockbridge, MA 01262

Lee & Don Weitz, Owners

ISAIAH JONES HOMESTEAD

	5 Rooms, $75-$124 B&B
	Visa, MC, Amex, Discov.
	All Private Baths
	Open Year-round
	Children over 12 accepted; No Pets
	Museums, Antiques, Gift Shops, Beach, Fishing, Whale Watching, Tennis, Golf, Biking, Hist. Sites
	Breakfast & Afternoon Tea; Warm Cider by Fireside or Lemonade on Porch. Low Cholesterol Cooking featured
	No Smoking

Rte. 6 (mid-Cape-Hwy.) Exit 2, L on Rte. 130 and bear R. at fork for 2/10 mi. on L.
TEL. 508-888-9115 or 800-526-1625
165 Main Street
Sandwich, MA 02563
Shirley Jones Sutton, Innkeeper

This 1849 Italianate Victorian in the historic village of Sandwich, Cape Cod's oldest town, is within walking distance of most points of interest and fine restaurants. Beautifully furnished with antiques, oriental carpets, and fresh flowers, its quiet elegance harks back to a time when life was tranquil and travelers were pampered. Enjoy the elegant rooms including the master suite with over-sized jacuzzi bath; the Beale Room with fireplace. All rooms have private baths. Breakfast is served by candlelight.

JARED COFFIN HOUSE

	60 Rooms, $85/$175 B&B
	Visa, MC, Amex, Diners, Discov
	All Private Baths
	Open Year-round
	Children & Pets Accepted with prior approval
	Excellent Bike Trail, Conservation Walk, Swimming, Sailing, Fishing (none on premises)
	All meals available on premises; Wine & Liquor available
	No Pipes or Cigars in Restaurant
	Conference Facilities (24)
	Wheelchair Access (6 rms., dining rm. & conf. fac.)

Flights available from NYC, Boston, New Bedford, & Hyannis. Or take Hyannis ferry, leaving car in Hyannis — cars unnecessary on Nantucket.
**TEL. 508-228-2400
Res: 800-248-2405 (M-F, 8-5); FAX 508-228-8549**
29 Broad St., P.O. Box 1580
Nantucket, MA 02554-1580
Philip & Margaret Read, Innkeepers

A collection of buildings from the mid-1800's tastefully restored to provide today's guest with the feeling of a gentler past. The inn is conveniently located in the Old Historic District near Main Street shops with easy access to island beaches and bike paths. The Tap Room and JARED's offer both casual and more formal dining featuring American cuisine. The inn is open for the Thanksgiving, Christmas, and New Year holidays and offers guests the friendly feeling of a home away from home.

MASSACHUSETTS
THE LENOX HOTEL

🛏	219 Rooms, $140/$215 EP 3 Suites, $235/350 EP
💳	Visa, MC, Amex, Enroute, Discov, Diners, CB
🛁	All Private Baths
🛎	Open year-round
🐕	No Pets; Children under 18 free in same room with parent
⚡R	Free exercise room on property; Sing-a-long in Diamond Jim's Piano Bar
🍷	Breakfast & Lunch in the Pub, Dinner in the Up- stairs Grille, Wine & Li- quor available
🚭	Smoking Restrictions
👥	Conference facilities (7 rms.)
♿	Wheelchair access (conf. fac.)

Turn of the century traditional hotel with the ambiance of a country inn. This small hotel has been run by the same family for over 25 years. In the Back Bay area, next to Copley Square, the hotel offers several rooms with decorative or working fireplaces and many with country inn touches. All rooms are equipped with a hair dryer, a shaving mirror, voice mail, and modem hook-up. Diamond Jim's Piano Bar and the Pub and Grill are popular attractions. New self-controlled heating and air conditioning has just been installed. Valet parking service.

Mass. Tpke., Exit 22, Copely Square ramp to L. on Dartmouth, 2 blocks to L. on Newbury St., 1 block to L. on Exeter, 1 block to hotel at corner of Exeter & Boylston.

TEL. 800-225-7676
IN MASS: 617-536-5300
710 Boylston St.
Boston, MA 02116

The Saunders Family,
Innkeepers

LONGFELLOW'S WAYSIDE INN

🛏	10 Rooms, $90
💳	All Major
🛁	All Private Baths
🛎	Closed Dec. 25th & July 4th
🐕	Children Accepted No Pets
⚡R	Historic sites, Famous Revolutionary War landmarks
🍷	All Meals (overnight guests only); Wine & Liquor available
🚭	No Smoking in Public Areas
👥	Conference Facility (50)
♿	Wheelchair Access (din- ing rm. & conf. fac.)

Immortalized in 1863 by Longfellow in his *Tales of a Wayside Inn*, the inn is located off U.S. Rt. 20 on Wayside Inn Road. Next to the inn is a working gristmill, (open April-November); the Red Stone School House of *Mary and Her Little Lamb* fame (open seasonal weather) and the Martha Mary Chapel for weddings. Reservations for lodging and for dining made well in advance.

Between Boston & Worcester off Rte. 20. 11 mi. (W) of Rte. 128 & 7 mi. (E) off Rte. 495. Sign on R., for Wayside Inn Rd.

TEL. 508-443-1776
FAX 508-443-2312
Wayside Inn Rd. off Rte. 20
South Sudbury, MA 01776

Robert H. Purrington,
Innkeeper

THE QUEEN ANNE INN

29 Rooms, $115/$265
B&B; 1 Suite, $300 B&B

Visa, MC, Amex, Diners

All Private Baths;
2 Jacuzzis

Closed Jan. 1–April 15

Children Accepted
Kennel nearby for Pets
Outdoor Swimming Pool;
Indoor Spa, 3 Tennis Cts,
Bikes, Boating, Scuba
Diving, Fishing, Golf
Continental Breakfast,
Dinner, Dining room
closed Tues.; 12/1- 5/17
Wine & Liquor Available
Smoking discouraged

Conference Facilities (30)

Rte. 6 (E) to Exit 11, R. on Rte. 137 and
L. on Rte. 28 for 3.5 mi. to light and R.
fork to Queen Anne Rd. and up hill to
inn.
TEL. 508-945-0394
RES.800-545-INNS
FAX 508-945-4884
70 Queen Anne Rd.
Chatham, MA 02633

Guenther Weinkopf,
Innkeeper

Spacious guest rooms, antiques, garden views, private balconies, working fireplaces, and private whirlpool baths are a few of the amenities that may be found here on Cape Cod's picturesque south shore. The intimate restaurant features superb cuisine, and pursuits to beguile quiet hours or to engage the energetic are all around.

RALPH WALDO EMERSON INN

34 Rooms, $80/$133 EP
2 suites, $95/$133

Visa, MC, Discov.

All Private Baths

Open May 1–Oct. 31
Children Accepted
No Pets
Heated Saltwater Swim-
ming Pool, Theater with
Projector TV & Video
Movies, Sauna & Whirl-
pool, Bike Rental at Inn,
Hiking Trails from Inn,
Whale Watches, Shops
Galleries & Golf nearby
Breakfast (all months
open) & Dinner (July-
Aug)
Smoking Permitted
Conference Facilities (35)
Wheelchair Access (2
rms., dining rm.)

Rte. 128 (N) to traffic light in
Gloucester, right on 127 to our sign in
Pigeon Cove (Phillips Ave.)
TEL. 508-546-6321
FAX 508-546-7043
Phillips Ave., Box 2369
Rockport, MA 01966

Gary & Diane Wemyss, Inn-
keepers

One of the last of the old summer hotels on Cape Ann, the Emerson's broad porches and Greek Revival architecture give it a classic majesty. Preserving the charm of yesteryear while keeping up with the times, the inn features a heated saltwater pool, a whirlpool and sauna, and a theater for movies. Popular seafood and shore specialties are always included on the menu. The Inn is right on the ocean and many rooms have an excellent ocean view.

THE RED LION INN

91 Rooms, $65/$155 EP
17 Suites, $165/$235 EP

Visa, MC, Amex, Diners, Discov

Private & Shared Baths

Open Year-round

Children Accepted
No Pets

Exercise room, Pool, Golf, Tennis, Tanglewood, Jacobs Pillow, Berkshire Theatre Festival, Norman Rockwell Museum, Chesterwood

Breakfast, Lunch, Dinner; MAP available for groups Wine & Liquor available

Non-smoking area in dining room

Conference Facilities (6-90)

Wheelchair Access (1 rm., dining rm)

This grand old inn in the Berkshire Hills is still the lively, delightful focus of village activity it has been since 1773. Its rambling porch, hung with summer pots of glowing fuchsias and festooned in winter with garlands and Christmas trees, welcomes travelers with cheerful cordiality, born of long tradition. Beautiful antiques and heirlooms abound. Massage therapist on premises. Breakfast, lunch, and dinner served daily. Dine on traditional New England fare in the formal main dining room, cozy tavern, or outdoor courtyard.

I-90, Exit 2 at Lee, to Rte. 102 (W) to Stockbridge.

TEL. 413-298-5545
FAX 413-298-5130
Main St.
Stockbridge, MA 01262

Jack & Jane Fitzpatrick, Owners

C. Brooks Bradbury, Innkeeper

THE VILLAGE INN

32 Rooms, $50/$160 EP
1 Suite, $225/$315 EP

Visa, MC, Amex,Discov, CB

All Private Baths
4 Jacuzzis

Open Year-round

Appropriate for Children over 6; No Pets

Downhill & XC Skiing, Golf, Riding, Tennis, Swimming, Fishing

Breakfast, English tea with homemade scones, Dinner of fine American regional cuisine exc. Mon. & Tues.

Smoking Permitted only in common rooms

Conference Facilities (50)

Wheelchair Access (6 rms.)

In the historic district of the Berkshire village of Lenox, this Colonial Inn, built in 1771, is near shops, galleries, library, churches, beautiful parks and wooded trails, Tanglewood and summer theatre and dance festivals, winter downhill and cross-country skiing, fall foliage and spring flower excursions, and year-round museums such as the Norman Rockwell, Clark, Grandma Moses, and Hancock Shaker Village. Every room is individualy furnished with country antiques, some 4-posters and fireplaces, all with private baths and telephones.

Mass. Tpke. (I-90), Exit 2, Rte. 20(W) to Rte.183(S). Turn L. for 1 mi. to R. on Church St. & inn. From Rte. 7 to Rte. 7A & Church St. in Lenox.

TEL. 413-637-0020
800-253-0917
FAX 413-637-9756
16 Church St. P.O. Box 1810
Lenox, MA 01240
Clifford Rudisill and
Ray Wilson, Innkeepers

THE WEATHERVANE INN

🛏	10 Rooms, $110/$190 MAP; $95/130 B&B
💳	Visa, MC, Amex
🛁	All Private Baths
🌳	Open Year-round
🐕	Appropriate for Children Over 7; No Pets
☀	Pool, Nature walks, Antiques, Museums, Tennis, Golf, Skiing, Tanglewood, Summer Theater
☕	Breakfast & Dinner; B&B rates available weekdays Wine & Liquor available
🚭	Smoking is restricted next to smoking logo
🪑	Conference Facilities (25)
♿	Wheelchair Access (2 rms.)

From NYC, Taconic Pkwy. to Rte. 23(E) 13 mi. to inn on R. From Mass. Tpke., Exit 2 & Rte. 102 to Rte. 7(S) to Rte. 23(W) to inn on L.

TEL. 413-528-9580
FAX 413-528-1713
P.O. Box 388, Rte. 23
South Egremont, MA 01258
Murphy Family,
Innkeepers

Renowned and caring Murphy family has been providing hospitality to their guests for the past 14 years in an elegant farm and coach house on ten acres in a quaint Berkshire village in southwestern Massachusetts. The charming fireside room with three common rooms and honor bar beckons guests seeking recreation and recuperation before experiencing the inns superb cuisine. A full breakfast is offered daily and when dinner is served a host of delectable appetizers and entrees entice you. An all seasons inn. (AAA 3 diamonds)

WHALEWALK INN

🛏	7 Rooms, $80/$115 B&B 5 Suites, $120/$165
💳	VISA, MC
🛁	All Private Baths
🌳	Open April-November
🐕	Children over 12 Welcome; No Pets
☀	Cape Cod National Seashore, Boating, Fishing, Biking, Golf, Whale Watching, Antiquing, Theater
☕	Breakfast
🚭	No Smoking
🪑	Conference Facility (10)

Rte. 6 to Orleans Rotary. Rock Harbor exit off rotary. Left onto Rock Harbor Road. Right onto Bridge Road. Driving time from Boston 2 hours.

TEL 508-255-0617
FAX 508-240-0017
220 Bridge Road
Eastham MA 02642
Carolyn and Richard Smith,
Innkeepers

The owners of this inn promise you an unspoiled environment on outer Cape Cod, one of the country's most beautiful areas. This 1830's home has been authentically restored and decorated with handsome antiques. The site consists of three acres, located on a back road, only minutes by car or bike to beaches, bike trials, or Orleans Village. All 12 guest rooms have private baths and are beautifully decorated. Five of them are suites with kitchens. A full breakfast is served. Hor d'oeuvres provided each evening.

MASSACHUSETTS
YANKEE CLIPPER INN

	26 rooms, $99/$210 B&B 13 Rooms w/ocean view
	Visa, MC, Amex, Discov
	All Private Baths
	Closed Jan. 1–Feb. 14, Week before Christmas & Christmas Day
	Appropriate for Children over 3; No Pets
	Swimming pool, Tennis, Golf, Whale-watching, Deep Sea Fishing, Hiking, Biking
	Breakfast & Dinner, BYOB
	No Smoking Rooms Available, Non-smoking Dining Rm., No Cigars or Pipes
	Conference facilities (50)
	TDD Accessible

Fresh ocean breezes and sweeping panoramic views have greeted guests here for over 47 years. The Inn and the 1840 Bulfinch House, both with antique furnishings, and the more contemporary Quarterdeck all offer country inn blandishments. There are historic sites in Boston, Salem, Concord and Lexington, and life can be lazy or exciting with Rockport's famous art colony close by. The Inn has a lovely heated outdoor saltwater pool on a landscaped terrace overlooking the gardens and ocean. Our dining room features New England gourmet cuisine and is open to the public.

Rte. 128 (N) to Cape Ann thru Gloucester. L. on Rte. 127 for 4 mi. to Rockport's 5 Corners & sharp L. & Pigeon Cove sign. Continue 1 mi. to inn.

TEL. 508-546-3407
800-545-3699
FAX 508-546-9730
96 Granite St., P.O. Box 2399
Rockport, MA 01966
Bob & Barbara Ellis, Innkps.

WHAT MAKES COUNTRY INNS "DIFFERENT"?

There are various reasons why one country inn seems different from any other country inn. Here are some of the things, chosen at random, that make country inns special:

Gardens — formal English gardens with topiary bushes, "natural" gardens with wild flowers, vegetable and herb gardens, and everything in between . . .

Displays or use of local arts & crafts — paintings, sculpture, ceramics, baskets, handmade quilts and wallhangings . . .

Collections of artifacts & memorabilia—walking sticks, Revolutionary War firearms, antique pump organs, nickelodeons, ship models, African masks, Oriental tapestries, carved pipes, bells, and other objects from "the old country," farm tools . . .

Museum-quality collections—ancient documents and maps, antique china teapots, rare china, crystal, pewter, "Nanking Cargo" porcelain, Shaker pieces, clocks . . .

Historical references—pictures and books tracing the early history and development of a region, portraits of former owners, printed histories of the inns . . .

Amusing & interesting collections—antique dolls, shoes, & kaleidoscopes, folk art, samplers, hand-cut jigsaw puzzles, stuffed animals . . .

Community involvement—events such as 4th of July celebrations, blueberry or apple festivals, antique car meets, bike or foot races, pumpkin-carving contests, Easter egg hunts, and art shows . . .

Homage to poets—One inn has an Edna St. Vincent Millay Room, where the poet first recited one of her poems: another has many Scottish references, with poems, quotations, and portraits of Robert Burns and Walter Scott and other famous Scots . . .

Miscellaneous—Christmas festivities with huge, festooned trees and all sorts of entertainments and events sometimes including sleigh rides. A 1958 Bentley or a London taxicab for transporting guests to and from the airport . . . — **by Virginia Rowe**

1. Stafford's Bay View Inn, Petoskey
2. Montague Inn, Saginaw
3. Dusty's English Inn, Eaton Rapids
4. National House Inn, Marshall
5. Victorian Villa, Union City

DUSTY'S ENGLISH INN

7 Rooms, $75/$175 B&B
1 Suite, $125/$195 B&B
2 Cottage, $110/$175 B&B
Visa, MC, Discov

All Private Baths

Open Year-round

2 Persons per room limit
Children not encouraged;
No Pet facilities

Golf, Fishing, Canoeing,
Hiking, Biking, XC-
Skiing, Antiquing

Breakfast, Lunch, Dinner;
Authentic English pub;
Wine, Beer, Ales, Liquor

Smoke-free Inn

Conference Facilities (50)
Wheelchair Access (4 rms.,
dining rm & conf. fac.)

From I-96 in Lansing, take M-99 (S) 8
mi. From I-94, take M-99 (N) 22 mi.
Ninety miles west of Detroit. 20 miles
south of State Capitol (Lansing) and
Michigan State Univ. (E. Lansing).

TEL 517-663-2500
FAX 517-663-2643

728 S. Michigan Rd.
Eaton Rapids, MI 48827

Dusty Rhodes, Innkeeper

A 1927 built Tudor-style riverside mansion on 15 acres. Rolling countryside with 2 miles of nature (xc-skiing in winter) trails along the Grand River and through woods. A 3 room suite and master bedroom are in the cottage complete with pool and fireplace sitting room. Six bedrooms in the inn find fireplaces, dining rooms, and walnut-paneled pub for cocktails, or pints of English ale.

MICHIGAN
MONTAGUE INN

🛏	17 Rooms, 1 Suite, $65/$150 B&B
💳	Visa, MC, Amex
🛁	16 Private Baths 1 Shared Bath
🌳	Open Year-round
🐕	Children Accepted; No Pets
☀	Library, Herb Garden, Antiquing, Marshall Frederick Gallery, Saginaw Art Museum, Japanese Tea House
🍷	Breakfast; Lunch & Dinner Tues.–Sat. Wine & Liquor available
🚭	No Smoking in guest rooms
🏛	Conference Facilities (2)
♿	Wheelcheer Access (3 rms., dining rm. & conf. fac.)

This Georgian Mansion, restored to its original splendor, is surrounded by spacious lawns with flower and herb gardens. Summer evenings may be spent under the trees watching the sun set over the lake. Enjoy winter evenings curled up in front of a roaring fire in our library. Fine cuisine is offered in our intimate dining room overlooking the beautiful grounds. The Montague Inn provides a peaceful and elegant oasis in the heart of the city.

From I-75 exit west on Holland Ave. (W) for approx. 3.5 mi. Go L. on Washington Ave., 2 blocks to inn.

TEL. 517-752-3939
FAX 517-752-3159
1581 S. Washington Ave.
Saginaw, MI 48601

Willy Schipper, Innkeeper

THE NATIONAL HOUSE INN

🛏	16 Rooms, $69/$110 B&B 2 Suites, $110/$115 B&B
💳	Visa, MC, Amex
🛁	All Private Baths
🌳	Closed Dec. 25
🐕	Children Welcome No Pets
☀	Gift shop, Garden, Park, Tennis, Antiquing, XC Skiing, National Historic Landmark District Tours
🍷	Breakfast & Catered Dinners; Wine Available
🚭	Area Smoking
🏛	Conference facilities (36)
♿	Wheelchair Access (dining rm. & conf. fac.)

Marshall, a National Historic Landmark District and home of Win Schuler's restaurant, has many citations for its 850 structures of 19th-century architecture, including the National Register of Historic Places, on which this inn is also listed. Michigan's oldest operating inn, the first brick building in the county has been restored as a warm, hospitable inn, beautifully furnished, and lovely gardens. Afternoon Tea, Lectures, Candlelight Home Tours, Mystery Weekends, Historic Garden Tours.

I-94 to Exit 110; Rte. 27 (S) 2 mi. to Michigan Ave. Turn R. Marshall is halfway between Detroit & Chicago.

TEL. 616-781-7374
102 So. Parkview
Marshall, MI 49068

Barbara Bradley, Innkeeper

STAFFORD'S BAY VIEW INN

22 Rooms, $88/138 B&B
9 Suites, $145/$175 B&B

Visa, MC, Amex

All Private Baths

Open mid May-Oct. full
time. Open Christmas
Holiday Season & Jan.-
March on weekends
Children Welcome
No Pets; Kennel nearby

Complimentary Croquet,
Bikes. Hiking, XC Skiing,
Beach, Golf, Tennis, Boat-
ing, Scenic Drives

Breakfast, Lunch, Dinner,
& Sun. Brunch in summer,
Sat. Dinner in winter

Non Smoking Dining
Rm.16 Non-Smoking Rms.

Conference Facilities (60)

Wheelchair Access, most
rooms

From Detroit, I-75 (N) to Gaylord exit,
Rte. 32 (W) to Rte. 131 (N) Petoskey.
From Chicago, I-94 to Rte. 196 (N) to
Rte. 131 (N) to Petoskey.

TEL. 616-347-2771

613 Woodland Ave.
P.O. Box 3
Petoskey, MI 49770

The Stafford Smith Family,
Innkeepers

Judged one of the "Ten Best Inns" in the nation, this grande dame of classic Victorian architecture on Little Traverse Bay in the Historic Landmark Victorian cottage community of Bay View, sets the standard in fine dining and gracious service. Guests swim, sail the Great Lakes, rock on the front porch, cross-country ski out the front door, or enjoy the finest Alpine skiing in the Midwest.

THE VICTORIAN VILLA INN

6 Rooms, $75/$95 B&B
4 Suites, $95/$125 B&B
MAP rates available
Visa, MC, Discov, Diners

All Private Baths

Open year-round

Children Accepted
No Pets

Antiquing, Hiking, Ca-
noeing, Golf, Tandem Bi-
cycles, Croquet, Fishing,
Lawn Games, Special
Weekends, Summertime
Villa Dinner Theatre Pro-
ductions

Breakfast, Afternoon Tea,
Dinner, Picnic baskets,
Victorian theme Dinners
No Smoking

Conference Facilities (24)
Wheelchair Access (1 rm.,
dining rm.)

From I-69, exit M-60 (Exit 25); 7 mi.
(W) to Union City & left on Broadway
St. (the Main St. of town). Continue to
inn on No. Broadway.

**TEL. 517-741-7383; 800-34-
VILLA; FAX 517-741-4002**

601 No. Broadway St.
Union City, MI 49094

Ron Gibson, Cynthia Coats,
Innkeepers

A quiet and unhurried reflection of the 19th Century, the elegant and romantic Victorian Villa Inn offers distinctively furnished guest chambers, delicious hearty breakfasts, afternoon English Teas, and seasonal lunches. The Victorian Villa Inn also offers 19th Century gourmet 7-course Victorian dining, which has achieved national recognition in *Victoria Magazine, Midwest Living*, and *Wine Spectator*. Guests may also choose a special selection from over 200 wines from the Villa's own wine cellar, awarded *Wine Spectator*'s "Best of Award of Excellence."

71

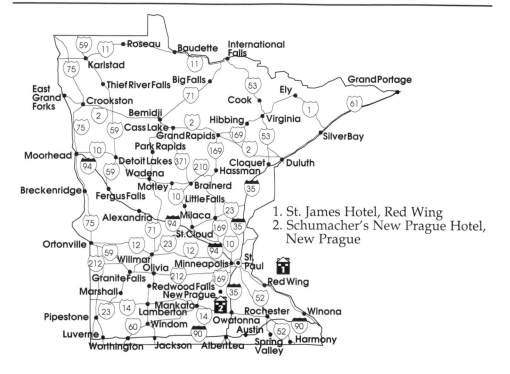

1. St. James Hotel, Red Wing
2. Schumacher's New Prague Hotel, New Prague

ST. JAMES HOTEL

- 60 rooms, $100/$155 EP
- Visa, MC, Amex, Disc., Diners, Carte Blanche
- All Private Baths, Some Whirlpools
- Open year-round
- Children accepted No Pets
- Shopping, Antiquing, Golf, Downhill & XC Skiing, River boat cruise
- Breakfast, Lunch, Dinner; Sun. Brunch Wine & Liquor available
- 20 Non-smoking Guest Rooms
- Conference facilities (300)
- Wheelchair access (100%)

Since 1875, a magnet for travelers to the scenic Mississippi River city of Red Wing. Nestled between limestone bluffs, this small, bustling hotel has been elegantly restored and outfitted. Impressive period furnishings, beautifully crafted quilts, genuine hospitality, and such special touches as complimentary champagne and turn-down service are a few of the pleasures you'll find.

From Minneapolis./St. Paul, take I-94E to US 61 S. To Red Wing .

TEl. 612-388-2846
800-252-1875
406 Main St.
Red Wing, MN 55066

Gene Foster,
General Manager

SCHUMACHER'S NEW PRAGUE HOTEL

11 Rooms, $105/$155 EP

Visa, MC, Amex, Discov

All Private Baths
11 Whirlpool Tubs

Year-round except Dec.
24–25

No Pets

18-hole Golf course, XC
Skiing, Biking, Fishing,
Casino

Breakfast, Lunch, Dinner
Wine, Beer & Liquor available

Smoking Permitted; No
Pipes or Cigars

Conference Facilities (11)

Wheelchair Access (din-
ing rm.)

From Mpls., 35W (S) to Exit 76 Elko,
New Market (County Rd. 2), W, turn
R for 10 mi. At 13, turn L, S, follow 13
2 mi., merges w/19 W, follow 2 Hwys
into New Prague. Hotel is on left hand
side past center of New Prague.
TEL. 612-758-2133
FAX (612) 758-2400
212 W. Main St.
New Prague, MN 56071
Kathleen & John Schumacher,
Innkeepers

 Named one of the "Ten Best Inns," 1992, one of the "Top Twelve Inns, 1991," and "National Pork Restaurant of the Year," 1992 and consistently named one of the favorite restaurants in Greater Minnesota, this charming Central European Inn is internationally known for its superb Czech and German cuisine by Chef/Proprietor John Schumacher. Bavarian folk painted furniture, eiderdown comforters, whirlpool tubs, gas fireplaces, Bavarian bar, and European gift shop add to the uniqueness of this inn.

Rates are quoted for 2 people for 1 night and do not necessarily include service charges and state taxes. An asterisk after the rates indicates a per-person rate for AP and MAP plans. For more detailed information, ask the inns for their brochures.

AP — American Plan (3 meals included in room rate)

MAP — Modified American Plan (breakfast & dinner included in room rate)

EP — European Plan (meals not included in room rate)

B&B — Bed & Breakfast (breakfast included in room rate)

— Represents recreational facilities and diversions either on the premises of an inn or nearby

1. The Duff Green Mansion, Vicksburg
2. Monmouth Plantation, Natchez
3. The Burn, Natchez

THE BURN

5 rooms, $90/$110 B&B
2 suites, $125/$135 B&B

Visa, MC, Amex, Diners

All Private baths

Open Year-round

School-age Children
No Pets

Private TV's, Swimming
Pool. Golf and Tennis
nearby.

Plantation Breakfast; spe-
cial Dinners, Lunches,
Picnics for groups of 20 +,
Wine & Liquor available

Conference Facilities (50)
Wheelchair Access (2
rooms)

The Burn: c. 1834 historic elegance combining the traditions of the antebellum South with present-day comfort.
Exquisite antiques and canopied beds in 7 warm, inviting
rooms. Nightly turn-down with sweets and wine. Guests
feast on a full-seated hot southern breakfast. Pool, Independent Innkeepers Association.

From I-55 at McComb, MS, exit to
Hwy. 98 (Natchez). Meadville to
Hwy. 98/84 to end & Hwy. 61 at
Washington. Turn L. (W) to Natchez.
R. onto No. Union to inn on L.

Tel. 601-442-1344
800-654-8859
FAX 601-445-0606
712 No. Union St.
Natchez, MS 39120
Larry & Debbie Christiansen,
Innkeepers

THE DUFF GREEN MANSION

4 Rooms, $85/$160 B&B
3 Suites, $95/$150 B&B
8% Sales Tax
Visa, MC, Amex

Private Baths

Open Year-round
Children Welcome
Small Pets Accepted,
Swimming pool on
grounds; Golf, Tennis,
Fishing, Hunting nearby;
many Historic Sites within walking distance
Plantation Breakfast,
Lunch, Dinner, Refreshments, Wine & Liquor
Available
Smoking in designated
areas
Conference Facilities (75)
Wheelchair Access (4
rms., dining rm.)

From I-20 Exit 4B to Clay St. Turn R. on Adams to First East St. Continue to inn.
TEL. 601-636-6968; 638-6662; 800-992-0037; FAX 601-634-1061
1114 First East St.
Vicksburg, MS 39180

Harry & Alicia Sharp,
Innkeepers

One of the finest examples of Palladian architecture in the state (National Register of Historic Places), this 1856 mansion was pressed into service as a hospital for Confederate, and later Union, soldiers during the famous siege of Vicksburg. The 12,000-sq.-foot mansion in the historic Old Town was restored in 1985 and is luxuriously furnished in period antiques and reproductions.

MONMOUTH PLANTATION

12 Rooms, $95/$135
13 Suites, $125/$165
AAA Four Diamond
Visa, MC, Amex

All Private Baths

Open Year-round

No Pets; Children over 14

Fishing, Golf, and Tennis
1/2 mile away

Breakfast and Dinner

No Smoking

Conference Facility (100)
Wheelchair Access (4 rms.,
dining rm. & conf. fac.)

One-half mile from center of Natchez. 1 1/2 hours from Jackson, MS and Baton Rouge, LA. 2 1/2 hours from New Orleans.
TEL. 601-442-5852
800-828-4581
FAX 601-446-7762
36 Melrose Avenue
Natchez, MS 39120
John Holyoak, Manager
Ron Riches, Owner

Monmouth Plantation, a National Historic Landmark circa 1818, a glorious return to the antebellum South. Rated "One of the ten most romantic places in the USA" by *Glamour Magazine* and *USA*. Today it tranquilly waits to enfold you in luxury and service. Walk our 26 beautifully landscaped acres. Twenty-five rooms and suites in the mansion and the 5 other historic buildings hold priceless art and antiques while providing every modern comfort. Mornings begin with a delightful complimentary Southern breakfast. Nights sparkle under candlelight and crystal during 5-course dinners.

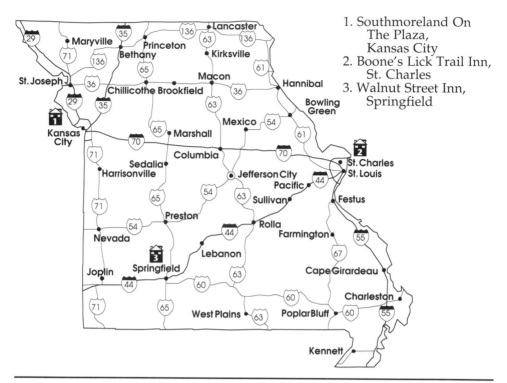

1. Southmoreland On
   The Plaza,
   Kansas City
2. Boone's Lick Trail Inn,
   St. Charles
3. Walnut Street Inn,
   Springfield

BOONE'S LICK TRAIL INN

	4 Rooms, $65/$95 B&B 1 Suite, $85/$125 B&B
	Visa, MC, Discov, Diners, Personal Checks
	All Private Baths
	Open Year-round
	Children Accepted; No Pets; Kennels nearby
	Historic District, Winery Antiquing, Dining, Riverboat Excursions, Goldenrod Showboat, Riverboat Gaming Casino, Biking/Hiking, State Park
	Full Breakfast; Lunches for Hikers/Bikers on re- quest
	No Smoking
	Conference Facilities (10- 16)
	Wheelchair Access Lim- ited (2 Rooms)

It was THE highway west, predating the Santa Fe & Oregon Trails. At first, they called it the "Boone's Lic" Trail. In the 1840's, a Federal style building rose in the village of St. Charles at the corner of Main Street and the Boonslick Road. Today, the inn, on the waterfront of "the Wide Missouri" River is surrounded and scented by rose and herb gardens, dressed in regional antiques, sprinkled with touches of Folk Art, and serves delicacies like lemon "sandbag" biscuits. Guests stroll the cobblestoned street of Missouri's largest Historic District. (Six miles to airport; 25 minutes to St. Louis.)

I-70 to exit 229 St. Charles Fifth St.,
(N) 3 blocks to Boonslick Rd. R. 4
blocks to Main St. Inn on SE corner of
Main & Boonslick

TEL. (314) 947-7000
(800-366-2427 9-5 CST)

1000 South Main St.
St. Charles, MO 63301

V'Anne and Paul Mydler,
Innkeepers

SOUTHMORELAND ON THE PLAZA

12 Rooms $100/$135 B&B

Visa, MC, Amex

All Private Baths

Closed Christmas Eve & Christmas Day

Children over 13; No Pets

Nelson-Atkins Museum of Art, Country Club Plaza, Dining & Shopping, Theater, Dinner Playhouse, Tennis, Swimming, Royals Baseball, Chiefs Football, Crown Center, Historic Westport & River Market

Breakfast, Wine & Hors d'oeuvres nightly

Smoking areas designated

Conference Facilities; A-V Equip. Available (14)

Wheelchair Accessible First Floor

From I-70, I-35, I-29 in downtown Kansas City, Missouri, take the Main Street exit S. several miles to E 46th St., turn E (L), go 1 1/2 blocks to the Inn on the left.

TEL. (816) 531-7979
FAX (816) 531-2407

116 E. 46th St.
Kansas City, MO 64112

Susan Moehl &
Penni Johnson, Innkeepers

 Award-winning Southmoreland's 1913 Colonial Revival styling brings New England to the heart of Kansas City's Historic, Arts, Entertainment and Shopping district—The Country Club Plaza. Business and leisure guests enjoy individually decorated rooms offering decks, fireplaces or double-Jacuzzi baths. Business travelers find respite at Southmoreland with its rare mix of business support services; in-room phones, FAX, message center, modem connections, 24-hour access and switchboard, and photocopier. Mobil Four-Star.

WALNUT STREET INN

14 Rooms, $80/$150 B&B

Visa, MC, Amex, Discov, Diners

All Private Baths

Open Year-round

No Pets; limited provisions for children

Nearby Lakes & Rivers, Golf, Tennis, Bass Pro, Caves, Bluffs, and Hiking Trails at the Nature Center. 45 min. from Branson, MO and Silver Dollar City

Breakfast; Wine & Beer Available

No Smoking except outside porches & balconies

Wheelchair Access (1 rm., dining rm.)

From I-44 take 65 S to Chestnut Expressway. West on Chestnut Expressway to Sherman Parkway; turn S 4 blocks to Walnut St.

TEL. 417-864-6346
FAX 417-864-6184

900 E. Walnut St.
Springfield, MO 65806

Nancy Brown & Karol Brown, Innkeepers

 One of the "Top Twelve Inns in the Country" and recommended by *Glamour Magazine,* the 14-room luxury urban inn is in Springfield's Historic District and thirty minutes from Branson. Enjoy fireplaces, jacuzzis, private porches, and feather comforters for leisure travelers. In-room phones and fax for business travelers. Relax on the front porch swing, read a book by the fire, walk to the great Hall for the Performing Arts, museums, theaters and restaurants, or enjoy the Ozarks fine natural attractions.

NEW HAMPSHIRE

1. Philbrook Farm Inn, Shelburne
2. Christmas Farm Inn, Jackson
3. Darby Field Inn, Conway
4. Stafford's in the Field, Chocorua
5. Corner House Inn, Center Sandwich
6. Lyme Inn, Lyme
7. Moose Mountain Lodge, Etna
8. Dexter's Inn and Tennis Club, Sunapee
9. Hickory Stick Farm, Belmont
10. Colby Hill Inn, Henniker
11. Inn at Crotched Mountain, Francestown
12. John Hancock Inn, Hancock
13. Chesterfield Inn, West Chesterfield

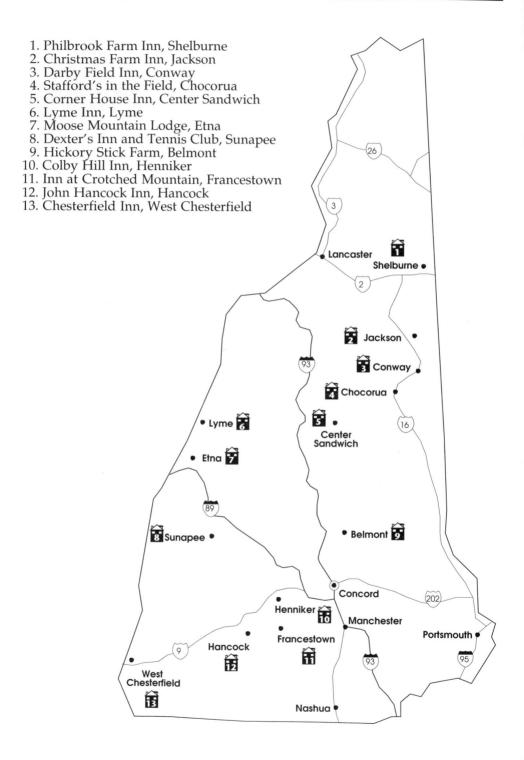

CHESTERFIELD INN

- 11 Rooms, $110/$150 B&B
  2 Suites, $150/$165 B&B
- Visa, MC, Amex, Discov, Diners
- All Private Baths
- Open Year-round except Christmas Eve & Day
- Children & Pets Welcome
- Arts, Crafts, Music in Keene & Brattleboro. Swimming & Boating on Spofford Lake
- Breakfast Daily; Dinner Tues. thru Sat.; Foliage Season, 7 days; Wine & Liquor available
- Conference Facilities (20)

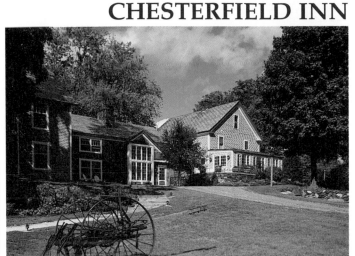

From I-91, take Exit 3 to Rte. 9 (E). Continue on Rte. 9 for 2 mi. to inn on L.

TEL. 800-365-5515
Route 9
West Chesterfield, NH 03466

Judy & Phil Hueber, Innkeepers

 Serving since 1787 as a tavern, a farm, and a museum, the inn's guest rooms today are spacious; some with fireplaces, or outdoor balconies, all with private baths, air conditioning, TV & telephone. Outside, the meadow overlooks Vermont's Green Mountains. Guests enjoy the cuisine of chef Carl Warner and enter the dining room through the kitchen to observe his magic in action. Chesterfield Inn is a wonderful place to relax in comfortable elegance.

CHRISTMAS FARM INN

- 20 Rooms, $136/$160 MAP; 10 Suites, $170/$180 MAP; In-room phones exc. M. Inn
  Visa, MC, Amex
  All Private Baths, 5 Jacuzzis
- Open Year-round
- Children Most Welcome
  No Pets
- Swimming Pool, Putting Green, Game Room, Shuffleboard, XC & Down-hill Skiing, Golf, Tennis
- Breakfast & Dinner
  Wine & Liquor available
- Non-Smoking Dining & Living Rooms
- Conference Facilities (50)
  Wheelchair Access (dining rm. & conf. fac.)

From Rte. 16 to Rte. 16A across covered bridge .5 mi. to schoolhouse. L. on Rte. 16B for .5 mi. to inn on R.

TEL. 603-383-4313
800-HI-ELVES
FAX 603-383-6495
Box CC, Route 16B
Jackson, NH 03846

Will Zeliff, Innkeeper

In a setting of majestic mountains, crystal-clear rivers and leafy woods, the cluster of buildings that make up this rambling inn invite you to share the good life. Whether inside in cozily decorated rooms, outside at the garden swimming pool, or in the candlelit dining room feasting on delectable, fresh meals, guests enjoy the at-home feeling.

COLBY HILL INN

	16 Rooms, $85/$155 B&B
	Visa, MC, Amex, Diners, Discov, CB
	Open Year-round
	All Private Baths
	Appropriate for children over 7; No Pets, enjoy ours
	Swimming, Games, Ice Skating, Skiing, Fishing, Books, Tennis, Antiques, and Canterbury Shaker Village
	Full Breakfast Daily(Inn guests only), Dinner Daily except Mon.–Tues., Wine & Liquor Available
	No Smoking except outside
	Conference Facility (32)

Congenial inn-dogs Bertha and Delilah await with a handshake and the cookie jar beckons at this rambling 1795 inn, a complex of farmhouse, carriage house, and barns on five village acres. 16 antique-filled guestrooms, some with working fireplaces, all with private baths and phones. And the food is memorable—from the bountiful breakfasts to the acclaimed candlelit dinners served in the gardenside dining room. Classic New England scenery abounds around this village on the river.

17 miles west of Concord off Route 202/9. South 1/2 miles on Rt. 114 to blinking light and Pharmacy. Turn right. Inn is 1/2 mile on the right.

TEL. 603-428-3281
800-531-0330
FAX 603-428-9218
The Oaks, PO Box 778
Henniker NH 03242
Ellie, John, and Laurel Day,
Innkeepers

CORNER HOUSE INN

	3 rooms, $80/$70 B&B
	Visa, MC, Amex
	All Private Baths
	Open Year-round exc.Thanksgiving, Dec. 25
	Children over 4 Well-behaved Pets allowed
	Crafts & Antique Shops, Museum, Art Gallery, Squam Lake, Tennis, Hiking, Skiing
	Breakfast, Lunch, Dinner Wine & Liquor available
	Smoking discouraged including dining rm.
	Conference Facilities (70)
	Wheelchair Access (dining rm. & conf. fac.)

The picturesque village of Center Sandwich and the surrounding lakes and mountain area, near "Golden Pond" (Squam Lake), offer delightful diversions in any season. A warm welcome awaits at the intimate 150-year-old Corner House, sparkling with country antiques and beautiful crafts made by many local artisans. The Inn boasts one of the area's most widely acclaimed restaurants.

I-93, Exit 23 & Rt. 104 (E) to Meredith. R. at light on Rt. 25 (E) to Ctr. Harbor. L. at 2nd light to Bean Rd. for 7 mi. to blinker. R. onto Main St. to inn.

TEL. 603-284-6219
800-832-STAY (7829)
FAX 603-204-6220
Main St., P.O. Box 204
Ctr. Sandwich, NH 03227
Jane & Don Brown,
Innkeepers

THE DARBY FIELD INN

15 Rooms, $65/$90 MAP
1 Suite, $55/$70 MAP (4)

Visa, MC, Amex

14 Private, 2 Shared Bath

Open Year-round exc. April

Children Accepted
No Pets

Swimming pool, XC ski trails, Canoeing, Golf, Tennis, Hiking, Rock climbing

Breakfast & Dinner
Wine & Liquor available

Smoking Restricted

Rte. 16 (N) toward Conway. Turn L. .5 mi. before Conway at inn sign. 1 mi. to 2nd inn sign. Turn R. & continue 1 mi. to inn.
TEL. 800-426-4147
603-447-2181
FAX 603-447-5726
P.O. Box D, Bald Hill
Conway, NH 03818
Marc & Maria Donaldson,
Innkeepers

Beguiling guests with a spectacular view of distant mountains from its dining room, many guest rooms, and terrace swimming pool, this 1830 inn on the edge of the White Mountain National Forest is a favorite with outdoor enthusiasts. Well-groomed ski and hiking trails past rivers and waterfalls, a cozy pub, a massive stone fireplace, and hearty, delicious food are part of the picture.

DEXTER'S INN & TENNIS CLUB

17 Rooms, $130/$170 MAP
1 Cottage, $187.50 MAP
Visa, MC, Discover

All Private Baths

Closed Nov. 1 to May 1

Children Accepted
Pets Accepted

3 Tennis Courts, Pool, Lawn Games, Lake activities, Hiking, Golf

Breakfast, Dinner
Wine & Liquor available

Non-smoking Dining area

Conference Facilities (25)

I-89 (N), Exit 12 & Rte. 11 (W) for 5.5 mi. to L. on Winn Hill Rd. for 1.5 mi. From I-91 (N), Exit 8 & Rte. 11/103 (E) for 18 mi. to Newport & Rte. 103 for .1 mi. to L. on Young Hill Rd. for 1.2 mi.
TEL. 800-232-5571
603-763-5571
Box 703IIA, Stagecoach Rd.
Sunapee, NH 03782
Michael Durfor & Holly
Simpson-Durfor, Innkeepers

Tennis buffs love Dexter's, but so do all the guests who come for the breathtaking views, idyllic gardens, green lawns, bright guest rooms and excellent, bountiful food. The Simpson-Durfor family runs the inn like a well-appointed private estate, which provides a perfect setting for weddings and family reunions. In addition to the outstanding tennis program and 3 excellent golf courses nearby, they offer friendly service and advice on the myriad diversions available in the area.

HICKORY STICK FARM

	2 Rooms, $70 B&B
	Visa, MC, Amex, Discov.
	All Private Baths
	Closed Mon.; Restaurant winter hours restricted
	Appropriate for Children over 7; No Pets
	Hiking, Nature trails, Birdwatching, Swimming, Boating, Skiing, Shaker Village
	Breakfast (guests only) & Dinner by reservation Wine & Liquor available
	Smoking Restricted
	Conference Facilities (25)

Since 1950 the Roeder family has been serving thoughtful meals in the delightful Early American atmosphere of their restaurant. The converted Colonial farm buildings offer great views over the back fields to the mountains from the dining room and screened gazebo. A varied menu is offered, with roast duckling the specialty. Two charming B&B rooms provide quiet relaxation to travelers.

I-93, Exit 20 & Rte. 3 toward Laconia, approx. 5 mi. over Lake Winnisquam bridge .3 mi. to R. on Union Rd. for 1.5 mi. & L. on Bean Hill Rd. for .5 mi. to inn.

TEL. 603-524-3333

60 Bean Hill Road
Belmont, NH 03220

Scott & Linda Roeder,
Innkeepers

INN AT CROTCHED MOUNTAIN

	13 Rooms, $100/$120 MAP
	No Credit Cards
	Private & Shared Baths
	Closed end of ski season to mid-May; late Oct. to Thanksgiving
	Children Accepted Pets Accepted
	Swimming pool, Tennis courts, XC and walking trails, Downhill Skiing, Ice Skating, Antique shops, Summer Theaters
	Breakfast, Dinner Wine & Liquor available
	Cigars or Pipes restricted
	Conference Facilities (26)
	Wheelchair Access (4 Rms.)

This 170-year-old colonial house is located on the northern side of Crotched Mountain. An awe-inspiring setting and a spectacular view of Piscataquog Valley makes all the difference at this out-of-the-way Colonial inn. Walking and ski trails thread the woods; vegetable and flower gardens supply food and adornment for tables and rooms. Rose Perry's savory home cooking has the added zest of an occasional Indonesian dish. John and Rose, who have been operating the inn since 1973, look forward to welcoming you.

From Manchester, Rte. 101 (W) to 114 (N) to Goffstown & 13 (S) to New Boston & 136 (W) to Francestown. R. at 47 (N) 2.5 mi. to L. on Mountain Rd. for 1 mi. to inn.

TEL. 603-588-6840
Mountain Rd.
Francestown, NH 03043

Rose & John Perry,
Innkeepers

THE JOHN HANCOCK INN

11 rooms, $88/$120 B&B

Visa, MC, Amex, Diners

All Private Baths

Open Year-round

Appropriate for Children over 12; No Pets

Historic Touring, Walking, Mountain Climbing, Skiing, Skating, Bicycling, Swimming, Antiquing, Summer Theater

Breakfast, Dinner, Wine & Liquor available

No Smoking

Conference Facilities (35)

Ramp for Access

From Keene, Rte. 9 (N) to Rte. 123 (E) to Hancock. From Peterborough, Rte. 202 (N) to L. on Rte. 123 to Hancock.
TEL. 603-525-3318
Outside N.H. **800-525-1789**
FAX 603-525-9301
Main Street
Hancock, NH 03449

Linda & Joe Johnston,
Innkeepers

This is the oldest original inn in New Hampshire. The Inn and the homes on this beautiful tree lined Main Street are in the National Historic Register. Stroll the well-worn cow paths. Pass the village store, country school house, gazebo, and white steepled church to Norway Pond. Celebrate the evening in our award-winning dining rooms, decorated with sponge painted walls, soft lighting and period fabrics. Dine on succulent roasts and Indian pudding. Retire in four poster comfort and let the Paul Revere church bell lull you to sleep.

THE LYME INN

13 Rooms, $55/$95 B&B
2 Suites, $75/$135 B&B
(Includes a tea)
Visa, MC, Diners, Discov

All Private Baths

Open Year-round

Pets Not Welcome; Children Welcome of All Ages

Dartmouth College, Skiing, Swimming, Golf, Tennis, Canoeing

Breakfast, Lunch, & Dinner; Wine & Liquor available

Smoking Restricted

Conference Facility (100)
Wheelchair Access (3 rms., dining rm. & conf. fac.)

I-91, Exit 14. Follow signs for Lyme. Inn is in center of town on the common.
TEL. 603-795-2222
FAX 603-795-4220
On the Common
Lyme, NH 03768

Tami & Mickey Dowd,
Innkeepers

An historic (1809) inn located at the head of the town common in picturesque Lyme, NH. Recently renovated. Adding modern amenities and restored to its original charm, our country tavern and dining rooms are known for their fine food and New England hospitality.

MOOSE MOUNTAIN LODGE

🛏	12 rooms, $160 MAP
💳	Visa, MC
🛁	5 Shared Baths
🌳🛋	Closed Mar. 21-May 31; Oct. 20 to Dec. 26
🐕👧	Appropriate for Children over 5; No Pets
☼R	Hiking & Skiing Trails, Swimming Pond, Large Porch, Appalachian Trail, Connecticut River, Dartmouth College
🍽	Breakfast, Lunch & Dinner in winter; Breakfast & Dinner summer & fall
🚭	No Smoking
⊦₳₳₳⊣	
♿	

🏠 Perched high on the side of Moose Mountain, with hiking and ski trails threading through 350 acres of woods and meadows, this big, old, comfortable lodge offers ever-changing views of the Connecticut River Valley. Meals are healthy, plentiful and delicious; the welcome is warm and friendly. Far from the sounds of civilization, peace and quiet reign.

I-89, Exit 18 (N) to Rte. 120 for 0.5 mi. to R. at Etna Rd. for 3.6 mi. to R. on Rudsboro Rd. for 2 mi. to L. on Dana Rd. for 0.4 mi. up mtn. to lodge.

TEL. 603-643-3529
Hanover, NH
Moose Mountain Rd.
P.O. Box 272
Etna, NH 03750

Peter & Kay Shumway,
Innkeepers

PHILBROOK FARM INN

🛏	19 Rooms, $100/$130 MAP (Rate change July 1) 4 Cottages $450/week
💳	No Credit Cards
🛁	Private & Shared Baths
🌳🛋	Closed April 1 to May 1; Nov. 1 to Dec. 26
🐕👧	Children Welcome Pets Accepted in Cottages
☼R	Swimming pool, Game room, Major Ski areas, Nat'l. forest Hiking, Golf
🍽	Full Breakfast, Trail Lunches to order, Dinner; B&B rates avail. BYOB
🚭	
⊦₳₳₳⊣	
♿	Wheelchair Access (1 rm.)

🏠 The latchstring has been out at this venerable (National Register of Historic Places) inn since 1861 and 5 generations of the Philbrook family have been dispensing New England hospitality and wholesome, hearty, home-cooked New England meals ever since. As they say, "you will find simplicity rather than luxury, genuineness rather than pretension" at this peaceful retreat.

U.S. Rte. 2 (W—20 mi.) from Bethel, ME. or (E—6 mi.) from Gorham, NH. At inn sign turn on Meadow Rd. for 1 mi. to R. at North Rd. for .5 mi. to inn.

TEL. 603-466-3831
881 North Rd.
Shelburne, NH 03581

The Philbrook & Leger
Families, Innkeepers

STAFFORDS-IN-THE-FIELD

10 Rooms, $80/$160 B&B DBL Occ.; $140/$200 MAP DBL Occ.— 3 Cotts, $90/$160 B&B DBL Occ.; $170/$200 MAP DBL Occ.

Visa, MC

8 Private, 3 Shared Baths

Open Year-round

Inquire Regarding Children; No Pets, Kennel Nearby

Walking Trails, Tennis, Croquet, XC Skiing, Golf, Swimming, Climbing, Antiques, Wedding Receptions in Restored Barn

Breakfast & Dinner, Picnic Lunches; Wine & Liquor Available

Smoking Restricted

Conference Facility (50-200)

Wheelchair access (cotts, dining rm. & conf. fac.)

From Chocorua Village & Rte. 16, take Rte. 113 (W) 1 mi. to inn sign. From Rte. 93, Exit 23 to Rtes. 104 & 25 (E) to Rte. 16 (N) to village & Rte. 113 as above.

TEL. 603-323-7766

FAX 603-323-7531

Box 270

Chocorua, NH 03817

The Stafford Family, Innkeepers

This New England farmhouse circa 1778, set amidst rolling fields & hidden from view by the surrounding forest, celebrates its centennial this year as a country Inn. Known the world over for its gourmet country dining. The herbs from Ramona's kitchen garden flavor the scrumptious dishes served in the lantern-lit dining room. Walk in the woods, sleep under down filled quilts, enjoy the peace and quiet of the country.

The IIA Gift Certificate

A Lovely Gift for Someone Special

The gift of an overnight stay or a weekend at a country inn can be one of the most thoughtful and appreciated gifts you can give your parents or children, dear friends, or valued employees for Christmas, a birthday, an anniversary, or any special occasion. Innkeepers and other employers are discovering this is an excellent way of rewarding their employees, while at the same time giving them some much needed rest and relaxation.

An IIA gift certificate means that you can give the gift of a stay at any one of over 250 member inns from Kennebunkport, Maine to Southern California; from Quebec, Canada to Key West, Florida; from Martha's Vineyard, Massachusetts to Seaview, Washington. We have inns in the Blue Ridge Mountains, on ranches in the western desert, near state parks and forests and nature preserves, in restored villages in historic districts, on lakes and by the sea. Choose your pleasure.

An IIA gift certificate is good for two years and may be purchased through the IIA office by personal check or Mastercard or Visa. With each gift certificate we send along a brand new copy of the *Innkeepers' Register*. For further information call **800-344-5244**.

A five dollar ($5) postage and handling fee will be added to all gift certificate purchases.

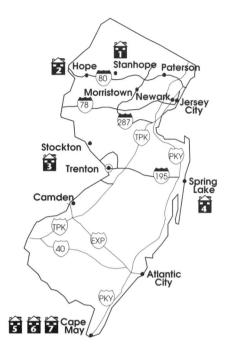

1. Whistling Swan Inn, Stanhope
2. Inn at Millrace Pond, Hope
3. Stockton Inn, "Colligan's," Stockton
4. Sea Crest By The Sea, Spring Lake
5. Mainstay Inn & Cottage, Cape May
6. Manor House, Cape May
7. The Queen Victoria, Cape May

THE INN AT MILLRACE POND

17 Rooms, $85/$150 B&B Corp. Rate Sun.– Thurs.

Visa, MC, Amex, Diners
All Private Baths

Open Year-round
Dining Room Closed for Dinner Christmas Day

Children Accepted (limited); No Pets

Tennis, Antiquing, Hiking, Fishing, Canoeing, Skiing, Golf, Bicycling, Winery tours, Waterloo Village.

Breakfast; Dinner daily Sunday Lunch or Dinner served Noon- 8:00 p.m.

Wine & Liquor available
Smoking in designated rooms and areas

Conference Facilities (30)
Wheelchair Access (restaurant)

Originally a grist mill complex, Circa 1769, the original innkeepers restored these historic buildings in 1986, creating a lovely inn along Beaver Brook. Authentically decorated rooms in the Grist Mill, Millrace House, and stone Wheelwright's Cottage blend the quiet elegance of Colonial America with modern amenities. The Mill's rich industrial heritage is evident while enjoying the restaurant's acclaimed seasonal menu. Colonial traditions of hospitality, value and gracious service highlight a visit to historic Hope. AAA ◆◆◆ Mobile ★★★

From I-80, Exit 12, take Rte. 521 (S) 1 mi. to 4-way stop., L. on Rte. 519 (N), .2 mi. to inn. From the south, Rte. 78 to Rte. 22 to Rte. 519 (N), travel 18 mi., take R. at blinker/4-way .2 mi. to inn.

TEL. 908-459-4884
Rte. 519, P.O. Box 359
Hope, NJ 07844
Cordie & Charles
Puttkammer, Innkeepers

MAINSTAY INN & COTTAGE

- 16 rooms, $105/$185 B&B
  7 suites, $115/$195 B&B
- No Credit Cards; Personal Checks
- All Private Baths
- Open Year-round
- Appropriate for children over 12; No Pets
- Swimming, Biking, Hiking, Tennis, Golf, Birdwatching, Historic Attractions
- Breakfast, Afternoon Tea
- No Smoking
- Conference facilities (24)
- Wheelchair Access (1 unit)

Take Garden State Pkwy. (S). In Cape May, Pkwy. becomes Lafayette St. Take L. at first light onto Madison Ave. Go 3 blocks, R. at Columbia Ave. Inn on R.

TEL. 609-884-8690
635 Columbia Ave.
Cape May, NJ 08204

Tom & Sue Carroll,
Innkeepers

Once an exclusive gambling club, the Mainstay is now an elegant Victorian inn furnished in splendid antiques. Breakfast and afternoon tea are served each day either in the formal dining room or on the wide veranda. Located in Cape May's famous historic district, the inn is within walking distance of beaches, interesting shops and a vast selection of fine restaurants.

MANOR HOUSE

- 8 Rooms, $68/$145 B&B
  1 Suite, $95/$165 B&B
- Visa, MC, Discov, Carte Blanche
- 7 Private, 2 Shared Bath
- Open Feb. 1–Jan.1
- Appropriate for Children over 12, Unable to Accommodate Pets
- Ocean swimming, Beach walking, Porch sitting, Birding, Golf, Historic Homes Tours, Napping
- Breakfast, Afternoon Tea
- Smoking Restricted
- Conference Facilities (12)

From zero-mi. mark on Garden State Pkwy. to Rte. 109 South becoming Lafayette St., turn L. on Franklin for 2 blks. to R. on Hughes for 1 1/2 blks. to inn on L.

TEL. 609-884-4710
612 Hughes St.
Cape May, NJ 08204-2318

Mary & Tom Snyder,
Innkeepers

On a tree-lined residential street in the heart of the historic district, Manor House offers guests an exceptionally clean and unpretentiously comfortable homestyle inn. Fluffy robes in the rooms and a generous cookie fairy are but a few of the fun touches found here. Relaxing on the porch, reading in the garden, or roaming the beaches and streets of Cape May occur with little effort. Mary's esteemed sticky buns and made-from-scratch breakfasts and Tom's good-humoredness give the inn its reputation for fine food and its character.

THE QUEEN VICTORIA®

🛏	17 Rooms, $70/$180 B&B 6 Suites, $110/240 B&B
💳	Visa, MC
🛁	All Private Baths
🛋	Open Year-round
🐕	Children Accepted No Pets
☀R	Ocean swimming, Historic tours, Birding, Shopping, Dining, Biking (free inn bikes), Tennis, Golf, Fishing
🍷	Full Breakfast, Afternoon Tea, B.Y.O.B.
🚭	No Smoking Inside
🏨	Conference Facilities for 10-20
♿	Wheelchair Access (1 suite)

The Wells family welcome you to three restored Victorian homes in the center of the Historic District with warm hospitality and special services. Relax on porches overlooking Victorian gardens. Fortify yourself with a hearty breakfast and afternoon tea for bicycle riding, antique shopping, historic touring or nature walks. Dine at several of New Jersey's best restaurants. Victorian ambiance yet modern amenities—air conditioning and whirlpool tubs. December, devoted to Christmas.

Garden State Parkway to southern end: continue straight over bridge, past marinas and onto Lafayette St. At second light turn left onto Ocean Street. Go 3 blocks. Turn right on Columbia and right into loading areas.

TEL. 609-884-8702
102 Ocean St.
Cape May, NJ 08204
Joan & Dane Wells,
Innkeepers

SEA CREST BY THE SEA

🛏	11 Rooms, $92/$159 B&B 1 Suite, $189/$239 B&B
💳	Visa, MC
🛁	All Private Baths
🛋	Open Year-round
🐕	No Children or Pets
☀R	Ocean Beach, Tennis, Golf, Playhouse, Race Track, Antiquing, Biking, Fishing, Sailing
🍷	Breakfast, Afternoon Tea
🚭	Smoking Outdoors Only
🏨	Conference Facility (11)
♿	

Your romantic fantasy escape. A Spring Lake Bed & Breakfast Inn just for the two of you. Lovingly restored 1885 Queen Anne Victorian for ladies and gentlemen on seaside holiday. Ocean views, open fireplaces, luxurious linens, feather beds, antique filled rooms, sumptuous breakfast and afternoon tea. A *Gourmet Magazine* "top choice." John & Carol Kirby welcome you with old fashioned hospitality to an atmosphere that will soothe your weary body and soul.

From NY & N Garden Pkwy to 34. From Phil. & S I-195 to 34. On 34 go south to first traffic circle and 3/4 around to 524 east to ocean. Go 1 blk. and turn right on Tuttle Avenue.

TEL. 908-449-9031
19 Tuttle Ave
Spring Lake, NJ 07762

John & Carol Kirby,
Innkeepers

THE STOCKTON INN

3 rooms, $60/$105 B&B
8 suites, $85/$145 B&B

Visa, MC, Amex, Discov

All Private Baths

Closed Dec. 25
Children limited
No Pets
Canoeing, Rafting, Tubing, Ballooning, Fishing, Hiking, Riding, Antiquing, Museums, Galleries, Theater, Historic Sites & Parks, Shopping Outlet Centers
Lunch, Dinner, Sun. brunch, Banquets to 200
Wine, Liquor & Beer available

Conference Facilities (60)
Wheelchair Access (dining rm.)

N.J. Rte. 202 to N.J. Rte. 29 (River Rd.) 3 mi. (N) to Stockton. Inn is in center of town on Main St. (Across the river from New Hope, PA.)

TEL. 609-397-1250
Main St., P.O.Box C
Stockton, NJ 08559

Andrew McDermott,
Innkeeper

The centerpiece of a small Delaware River town dates from 1710, serving travelers & neighbors since 1796. A colorful history and equally colorful guests include Rodgers & Hart, who were inspired to write the song "There's A Small Hotel (with a wishing well)." Romantic suites & bedrooms, many with fireplaces, in the Main Inn, Wagon, Carriage and Federal Houses. The restaurant boasts " 3 Star" Contemporary American & Continental Cuisine, fireplaces, murals of colonial Hunterdon & Bucks Counties, live entertainment & dancing. Seasonal Garden Dining.

WHISTLING SWAN INN

9 Rooms, $75/$95 B&B
1 Suite, $100/$110 B&B

Visa, MC, Amex, Discov

All Private Baths

Open Year-round

Children over 12 are Welcome; No Pets Please
Near Waterloo Village, Wineries, Antiquing, Winter Sports, State forests, Shopping, Fairs, Shows, Flea Markets
Full Buffet Breakfast, Wine, Lemonade, Coffee, Tea, Cider
No Smoking

Conference (10-12)

Bus & Train via N.J. Transit to Netcong/Stanhope. Exit 27 off I-80 via route 183/206 one mile to Hess gasoline station. Turn on Main St. across from Hess.

TEL 201-347-6369
FAX 201-347-3391
110 Main St.
Stanhope, NJ 07874
Joe Mulay and Paula
Williams , Innkeepers

Nestled in northwestern New Jersey's Skylands Tourism region only 45 miles west of New York City, this 1905 Victorian home has been converted to a B&B and renovated in two major segments of time. Each room has a private bath, queen size bed and period furnishings. Much of what is in the house is from Paula's grandmother's home in Oklahoma. Enjoy the porch swing, hammock and picnic table or sherry, movies, fireplaces and Tubs-for-Two bathroom. We work with any dietary requirements.

89

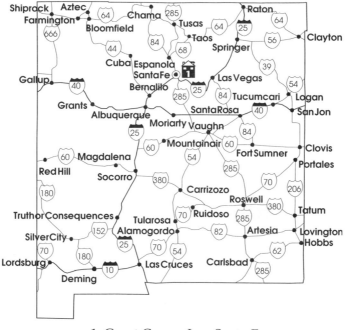

1. Grant Corner Inn, Santa Fe

GRANT CORNER INN

12 Rooms, $60/$140 B&B
Hacienda, $100/$115 B&B

Visa, MC

10 Private Baths, 1 Shared Baths

Open Year-round

Appropriate for Children over 6; No Pets

Skiing, Hiking, Fishing, Golf, Tennis, Swimming (fee)

Complimentary Breakfast; Picnic Lunches, Catered Dinners, Restaurant Serving Brunch to Public Sat. & Sun. Complimentary Wine

Smoke-free inn

Conference Facilities (20)

Wheelchair Access (1 rm.)

This delightful inn has an ideal location just two blocks from the historic plaza of downtown Santa Fe, among intriguing shops, galleries, and restaurants. Lush gardens, beautifully appointed guest rooms, fabulous gourmet breakfasts, and the gracious hospitality of the Walters family make this an experience not to be missed. Ample parking on the premises.

From Albuquerque, I-25 (N) Exit St. Francis L. (N) 3 mi.to R. at Alameda (W) .6 mi. L. (N) on Guadalupe .1 mi., R. (W) on Johnson .1 mi., parking on L.

TEL. 505-983-6678
122 Grant Ave.
Santa Fe, NM 87501

Louise Stewart & Pat Walter, Innkeepers

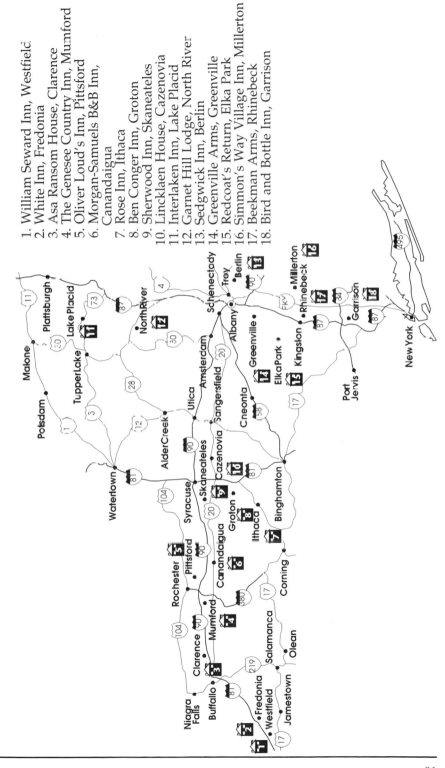

1. William Seward Inn, Westfield
2. White Inn, Fredonia
3. Asa Ransom House, Clarence
4. The Genesee Country Inn, Mumford
5. Oliver Loud's Inn, Pittsford
6. Morgan-Samuels B&B Inn, Canandaigua
7. Rose Inn, Ithaca
8. Ben Conger Inn, Groton
9. Sherwood Inn, Skaneateles
10. Lincklaen House, Cazenovia
11. Interlaken Inn, Lake Placid
12. Garnet Hill Lodge, North River
13. Sedgwick Inn, Berlin
14. Greenville Arms, Greenville
15. Redcoat's Return, Elka Park
16. Simmon's Way Village Inn, Millerton
17. Beekman Arms, Rhinebeck
18. Bird and Bottle Inn, Garrison

ASA RANSOM HOUSE

🛏	6 Rooms, $85/$125 B&B 3 Suites, $145 B&B
💳	Visa, MC, Discov
🛁	All Private Baths
🍽	Closed Fri.; month of Jan.
🐕	Well-supervised Children welcome; No Pets
R	Niagara Falls, many Antique Shops within walking distance
🍷	Breakfast for House-guests; Dinner Sun. thru Thurs. (Sat.-Houseguests only); Wine & Liquor available
🚭	No Smoking
⊢▥⊣	Conference Facilities (40)
♿	Wheelchair Access

On the site of the first gristmill built in Erie County (1803), this historic village inn offers country gourmet dining and fine New York State wines. Guests are romanced in the winter by the glowing fireplaces in the guest rooms, and enchanted in the summer by spacious grounds full of herbs and flowers. Some rooms have porches or balconies and a full country breakfast is included for all guests. Clarence is known throughout the East for its antiques and treasures. Only 25 miles from Niagara Falls.

Traveling (E): I-90, Exit 49, L. on Rte. 78 for 1 mi. to R. on Rte. 5 for 5.3 mi. Traveling (W): I-90, Exit 48A & R. on Rte. 77 for 1 mi. to R. on Rte. 5 for 10 mi. to inn.

TEL. 716-759-2315
FAX 716-759-2791
10529 Main St. (Rte. 5)
Clarence, NY 14031-1684
Robert Lenz & Judy Lenz,
Innkeepers

BEEKMAN ARMS

🛏	59 Rooms, $80/$110 EP 2 Suites, $125/$140 EP
💳	Visa, MC, Amex
🛁	All Private Baths
🍽	Open Year-round
🐕	Children Accepted; No Pets exc. motel unit
R	Hyde Park, Rhinebeck WW1 Aerdrome, Culi- nary Instit. of Amer., Golf, Swimming, Fishing, XC Skiing Nearby
🍷	Breakfast, Lunch, Dinner Wine & Liquor available
🚭	4 rooms Non-smoking Non-smoking Dining area
⊢▥⊣ ♿	Conference Facilities (25) Wheelchair Access (2 rms, dining rm. & conf. fac.)

The focus of activity in bustling, historic Rhinebeck, this inn has seen history being made since 1766 when its original section was built. Today its offers authentically furnished guest rooms, some with working fireplaces, a Colonial Tap Room and a beautiful greenhouse dining area where casual but elegant country fare is served.

NY Thruwy. (I-90) Rhinecliff Bridge Exit to Rte. 9 (S) 2 mi. to Rhinebeck Village. From Taconic Pkwy. take Rte. 199 (W) to L. on Rte. 308 to Rhinebeck Village.

TEL. 914-876-7077
FAX 914-876-7077
4 Mill St., Route 9
Rhinebeck, NY 12572

Chuck LaForge, Innkeeper

BENN CONGER INN

1 Room, $90/$120 B&B
3 Suites, $110/$220 B&B

Visa, MC, Amex, Diners

All Private Baths

Open Year-round

Children Welcome
No Pets—Kennel nearby

Hiking, Biking, XC Skiing,
Golf, Tennis, all Lake
Sports, Antiques, Wineries

Breakfast, Dinner
Wine & Liquor available

Smoking limited

Conference Facilities (40)

From I-81, Exit 12 (Homer) (S) on Rte.
281 for 2 mi. R. (W) on Rte. 222 for 9
mi. to Groton. Cross Rte. 38, making
no turns. Inn is up hill on R.
TEL. 607-898-5817
206 W. Cortland St.
Groton, NY 13073

Alison & Peter Van der
Meulen, Innkeepers

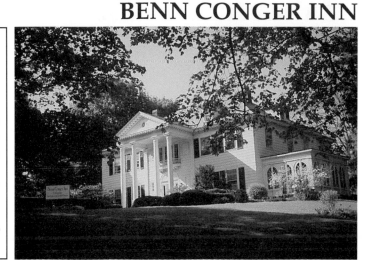

A revival mansion built for industrialist Benn Conger, the Inn is best known as a hideaway for mobster Dutch Schultz. Eighteen pastoral acres, gracious public rooms, including a library and conservatory, oversized suites, antiques, imported linens, amenities, Mediterranean-inspired cuisine and over 100 fine wines will please the most discriminating traveler. ("Wine Spectator" Award 1987-93).

THE BIRD & BOTTLE INN

2 Rooms, $195/$215
MAP
2 Suites, $215/$225 MAP

Visa, MC, Amex, Diners

All Private Baths

Closed Jan. 1 - 20

Not appropriate for Children; Pets not accepted

Hiking, Nature walks,
Golf, XC Skiing, Boating

Breakfast, Dinner, Sun.
brunch; Wine & Liquor
available

Smoking accepted

Conference Facilities (50)
From Rte. I-84: Fishkill: (S) 8 mi. on
Rte. 9. Inn on L. From NYC and
Westchester: (N) on Rte. 9A and 9,
past Croton and Peekskill. Inn 8 mi.
beyond Peekskill on Rte. 9 in Garrison area.
TEL. 914-424-3000
Old Albany Post Rd. (Rte. 9)
Garrison, NY 10524

Ira Boyar, Innkeeper

A famed landmark on the old Albany-New York Post Road since 1761, this inn continues to welcome travelers with traditional Hudson River Valley hospitality. An authentic old country inn, it is internationally renowned for its gourmet cuisine served in 3 dining rooms with working fireplaces and comfortable, cozy rooms with woodburning fireplaces, 4 poster or canopied beds and private bath, and Colonial furnishings. *Hudson Valley Magazine* voted . . . "Best Restaurant Putnam County, NY 1993."

NEW YORK
GARNET HILL LODGE

🛏	22 Rooms, $120/$170 MAP
💳	Visa, MC
🛁	All private baths
🕯	Closed Nov. 20–30
🐕	Supervised Children Welcome; No Pets
⚡R	Swimming, Tennis, Hiking, Boating, Fishing, XC Skiing, Museums, Downhill Skiing
🍷	Breakfast, Lunch, Dinner Wine & Liquor Available
🚭	Non-smoking Dining Area
┣╋╋┫	Conference Facilities (60)
♿	

12 Garnet Hill is nestled in the Adirondack mountains and overlooks beautiful Thirteenth Lake. This rustic resort-inn was built in 1936 in the area of a historic garnet mine. Guests are welcomed into a dining/living room with great log pillars and a large garnet stone fireplace. The inn features distinctive guest rooms and a menu highlighted by homebaked breads and desserts, special vegetarian dishes, and heart-healthy entrees.

From Albany on I-87 Exit 23 (Warrensburg). (N) on Rte. 9 to Rte. 28. (W) on Rte. 28, 22 mi. to North River. L. on 13th Lake Rd. 4.5 mi. to inn.

TEL. 518-251-2444
FAX 518-251-3089
13th Lake Rd.
North River, NY 12856

George & Mary Heim,
Innkeepers

THE GENESEE COUNTRY INN

🛏	8 Rooms, $85/$125 B&B 2 nite min (some wkends)
💳	Visa, MC, Diners
🛁	All Private Baths
🕯	Closed Dec. 24 & 25; Also Sun. Noon to Tues. Noon Nov.-Apr. exc. Holidays
🐕	No Pets
⚡R	Trout fishing, Walking, Biking, Genesee Country Museum, Letchworth St. Pk., Rochester, Discount shopping, Gift Shop
🍷	Breakfast houseguests; Luncheon for conferences; Tea, Cheese & Crackers; BYOB
┣╋╋┫	Conference Facilities (14)
♿	Wheelchair Access (1 rm)

4 GIVE YOURSELF A HIDEAWAY BREAK . . . Savor the magic quiet of our award-winning historic storybook stonemill in the century village of Mumford. See blue heron as you flyfish secluded "A-rated" troutstreams, visit nearby village-museum, our "18th century Williamsburg of Western NY," or Letchworth Park known as "The Grand Canyon of the East," then just relax and enjoy our hospitality. Tea, breakfast, some fireplaces, canopy beds, giftshop. Near fine restaurants. AAA, MOBIL, *Country Inns and Backroads*.

From NY Thrwy. (I-90) take Exit 47 and Rte. 19 S. to LeRoy. Go (E) on Rte. 5 to Caledonia, (N) on Rte. 36 to Mumford. L. on George St.

TEL. 716-538-2500
FAX 716-538-4565
948 George St.,
Mumford, NY 14511-0340
Glenda Barcklow, Proprietor, Kim Rasmussen,
Innkeeper

GREENVILLE ARMS

	12 Rooms, $88/$145 B&B 1 Suite, $145 B&B
	Visa, MC, Discov, Diners
	All Private Baths
	Open May 1–Dec. 1
	Well-supervised Children over 12; No Pets
R	Swimming pool, Tennis, Golf, Bicycling, Hiking, Hudson Valley & Catskill Sightseeing
	Breakfast for houseguests Dinner by reservation Wine available
	No Smoking
	Conference Facilities (30)

From NYC: 2 hrs. (N) on I-87 to Exit 21 & Rte. 23(W) for 9 mi. Then (N) on Rte. 32 for 9 mi. to Greenville. Inn is on L., before traffic light.

TEL. 518-966-5219
P.O. Box 659, South St.
Greenville, NY 12083-0659

Tish Dalton & Eliot Dalton, Innkeepers

Built in 1889 in the foothills of the Northern Catskills, this lovely Queen Anne Victorian inn is set on 6 lush acres of lawns and shade trees, with gardens and swimming pool. Antiques, original artwork and Victorian details add to an atmosphere of warmth and relaxed comfort. After a full country breakfast, guests enjoy hiking, biking, sightseeing or relaxing by the pool. In the evening the inn features intimate fireside dining in The Vanderbilt Room, where Creative American Cuisine wins accolades.

INTERLAKEN INN

	11 Rooms, $50/$110 B&B $100/$170 MAP 1 Suite, $170 MAP 1 Cottage, $125 B&B
	Amex, MC, Visa, Enroute All Private Baths
	Open Year-round
	Children accepted over 5 No Pets
R	Golf, Skiing, Boating, Skating, Canoeing, Hiking, Biking, X-Country Skiing, Olympic Venues
	Full Breakfast, Dinner, Afternoon Tea, Sherry in each room, Wine & Liquor Available
	Smoking limited to common rooms
	Conference Facilities (20)

I-87 to 73 to Lake Placid, 1st stoplight left (Main St.) to Mirror Lake Dr. to Interlaken

TEL. 518-523-3180
800-428-4369
15 Interlaken Ave.
Lake Placid, NY 12946

Roy and Carol Johnson, Inn keepers

In the heart of the Adirondack Mountains, site of the 1932 and 1980 winter Olympics, this 1906 Victorian Inn offers a wonderfully romantic setting with uniquely decorated, antique furnished rooms. Enjoy a peaceful setting and four seasons of outdoor activities. The Inn offers fine dining using the season's freshest bounty to provide guests with a unique dining experience.

NEW YORK
LINCKLAEN HOUSE

🛏	18 rooms, $70/$99 B&B 3 suites, $115/$130 B&B
💳	Visa, MC,
🛁	All Private Baths
💡	Open Year-round
🐕	Children accepted Pets accepted
☀	Swimming, Golf, Tennis, Downhill & XC Skiing
🍷	Lunch, Dinner; Sun. Brunch Buffet Wine & Liquor available
🚬	Smoking accepted
⌂	Conference facilities (50) Banquet facilities (200)

Built in 1835 as a luxurious stopover for Colonial travelers, the Lincklaen House has long been a local landmark and has hosted such luminaries as President Grover Cleveland and John D. Rockefeller. The old-world atmosphere is now combined with modern comfort and gracious service, offering guests a return to an era of elegant hospitality.

From NY Thruwy. (I-90): Exit 34, take Rte. 13 (S) to Cazenovia. R. on Rte. 20, 1 block. From I-81: Exit 15 (La Fayette), E. on Rte. 20. 18 mi. to Cazenovia.

TEL. 315-655-3461
FAX 315-655-5443
79 Albany St., Box 36
Cazenovia, NY 13035

Howard M. Kaler,
Innkeeper

MORGAN-SAMUELS B&B INN

🛏	5 Rooms, $99/$195 B&B 1 Suite, $150/$175 B&B Business Room/$69
💳	All rms. have fireplaces Visa, MC, Discov
🛁	All Private Baths
💡	Open Year-round exc. Dec. 24–25
🐕	Children under 3 or over 10; Pets outdoors only
☀	Tennis, Golf, Nearby Lake, Wineries, Outdoor Symphonies & Concerts, Sonnerberg Gardens, Horse drawn Sleigh Rides, 2100-ft. elevation downhill skiing (11 m.)
🍷	Candlelit Gourmet Brkfast w/ Mozart, Dinner prix fixe by Reservation; BYOB
🚬	No Smoking
⌂	Conference Facilities (15)
♿	Wheelchair Access (dining rm.)

As you travel the 2,000-ft. tree-lined drive to the secluded 1810 English style mansion you sense the difference between ordinary and legendary. The Inn sits like a plantation on a rise surrounded by 46 acres. Four patios, a lily pond with waterfall, five acres of lawn and gardens are canopied by 250 noble trees. Three rooms with French doors and balconies, ten active fireplaces, and a tea room with stone wall with 6-ft. glass window and pot-bellied stove. Library, common room, large screened and furnished porch, 2 jacuzzis, museum quality antiques, oil paintings. Mobil ★★★ AAA ◆◆◆

I-90 from E Exit 43 R. on 21 to 488; L. 1st R. to stop sign continue 3/4 mile to Inn on R.

TEL. (716) 394-9232
FAX (716) 394-8044
2920 Smith Rd.
Canandaigua, N.Y. 14424

Julie & John Sullivan,
Innkeepers

OLIVER LOUD'S INN

🛏	8 Rooms, $135/$145 B&B
💳	Visa, MC, Amex, CB, Diners Club
🛁	All Private Baths
🏮	Open Year-round
🐕	Children over 12 welcome; No Pets; kennel nearby
R	Erie Canal towpath for hiking, Jogging, XC Skiing, Biking, Boating, Golf, Tennis, Museums, Sight-seeing
⊙	Cont. Breakfast hamper, Richardson's Canal House rest.; Wine & Liquor available
🚬	Smoking/non-smoking rms.
⊞	Conference Facilities (20)
♿	Wheelchair Access (1 rm.)

NY Thruwy. (I-90) Exit 45, to I-490 (W) for 3 mi. to Bushnell's Basin exit (#27), turn R. & continue to Marsh Rd. signal & bear R. to inn.

TEL. 716-248-5200
FAX 716-248-9970
1474 Marsh Rd.
Pittsford, NY 14534

Vivienne Tellier, Innkeeper

Feeding ducks, building snowmen, visiting nearby shops, or rocking on the porch over-looking the Erie Canal, are some ways to relax at this circa 1810 stagecoach inn. Authentically furnished with antiques and period artwork, guests are pampered with V.I.P. welcome trays, as well as a breakfast hamper delivered to your room. King sized and canopy beds available.

THE REDCOAT'S RETURN

🛏	14 rooms, $75/$95 B&B
💳	Visa, MC, Amex
🛁	Private & Shared Baths
🏮	Open Year-round
🐕	Inquire regarding Children; No Pets
R	Downhill & XC Skiing, Golf, Tennis, Swimming, Boating, Horseback Riding, Hiking, Antique Shopping
⊙	Breakfast Daily; Dinner served Fri.-Mon. only Wine & Liquor available
🚬	Pipes & Cigars restricted
⊞	Conference Facilities (20-30)
♿	Wheelchair Access (dining rm. & conf. fac.)

NY Thruwy (N), Exit 20 (Saugerties). L. to Rte. 32 (N). Rte. 32 merges with Rte. 32A and at light, with 23A (W). At Tannersville light, take L. onto County Rd. 16, 4.5 mi. to R. on Dale Lane. Inn on R.

TEL. 518-589-6379
Dale Lane
Elka Park, NY 12427

Tom & Peggy Wright, Innkeepers

Peg and Tom Wright's easy cordiality has been making guests comfortable for 21 years. Tom's English accent and his artistry in the kitchen (he was a chef on the Queen Mary) keeps them coming back for more. Whether it's snuggling up in front of a roaring fire, hiking, or enjoying spectacular views of the Catskills, it's always fun at this romantic, cozy inn.

ROSE INN

🛏	11 Rooms, $100/$160 B&B 4 Suites, $175/$250 B&B
💳	Visa, MC
🛁	All Private Baths
🏡	Open Year-round
🐕	Children over 10 or prior arrangements; No Pets, kennel next door
🎿	Cayuga Lake Sports, X-Country Skiing, near Downhill Skiing, Golf, Fishing, Wineries, Cornell University, Antiques
🍽	Breakfast, Dinner prix fixe by reservation; Wine & Liquor available
🚭	No smoking
♿	Conference Facilities (60) Wheelchair Access (conf. fac.)

🏠 A spectacular Inn in a lovely country setting. Located halfway between NYC and Niagara Falls, in the heart of the Finger Lakes. This 1850 Italianate mansion is a gem of woodcraft, with a stunning circular staircase of Honduran Mahogany. Large, high ceilinged rooms are luxuriously furnished with antiques from around the world accented by lush colors and fabrics. Extraordinary cuisine is romantically served in elegant private dining rooms. Sherry and Charles welcome you to New York's only Mobil ★★★★ and AAA ◆◆◆◆ inn.

10 m. N of Ithaca on 34 N. From Ithaca 13 exit, 34 N, 6 m. to "T" (red flashing light). R. for .5 m. to fork, stay L., Inn is 3.5 m. on R.

TEL. 607-533-7905
FAX 607-533-7908
Rte. 34 North, P.O. Box 6576
Ithaca, NY 14851-6576

Charles & Sherry Rosemann, Innkeepers

THE SEDGWICK INN

🛏	4 Rooms, $85/$95 B&B 1 Ste, $100/$120 B&B Annex $65/$75
💳	Visa, MC, Amex, Diners, Discov
🛁	All Private Baths
🏡	Open Year-round
🐕	Children accepted in annex; Pets accepted in annex
🎿	Library, Gift & Gourmet shops, Downhill & XC Skiing, Swimming, Theatre, Tanglewood Music Festival, Art Museums
🍽	Breakfast, Light lunches, Gourmet Dinners
🚭	Wine & Liquor available No Smoking in Inn bedrooms
♿	Conference Facilities (25) Wheelchair Access (annex, dining rm.)

🏠 This historic inn, once a stagecoach stop, sits on 12 acres in the beautiful Taconic Valley on the New York side of the Berkshires, within easy access to Albany, Western Massachussets and Southern Vermont. Comfortable, yet elegant, it has been described as "the quintessential country inn." Rooms are furnished in antiques. Fireplaces, fine art and interesting artifacts grace both the handsome living room and the well-stocked library where the original indentures, date 1791, are displayed. The restaurant is renowned for its fine food and the carriage house features unusual gifts.

From Albany: Rte. 787 N to Troy. Exit Rte. 7 E to Rte. 278. R. on 278 to Rte. 2, L. on Rte. 2 for approx. 15 m. to Rte. 22. R. on 22 S, 6 m. to inn. From N.Y.C.: Taconic Pkwy N, Exit Rte. 295 E to Rte. 22. L. on Rte. 22 N for 22 m.

TEL. 518-658-2334
800-845-4886
FAX 518-658-3988
Rte. 22, Box 250
Berlin, NY 12022
Edie Evans, Innkeeper

THE SHERWOOD INN

🛏	13 Rooms, $60/$80 B&B 5 Suites, $70/$145 B&B
💳	Visa, MC, Amex, Diners, CB
🛁	All Private Baths
💡	Open Year-round Peak rates effective Fri. & Sat. nights year-round
🐴	Children Accepted No Pets
☂R☂	Swimming, Boating, Golf, Downhill and XC Skiing, Fishing, Bicycling, Hiking, Antiquing
☕	Continental Breakfast, Lunch, Dinner; Dining room closed 12/24 & 25; Wine & Liquor available
🚭	Non-smoking dining area
🎎	Conference Facilities (100) Banquet (150)

From N. Y. Thruwy: Exit Weedsport, Rte. 34 (S) to Auburn. (E) on Rte. 20, 7 mi. to Skaneateles. From (S): Rte. 81 (N) to Cortland, Rte 41 (N) to Skaneateles. L. on Rte. 20 for 1 mi.
TEL. 315-685-3405
1-800-3-SHERWOOD
FAX 315-685-8983
26 West Genesee St.
Skaneateles, NY 13152
William Eberhardt and Claire O'Boyle Downey, Innkeepers

From the handsome lobby with its fireplace and gift shop to the pleasant guest rooms, many of which overlook beautiful Skaneateles Lake, gracious service and comfort are the keynotes here. American cuisine with a Continental touch has been featured in *Bon Appetit*, and is served in the dining rooms and the friendly, casual tavern. The lovely village of Skaneateles offers many activities.

SIMMONS' WAY VILLAGE INN

🛏	9 Rooms, $125/$150 EP (15% serv. chg. incl. B&B) 1 Suite, $265 EP
💳	Visa, MC, Amex
🛏	All Private Baths
💡	Open Year-round
🐴	Children Accepted No Pets
☂R☂	Skiing, Golf, Tennis, Swimming, Concerts, Summer Stock, Auto Racing, Antiquing, Historical sites
☕	Breakfast (guests only), Brunch, Dinner; MAP available
🚭	Wine & Liquor available Smoking in restricted areas
🎎	Conference Facilities (25)
♿	Wheelchair Access (dining rm. & conf. fac.)

From N.Y.C. (90 mi.): Taconic Pkwy. to Rte. 44(E) or I-684 to Rte. 22 (N) to Rte. 44 (E) (Main St.). From Boston (160 mi.): Mass. Tpke., Exit 2, Rte. 102 (W) to Rte. 7 (S) to Rte. 44 (W). From Hartford: Rte. 44 (W) to Millerton.
TEL. 518-789-6235
FAX 518-789-6235
33 Main St.
Millerton, NY 12546
The Carter Family, Owners & Innkeepers

Graceful retreat in grand Victorian elegance and civility. Located near CT border in Berkshire foothills. Antiques, fireplaces, porches and historic, candlelit silver service highlight memorable accommodations and internationally acclaimed cuisine and wine selections. Selected by American Express/Hertz as "Quintessential Country Inn 1991" for a national ad campaign. Simmons' Way has been awarded a rare distinction of 4-star rating at local, national and international levels.

THE WHITE INN

🛏	12 Rooms, $59/$89 B&B 11 Suites, $89/$159 B&B
💳	Visa, MC, Amex, DC, Discov.
🛁	All Private Baths
🛋	Open Year-round
🐕	Children accepted No Pets
ℝ	Antiquing, Wineries, Chautauqua Institution, SUNY college activities, Golf, Bicycling, XC/alpine skiing
☕	Breakfast included; Lunch, Dinner; Wine & Liquor available
🚭	Some Non-smoking rms. Non-smoking Dining area
⊢🏠⊣	Conference Facilities (60)
♿	Wheelchair access (dining rm. & conf. fac.)

🏠 Built on the 1868 homesite of the county's first physician, The White Inn features beautifully restored and decorated guest rooms and suites. Antiques and period reproductions adorn the guest rooms and public spaces. Superb cuisine has gained an enthusiastic following among guests and townsfolk. The Inn offers fine dining and banquets as well as casual and late-night fare.

NY Thruwy. Exit 59. At traffic light L. on Rte. 60 (S) to traffic light, R. on Rte. 20 (W), Main St. Inn on R.

TEL. 716-672-2103
FAX 716-672-2107
52 East Main St.
Fredonia, NY 14063

Robert Contiguglia & Kathleen Dennison, Innkeepers

WILLIAM SEWARD INN

🛏	14 Rooms, $85/$145 B&B
💳	Visa, MC, Discov.
🛁	All Private Baths
🛋	Open Year-round Children over 10 are welcome; No Pets, Boarding available nearby
ℝ	Chautauqua Institution, Lily Dale, Wineries, Antique & Speciality Shops, Skiing, Swimming, Boating, Tennis, Golf nearby.
☕	Full Breakfast; Prix Fix Dinner available Thursday-Sunday by advance Reservation only; BYOB
🚭	No Smoking inside
⊢🏠⊣	Conference Facilities (15)
♿	Wheelchair Access (2 Rms.)

🏠 Although Chautauqua Institution is a major attraction, many travelers come specifically to stay at this 1821 antique-filled inn for rest and relaxation. The formal but comfortable ambience created with period antiques (mid-1800s-early 1900s) in the 1821-1880 portion of Inn as well as the period reproduction setting in the new carriage house lend well to total relaxation for guests.

4 mi. S. on Rte. 394 from I-90, Exit 60. 2.5 hrs. NE of Cleveland, OH; 2.5 hrs. N of Pittsburgh, PA; 1.5 hrs. SW of Buffalo, NY; 3 hrs. SW of Toronto, Canada

TEL. 716-326-4151
FAX 716-326-4163
RR2, Box 14, S. Portage Rd.
Westfield, NY 14787
Jim and Debbie Dahlberg, Innkeepers

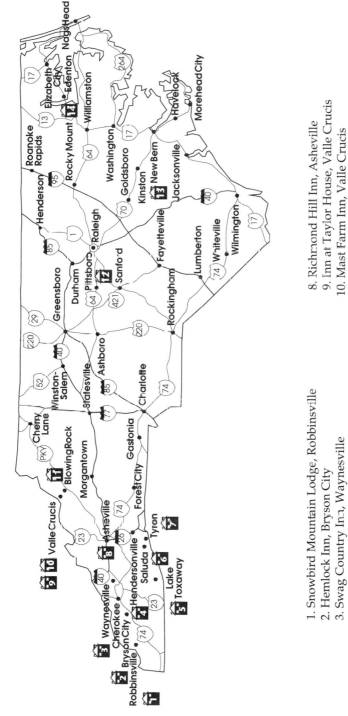

1. Snowbird Mountain Lodge, Robbinsville
2. Hemlock Inn, Bryson City
3. Swag Country Inn, Waynesville
4. Waverly Inn, Hendersonville
5. The Greystone Inn, Lake Toxaway
6. Orchard Inn, Saluda
7. Pine Crest Inn, Tryon

8. Richmond Hill Inn, Asheville
9. Inn at Taylor House, Valle Crucis
10. Mast Farm Inn, Valle Crucis
11. Gideon Ridge Inn, Blowing Rock
12. Fearrington House, Pittsboro
13. Harmony House Inn, New Bern
14. Lords Proprietor's Inn, Edenton

NORTH CAROLINA
THE FEARRINGTON HOUSE

	14 Rooms, $150 B&B
	9 Suites, $200/$250 B&B
	Visa, MC, Pers. Checks
	All Private Baths
	Open Year-round
	No children under 12; No Pets
	Swimming, Biking, Walking, Bird watching, Golf, Tennis, Sailing, Fishing, Antique Shopping
	Breakfast, Lunch, Dinner Outstanding Wine list; BYOB
	Smoking limited
	Conference facilities (40)
	Wheelchair Access (1 rm.)

In a cluster of low, attractive buildings surrounded by gardens and rolling countryside, this elegant inn offers luxurious quarters in a country setting. A member of Relais et Chateaux, the restaurant's sophisticated regional cuisine, prepared in the classical techniques, has received national acclaim, including AAA's 4–diamond award and Mobil's 4-star.

Chapel Hill, U.S. 15-501 (S) 8 mi. to Fearrington Village.
TEL. 919-542-2121
FAX 919-542-4202
2000 Fearrington Village Center
Pittsboro, NC 27312

Jenny & R.B. Fitch, Owners;
Richard Delany,
General Manager

GIDEON RIDGE INN

	9 Rooms, $100/$140 B&B
	Visa, MC, Amex
	All Private Baths
	Open Year-round
	Appropriate for Children over 12; No Pets
	Hiking, Horseback Riding, Golf, Tennis, Village & Crafts shops, Blue Ridge Pkwy. Grandfather Mtn.
	Full Breakfast, Dinners & Lunches for groups by prior request; BYOB
	Smoking limited
	Conference Facilities (12-16)

Surrounded by six stone terraces on top of Gideon's Ridge, the inn overlooks the Blue Ridge Mountains. This sturdy 1930 stone house, offers rooms decorated with antiques and family heirlooms. While at the inn, guests may relax in the library with its massive stone fireplace, enjoy an exceptional breakfast in the dining room and stroll through woods and gardens.

U.S. 321, 1.5 mi. (S) of village of Blowing Rock, turn (W) on Rock Rd., L. on Gideon Ridge Rd. at fork. Go to top of the ridge.
TEL. 704-295-3644
6148 Gideon Ridge Rd.
P.O. Box 1929
Blowing Rock, NC 28605

Cobb & Jane Milner,
Innkeepers

THE GREYSTONE INN

🛏	33 Rooms, $240/$350 MAP 1 suite $410/$450 MAP
💳	Visa, MC, Amex
🛁	All Private Baths
🛎	Open Apr. 1–Jan.1
🐕	Children Welcome; No Pets
☼R☼	On premises: Golf, Tennis, Swimming Pool, Croquet, Sailing, Water Skiing, Fishing, Hiking, Waterfalls, Party Boat Cruise
☕	High-Country Breakfast, Gourmet Dinner, Afternoon Refreshments; Wine & Liquor Available Non-smoking Dining Rm.
⌨	Conference Facilities
♿	Ramp to one Guest Room

From Asheville: I-40 to I-26 E., Rt. 280S (Exit #9) to Brevard. Us 64 W for 17 m. to Lake Toxaway Country Club/ Greystone Inn sign. Turn R. for approx. 3.5 mi. to inn.

TEL. 704-966-4700 (in NC)
800-824-5766

Greystone Lane
Lake Toxaway, NC 28747

Tim/Boo Boo Lovelace, Inkps.

 With all the diversions of spectacularly beautiful Lake Toxaway at its doorstep, this intimate, historic (National Register) resort-inn combines the lure of its wild mountain setting with the comfort of modern luxuries and an exceptional cuisine. Romantic and tranquil. Complimentary tennis, sailboat, bassboat, ski boat, canoe and daily party boat cruise at all times and complimentary golf certain months. ◆◆◆◆

HARMONY HOUSE INN

🛏	9 Rooms, $85 B&B
💳	Visa, MC, Amex
🛁	All Private Baths
🛎	Open Year-round
🐕	Children accepted No Pets
☼R☼	Historic district, Tryon Palace, 2 rivers, Croatan Forest, Golf, Tennis, Boating
☕	Full Breakfast; BYOB
🚭	No Smoking
⌨	Conference facilities (10-12)
♿	

I-95, Exit 70 (E) to 4th New Bern exit to E. Front St., then L. on Pollock St. Hwy. 17 runs 1 blk. (N) of Pollock St.

TEL. 919-636-3810

215 Pollock St.
New Bern, NC 28560

A.E. & Diane Hansen,
Innkeepers

 As the Ellis family grew, so did their ca. 1850 home, with additions ca. 1860 (the Union troops were billeted in this home) and ca. 1880. In 1900, the home was sawed in half by the Ellis brothers, moved apart and rejoined with a second front door, hallway and staircase plus a wonderful front porch. Located in the historic district, this unusually spacious Greek Revival inn is decorated with antiques, locally made reproductions, New Bern & family memorabilia and angels from Diane's collection.

NORTH CAROLINA
HEMLOCK INN

	23 rooms, $118/$134 MAP 3 cotts., $140/$162 MAP
	No Credit Cards
	All Private Baths
	Open mid-April-Oct.
	Children welcome No Pets
	Hiking, Ping-pong, Shuffle-board, Skittles, Smoky Mtn. Natl. Park, Tubing, Cherokee Indian Res.
	Breakfast at 8:30 A.M., Dinner at 6 P.M., Mon. to Sat. & 12:30 P.M. Sun.
	Non-smoking dining room
	Wheelchair access (8 rms.)

High, cool, quiet, and restful, this inn is beautifully situated on top of a small mountain on the edge of the Great Smoky Mountains National Park. There's a friendly informality in the family atmosphere and authentic country furniture. Honest-to-goodness home cooking and farm-fresh vegetables are served bountifully from Lazy Susan tables.

Hwy. 74, Hyatt Creek Rd.- Ela exit & bear R. to L. turn on Hwy. 19 for approx. 1 mi. to R. turn at inn sign. Take country road 1 mi. to L. turn at next inn sign.

TEL. 704-488-2885
Galbreath Creek Rd.
P.O. Drawer EE,
Bryson City, NC 28713
Morris & Elaine White; Ella Jo & John Shell, Innkeepers

THE INN AT THE TAYLOR HOUSE

	5 Rooms, $110 B&B 2 Suites, $145 B&B
	Visa, MC
	All Private Baths
	Open Apr. 15–Dec. 15
	Children by prior arrangement; No Pets
	Hiking, Fishing, Horseback riding, Canoeing, Championship Golf, Skiing, Grandfather Mtn., Blue Ridge Parkway, Shops & Restaurants
	Breakfast; Arrangements for private parties, weddings & family reunions
	Smoking on porch only
	Wheelchair Access (dining room)

A bit of Europe in the peaceful, rural heart of the Blue Ridge Mountains, this charming farmhouse is decorated with fine antiques, oriental rugs, artwork, and European goose-down comforters on all the beds. Bright fabrics, wicker furniture and flowering plants invite guests to rock on the wide wraparound porch, while the friendly hospitality and memorable breakfasts add to their pleasure.

Boone/Banner/Elk accessible from any direction. NC Hwy. 105(N) for 2.8 mi. to Valle Crucis. L. on Hwy. 194 for 8/10 mi. to inn.

TEL. 704-963-5581
FAX 704-963-5818
Highway 194, P.O.Box 713
Valle Crucis, NC 28691

Chip & Roland Schwab, Innkeepers

THE LORDS PROPRIETORS' INN

20 Rooms, $140/$180 MAP; B&B (Sun. & Mon.)

None. We will bill.

All Private Baths

Open Year-round Exc. Dec. 24 & 25

Children Welcome No Pets

Swimming at owners' country estate, Fishing, Tennis nearby, Golf privileges, Two Waterfront Courses

Breakfast, Dinner (Tues.–Sat.); Wine available with dinner

Smoking in parlors and on porches

Conference Facilities (30)

Wheelchair Access (1 rm., dining rm. & conf. fac.)

From N.C. 32 and U.S. 17 continue on Broad St. to the inn.

TEL 1 800 348-8933
FAX 919-482-2432
300 No. Broad St.
Edenton, NC 27932

Arch & Jane Edwards, Innkeepers

The Inn offers twenty spacious guest rooms in three restored homes on over an acre of grounds in Edenton's Historic District. Breakfast and dinner are served to guests in the Inn's dining room. Guest reactions: "We've enjoyed some fairly decent lodgings—Shepherds, the St. Francis, the George V. We have never felt as well cared for as at your Inn. The quality of the surroundings and management, the attention to detail, and the genuine friendliness you and your staff offer make the Lords Proprietors' Inn truly exceptional." "The food is unsurpassable."

MAST FARM INN

9 Rooms, $80/$140 MAP
3 Cabin Suites, $135/$165

Visa, MC

10 Private, 1 Shared Baths

Open Dec. 27–Mar. 6; Apr. 20–Nov. 6

Appropriate for Children over 12; No Pets

Fishing, Hiking, Skiing, Golf, Canoeing

Breakfast, houseguests only; Dinner, Tues.- Sat.; Sun. Lunch; BYOB

No Smoking

Wheelchair Access (1 rm., dining rm.)

Boone/Banner Elk area accessible from any direction. Watch for Valle Crucis sign on NC 105. Mast Farm Inn is 2.6 mi. from NC105 on SR1112.

TEL. 704-963-5857
FAX 704-963-6404
P.O.Box 704
Valle Crucis, NC 28691

Sibyl & Francis Pressly, Innkeepers

Nestled in the beautiful mountain valley community of historic Valle Crucis near the Blue Ridge Parkway, the inn sits on an 18-acre operating farm. The inn features extensive flower gardens and the farm's freshest vegetables and salads help provide guests with a special dining experience. Life at this restored, antique-filled inn (National Register of Historic Places) is pleasant and peaceful. Lodgings are in the main house or in the renovated blacksmith shop, woodwork shop or loom house.

THE ORCHARD INN

	9 Rooms, $95/$130 B&B 3 Cottages $125/$145 B&B
	MC, Visa; Pers. Checks
	All Private Baths
	Open Year-round
	Appropriate for children over 10; No Pets
	Walking Paths, Birding, Antiquing, Biltmore Estate, Blue Ridge Parkwy, Golf
	Breakfast included; Dinner by reservation; Picnics on request; BYOB
	Smoking restricted
	Conference Facilities (20)

Guests enjoy a truly memorable dining experience to the strains of Mozart and Schumann on the glassed-in, wraparound porch with a breathtaking view of the southern Blue Ridge Mountains. This turn-of-the-century country house has a touch of plantation elegance, with a large fireplace, many antiques, folk art, and masses of books and magazines to beguile guests.

I-26, NC Exit 28 & turn toward Saluda for 1 mi. to L. on Hwy. 176 for .5 mi. to inn on R.

TEL. 800-581-3800
FAX 704-749-9805
P.O. Box 725
Saluda, NC 28773

Ronnie & Newell Doty,
Innkeepers

PINE CREST INN

	22 Rooms, $125/$150 B&B 8 suites, $140/$165 B&B
	Visa, MC, Amex, Discov
	All Private Baths
	Open Year-round exc. Jan. Children Welcome
	Pets not accepted
	Golf, Tennis, Swimming, Hiking, Horseback riding, Biltmore House & Gardens, Blue Ridge Pkwy., Chimney Rock., Fence Equestrian & Nature Ctr.
	Full Breakfast, Picnic Baskets Available, Dinner; Liquor & Wine available
	Smoking Limited
	Conference Facilities (15 – 60)
	Wheelchair Access (conf. fac.)

The famed hunt country and foothills of the Blue Ridge Mountains are the setting for this classic Inn. Listed on the National Register, the Pine Crest Inn features luxurious guest rooms, fireplaces, verandas, crisp mountain air, exceptional dining, and gracious service. Fresh grilled seafood, Maryland crab cakes, rack of lamb, and roast duck are the Chef's specialties. An extensive library, intimate bar, and manicured grounds add to the atmosphere of casual elegance. Hiking trails, nature walks, and natural waterfalls are nearby. AAA Four Diamond Award.

From I-26, Exit 36 to Tryon. Follow Rte. 108/176 to town of Tryon. Turn on New Market Rd. Follow signs to inn.

TEL. 800-633-3001
704-859-9135
200 Pine Crest Lane
Tryon, NC 28782

Jeremy & Jennifer Wainwright,
Innkeepers

RICHMOND HILL INN

19 Rooms, $125/$295 B&B
2 Suites, $145/$295 B&B

Visa, MC, Amex

All Private Baths

Open Year-round

Children Welcome; Pets Not Permitted

Croquet Lawn on site, Biltmore Estate tours, Blue Ridge Pkwy., Antiques & Crafts Shopping

Breakfast, Dinner; Sun. Brunch; Wine & Liquor Available

Non-Smoking Guest Rooms

Conference Facilities (50)

Wheelchair Access (1 rm., dining rm. & conf. fac.)

From I-240, take 19/23 Weaverville exit. Take exit 251 (Unca). L. at bottom of Ramp, L. onto Riverside Dr., R. on Pearson Bridge Rd., R. on Richmond Hill Dr.

TEL. 704-252-7313
800-545-9238
FAX 704-252-8726
87 Richmond Hill Dr.
Asheville, NC 28806
Susan Michel, Innkeeper

This 1889 Queen Anne mansion was one of the most elegant and innovative structures of its time. Now on the National Register, the inn's rich oak paneling, handcarved fireplaces, and high ceilings provide an unusually luxurious setting in the Blue Ridge Mountains. Canopy and 4-poster beds, a highly-acclaimed gourmet restaurant, fresh mountain air are just a few of the attractions.

SNOWBIRD MOUNTAIN LODGE

19 Rooms, $112/$118 AP
12 Suites, $118/130 AP

Visa, MC, Discov

All Private Baths

Open mid-April–early Nov.

Children over 11 welcome; No Pets

Hiking, Rafting & Horseback riding nearby, Fishing, Boating, Cherokee Indian sites, Horseshoes, Billiards, Ping-pong, Shuffleboard

Breakfast, Lunch, Dinner BYOB

Smoking in restricted areas

Wheelchair Access (2 rooms and dining room)

Robbinsville, at Hardees, Rte. 129 N for 1. 5 mi. to L. on NC Rte. 1116 for 3.3 mi. to R. at stop sign (Rte. 1127) for 6.7 mi. to lodge.

TEL 704-479-3433
275 Santeetlah Rd.
Robbinsville, NC 28771

Bob & Connie Rhudy, Innkeepers

High up in Santeetlah Gap, not far from the giant hardwood trees of the Joyce Kilmer virgin forest, is this secluded, rustic and picturesque mountain lodge, built of chestnut logs and native stone. Huge fireplaces, comfortable beds in pleasant rooms, a spectacular view and plentiful, delicious meals make this an exceptional vacation retreat. The lodge is on the National Register of Historic Places.

NORTH CAROLINA
THE SWAG COUNTRY INN

🛏	14 rooms, \$175/\$300 AP 2 cottages, \$275/\$350 AP
💳	Visa, MC
🛁	All Private Baths
	May 18–October 30
👫	Children under 7 in cottages; No Pets
R	Hiking trails, Racquetball, Badminton, Croquet, Horseshoes, Pond with boat and dock
🍷	All 3 Meals, hors d' oeuvres; Coffee beans & grinders in rooms; BYOB
🚭	No inside Smoking
	Conference Facilities (20)
♿	Wheelchair Access (1 rm.; dining rm. & conf. fac.)

This mountain hideaway is built of hand-hewn logs and is situated on 250 acres of secluded and unspoiled land. The Swag Country Inn is perched at 5,000 feet, with a private entrance into The Great Smoky Mountains National Park. Guests enjoy 50-mile breathtaking views. It offers countless amenities, such as a fine library, fireplaces, Jacuzzis, and exceptional cuisine.

NC I-40, Exit 20 to Hwy. 276 for 2.8 mi. to Swag sign. Just after sign, turn R. 4 mi. up blacktopped road to Swag gate. L. on gravel driveway 2.5 mi. to inn.

TEL. 704-926-0430; 926-3119; FAX 704-926-2036
212-570-2071 Off Season
Hemphill Rd.,Rte. 2, Bx 280A
Waynesville, NC 28786
Deener Matthews, Innk.

THE WAVERLY INN

🛏	15 Rooms, \$89/\$109 B&B 1 Suite, \$165 B&B
💳	Visa, MC, Amex, Discov.
🛁	All Private Baths
	Open Year-round
👫	Children Welcome No Pets
R	Biltmore Estate, Flat Rock Playhouse, Antiquing, Golf, Blue Ridge Pkwy., Hiking, Horseback Riding, Fishing
🍷	Full Breakfast; Refreshments; Evening Social Hour; Arrangements for Private Parties, BYOB
🚭	Smoking Limited
♿	Wheelchair Access (dining room)

In an area rich with history and natural scenery, this National Register inn is the oldest surviving inn in Hendersonville's historic district. Walking distance to fine restaurants, exceptional shopping and antiquing. Polished wood, turn-of-the-century fittings, 4-poster beds, wide porches and rocking chairs are only part of the picture that brings guests back to this comfortable, friendly place. Join us for our daily social hour between 5 and 6 P.M. or just raid the cookie jar for one of Darla's famous inn house delectables.

From I-26, NC Exit 18B, US-64 (W); Continue 2 mi. into Hendersonville. Bear R. onto Rte. 25(N) for 800 yards. Inn is on L. at corner of 8th Ave. & N. Main.

TEL. 800-537-8195; 704-693-9193; FAX 704-692-1010
783 N. Main St.
Hendersonville, NC 28792

John & Diane Sheiry, Darla Olmstead, Innkeepers

108

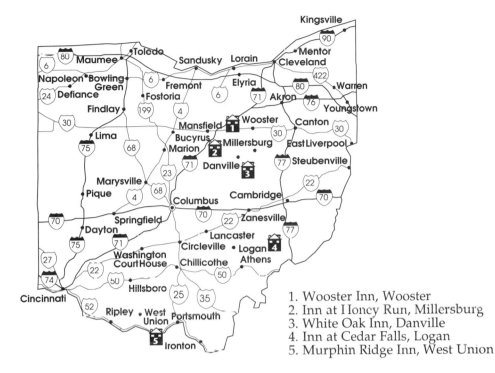

1. Wooster Inn, Wooster
2. Inn at Honey Run, Millersburg
3. White Oak Inn, Danville
4. Inn at Cedar Falls, Logan
5. Murphin Ridge Inn, West Union

THE INN AT CEDAR FALLS

9 Rooms, $75/$90 B&B
3 Cabins $110/$150 B&B

Visa, MC

All Private Baths

Open Year-round
exc. Dec. 25

Children's accommodations limited; No Pets

Hiking, Hammocks, Swimming, Canoeing, Riding

Breakfast; Dinner by reservation; Lunch for special occasions; BYOB

Specified Smoking areas

Conference Facilities (20)

Wheelchair Access (1 rm.)

From Columbus: Rte. 33 (S) to Logan exit, R. on Rte. 664, 9.5 mi. L. on Rte. 374. Inn is 1 mi. on L.

TEL. 614-385-7489

21190 State Route 374
Logan, OH 43138

Ellen Grinsfelder, Innkeeper

The restored and comfortably rustic 1840 Log House is an open kitchen-dining room, serving the most refined of gourmet dishes, prepared from home-grown produce. Guest rooms in the barn-shaped Inn building combine antique beds, private baths, and sweeping views of meadows, woods and wildlife. Fully-equipped 1800 log cabins, accommodating up to four, feature privacy. Facilities are appropriate for small business retreats, as well. The rugged and beautiful Hocking Hills State Park with glorious caves, waterfalls and forests flanks the Inn on three sides.

OHIO
THE INN AT HONEY RUN

🛏	37 rooms, $79/$150 B&B 2 two-room guest houses, $200/$275 (4 pers.) B&B
💳	Visa, MC, Amex
🛁	All Private Baths
🕯	Open Jan. 10 (94)–Dec. 23 (94), Dec. 26 (94)–Jan. 1 (95), Jan. 13 (95)—
🐕	Children accepted No pets
☼R	Birdwatching, Nat. trails, Game room, Amish Ctry, Cheese Factories, Craft Shops, Golf, Tennis
☕	Breakfast, Lunch, Dinner BYOB for guest rooms only
🚬	Some Non-smoking guest rooms, No smoking in dining room
⌂	Conference Facilities (72)
♿	

Located on sixty acres of woods and pasture, this prize winning, contemporary inn offers a serene blend of nature and luxury. Stay in the INN and watch birds from your picture window. Enjoy breakfast in your earth-sheltered Honeycomb Room with its stone fireplace and sliding glass door overlooking a wild flower meadow. Relax in a two-bedroom Guest House with panoramic views of Holmes Country hills. Explore the sights, crafts and backroads of scenic Holmes County, home to the world's largest Amish population.

From Millersburg: Rtes. 62/39 (E) for 2 blocks. L. on Rte. 241 (N) for 1.9 mi. R. (E) on County Rd. 203 for 1.5 mi.

TEL. 216-674-0011
FAX. 216-674-2623
6920 County Road 203
Millersburg, OH 44654

Marjorie Stock, Innkeeper

MURPHIN RIDGE INN

🛏	10 Rooms, $75/$85 B&B
💳	No Credit Cards
🛁	All Private Baths
🕯	Open Feb. 12–Dec. 31 exc. Dec. 24–25, Jan. 1–Feb. 11 and every Mon. & Tues.
🐕	Children Welcome; No Pets
☼R	Amish Shops, Serpent Mound, Appalachia Preserve, Golf, Herbs, Scenic Drives nearby
☕	Lunch & Dinner Wed. thru Sun.; BYOB for guest rooms only
🚬	No Smoking
⌂	Conference Facilities (25-30)
♿	Wheelchair Access (6 rms.)

An historic, tranquil 717-acre woodland farm is the setting for this prize-winning Inn. The brick farmhouse (1810) blends 3 attractive dining rooms, original fireplaces, unique Adams County crafted gifts and Art Gallery. Guests enjoy delicious entrees; homemade soups, made daily; luscious desserts from the professional kitchen staff. The custom furnished contemporary guesthouse includes fireplace rooms, porches, gathering room. Swimming, tennis, nature trails, horseshoes, shuffleboard, basketball, croquet on premises.

Rte 32 E. Rte. 41 S. To Dunkinsville 6 mi, R. on Wheatridge 1 1/2 mi. R. on Murphin Ridge 1/2 mi.

TEL. (513) 544-2263
750 Murphin Ridge Rd.
West Union, OH 45693

Mary & Robert Crosset Jr., Innkeepers

WHITE OAK INN

10 Rooms, $70/$150 B&B
(3 Rms. with Fireplaces)

Visa, MC, Discov

All Private Baths

Closed Christmas

Appropriate for Children
over 12; No Pets

Lawn games, Bicycling,
Amish country touring,
Antiquing, Golf, Fishing,
Canoeing, Hiking

Breakfast; Dinner by res-
ervation; Comp. Sherry
BYOB

No Smoking

Conference facilities (25)

From I-71: Rte 36 (E) or Rtes. 95 (E)
and 13 (S) to Mt. Vernon. Then U.S.
Rte 36 (E) 13 mi. to Rte 715. From I-77:
Rte. 36 (W) 43 mi. to Rte 715. Take Rte.
715 (E) 3 mi. to inn.

TEL. 614-599-6107

29683 Walhonding (S.R. 715)
Danville, OH 43014

Ian & Yvonne Martin,
Innkeepers

 Turn-of-the-century farmhouse in a quiet, wooded country setting. Antiques and period decor, fireplace and square grand piano in the common room, front porch with swings and rockers, a screened house, and elegant meals, all make your stay a memorable one. Experience simple country pleasures. The Inn is close to Ohio's Amish area for quilts, oak furniture, antiques, and cheeses. We also offer guest participation in our onsite archaeological dig and other special event packages.

THE WOOSTER INN

15 Rooms, $75/$85
2 Suites, $100/$120

Visa, MC, Amex, Diners,
Discov.

All Private Baths

Closed Dec. 25–26

Well Supervised Children
accepted; Pets Accepted

Golf, Tennis, Amish settle-
ments, Football Hall of
Fame in Canton, Wooster
College activities

Breakfast, Lunch, Dinner,
Wine & Beer available

Non-Smoking Dining
Room

Conference Facilities (50)

Wheelchair Access

I-71 (S) to Burbank. L. on Rte. 83 (S), 18
mi. Wooster Exit, R. at Rte. 585 (S) for
200 ft. R. at Wayne Ave. Inn .7 mi. on
L. I-71 (N) to US-30 E., 24 mi to Wooster
Exit at Madison R. Follow to Beaver
to Wayne Ave. 2 mi. Turn R, 2 blks. to
inn.

TEL. 216-264-2341
FAX 216-264-9951 (24 hr.)

801 E. Wayne Ave.
Wooster, OH 44691
Andrea Lazar, Innkeeper

The spacious campus of the College of Wooster is the setting for this pleasant inn, which overlooks the college golf course, where inn guests may play. Tastefully decorated rooms offer modern comfort and quiet, and cuisine in the attractive dining room is excellent and fresh. The Ohio Light Opera and college events provide cultural and recreational diversions.

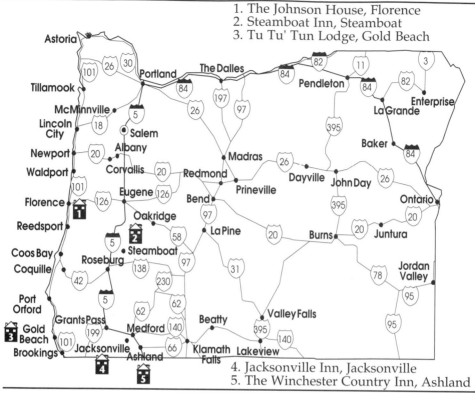

1. The Johnson House, Florence
2. Steamboat Inn, Steamboat
3. Tu Tu' Tun Lodge, Gold Beach

4. Jacksonville Inn, Jacksonville
5. The Winchester Country Inn, Ashland

JACKSONVILLE INN

8 rooms, $80/$125 B&B
1 Suite, $175 B&B

Visa, MC, Discov, Amex, Diners
All Private Baths

Open Year-round

Children Accepted
No Pets

Museum, Antiques, Hiking, Wineries, Swimming, White Riv. Rafting, Shopping, Shakespeare Fest., Britt Music Festival

Restaurant, Bistro
Sun. Brunch, Lounge
Wine & Liquor available
Non-smoking Rooms

Conference Facilities (80)

Housed in one of Jacksonville's early (1861) permanent structures, built during the gold rush, the inn has locally quarried sandstone walls flecked with bits of gold in the dining room and lounge. In addition to guest rooms furnished with restored antiques, the inn boasts one of Oregon's most award-winning restaurants, with superb dining and a connoisseur's wine cellar.

I-5(N), Ex. 30, R. Crater Lk. Hwy (Hwy. 62) to Medford. R. on McAndrews, L. on Ross Lane, R. on W. Main (238), R. on Calif. St. I-5(S), Exit 27, L. on Barnett, R. on Riverside; L. on Main St. R. on Calif.

TEL. 503-899-1900; 800-321-9344; FAX 503-899-1373

175 E. California St.
Jacksonville, OR 97530

Jerry & Linda Evans, Innkps.

THE JOHNSON HOUSE

6 rooms (including a small garden cottage), $75/$105 B&B
Visa, MC

Private Baths

Open Year-round

Appropriate for Children over 12; No Pets

Ocean Beaches, Dunes, Woods, Lakes, River, Whale-watching, Horseback Riding, Hiking, Fishing, Golf

Full Breakfast; Complimentary Wine; BYOB

Smoking on porches

1 block (N) of Siuslaw River; 2 blocks (E) of Coast Hwy. 101; corner First & Maple in Old Town.

TEL. 503-997-8000
216 Maple St.
PO Box 1892
Florence, OR 97439

Ronald & Jayne Fraese, Innkeepers

This is like "grandmother's house," with treasured heirlooms, amusing photographs and curios, where you are welcomed with a cup of tea. The faithfully restored 1892 Victorian inn is in the center of Old Town, a waterfront community on Oregon's scenic central coast. Just a block away from docks and small commercial fishing fleet. Blue and ivory guest rooms feature lace curtains, down comforters, and many books. Breakfasts are lavish and imaginative.

STEAMBOAT INN

8 Cabins, $85 EP
7 Cotts./suites, $125/$195

Visa, MC

All Private Baths

Closed Jan.–Feb. & limited service Mar.–Apr.

Children Accepted
No Pets

Fishing for steelhead, 35 mi. of public water, Backpacking, Hiking

Breakfast, Lunch, Dinner by reservation
Wine Available

No Smoking

Conference facilities (70 day mtg. & 40 overnight)

Wheelchair Access (2 rms., dining rm. & conf. fac.)

I-5 to Roseburg. Steamboat Inn is 38 mi. (E) on Rte. 138. Inn is 70 mi. (W) of Crater Lake and 40 mi. (W) of Diamond Lake, on Rte. 138.

TEL. 503-498-2411
FAX 498-2411 (1 ring +*2)
Steamboat, OR 97447-9703

Sharon & Jim Van Loan, Innkps.
Patricia Lee, Manager

Nestled among towering firs, choose from cozy streamside cabins, cottages in the woods or luxurious suites on the river. You may want a picnic for a days outing to Crater Lake, local waterfalls, swimming holes, hiking trails or the wineries of Douglas County. Be sure to be back for the evening dinner. This creative meal, featuring fresh local ingredients and Oregon wine, will add the perfect finish to an already perfect day!

OREGON
TU TU' TUN LODGE

	16 rooms, $90/$155 EP 4 Suites, Guesthouses, $90/$198 EP
	Visa, MC
	All Private Baths
	Closed Oct. 27-April 27; Year-round River Stes., Ghouse. Stes., Firepl. rms.
	Sept.-June Children Very Welcome; Pets Welcome
	Guided Fishing, White Water Boat Trips, Self-guided Hiking Trails, Beachcombing, 9-hole Golf Course, 4-hole Pitch & Putt, Horseshoes.
	Breakfast, Lunch (Reg. Guests Only), Dinner, MAP available; Wine & Liquor Available
	No Smoking in Dining Rm.
	Conference Facilities (40)
	Wheelchair Access (8 rms.)

Nestled on the banks of the Rogue River, Tu Tu' Tun Lodge combines the comforts of a first-class resort with the congeniality of a small hideaway. Guests enjoy hors d'oeuvre around the large stone fireplace, gourmet dining overlooking the river and madrone wood fires on the terrace at dusk. Come, partake in the serious challenge of the steelhead and salmon, experience the excitement of a white water excursion or simply enjoy some solitude.

Gold Beach, Hwy. 101 (E) 7 mi. along north side of Rogue River to Lodge.
TEL. 503-247-6664
FAX 504-247-0672
96550 North Bank Rogue
Gold Beach, OR 97444

Dirk & Laurie Van Zante, Innkeepers

THE WINCHESTER COUNTRY INN

	18 Rooms, $89/$160 B&B
	Visa, MC
	All Private Baths
	Open Year-round
	Children Accepted No Pets
	White water rafting, Hiking, XC & Downhill Skiing, Shakespeare Festival, Boating, Sailing, Music
	Breakfast, Sunday brunch, Dinner; Wine & Liquor available
	Smoke-free Inn
	Conference facilities (35)

A true country inn in the heart of the city, this handsomely restored, century-old Victorian home (National Register) invites you to enjoy an atmosphere of sophisticated country living. Beautiful tiered gardens and gazebo welcome guests each morning for breakfast. Guest rooms offer antiques, balconies and patios. Gourmet dinners and champagne Sunday brunch are served.

From I-5 (N), 1st Ashland exit. R. on Valley View, L. on Hwy. 99 for 3 mi. to Ashland. R. on 2nd St. From I-5 (S), 1st Ashland exit, for 4 mi. to Ashland. L. on 2nd St.
TEl. 503-488-1113
or 488-1115; 800-972-4991
35 So. Second St.
Ashland, OR 97520
Michael and Laurie Gibbs, Innkeepers

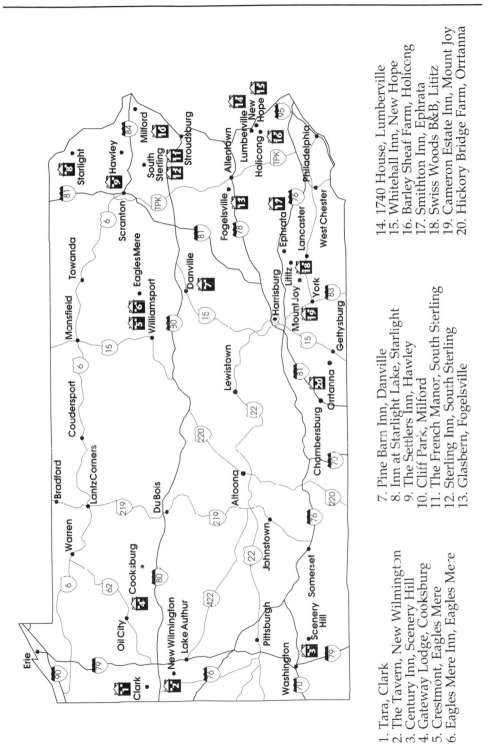

14. 1740 House, Lumberville
15. Whitehall Inn, New Hope
16. Barley Sheaf Farm, Holicong
17. Smithton Inn, Ephrata
18. Swiss Woods B&B, Lititz
19. Cameron Estate Inn, Mount Joy
20. Hickory Bridge Farm, Orrtanna

7. Pine Barn Inn, Danville
8. Inn at Starlight Lake, Starlight
9. The Settlers Inn, Hawley
10. Cliff Park, Milford
11. The French Manor, South Sterling
12. Sterling Inn, South Sterling
13. Glasbern, Fogelsville

1. Tara, Clark
2. The Tavern, New Wilmington
3. Century Inn, Scenery Hill
4. Gateway Lodge, Cooksburg
5. Crestmont, Eagles Mere
6. Eagles Mere Inn, Eagles Mere

BARLEY SHEAF FARM

	8 Rooms, $116/$155 B&B 2 Suites, $130/$175 B&B
	Visa, MC, Amex, Diners
	All Private Baths
	Closed only Christmas week
	Appropriate for Children over 8; No Pets
R	Pool, Croquet, Flea Markets, Shopping, Historic touring, Antiquing
	Full Breakfast
	Smoking allowed
	Conference Facilities (25) Wheelchair Access (2 rms., dining rm.)

Barley Sheaf is an early Bucks County farm comfortably situated on 30 acres at the end of a long tree-lined drive. Once owned by the playwright George S. Kaufmann, it was the gathering place in the 30's and 40's for some of Broadway's brightest illuminaries, ie. Dorothy Parker, Mose Hart, the Marx brothers, etc. A park-like setting provides beauty and seclusion ideally suited for a romantic getaway. Lovely guest rooms, gracious common rooms, exceptional hospitality and an outstanding breakfast are Barley Sheaf hallmarks.

On Rte. 202, .5 mi. (W) of Lahaska. From N.J. take Rte. 202. From Rte. 276 and south, take Rte. 263 (N) to Buckingham and Rte. 202 to inn.

TEL. 215-794-5104
FAX 215-794-5565
Route 202, Box 10
Holicong, PA 18928

Ann & Don Mills,
Innkeepers

CAMERON ESTATE INN

	18 Rooms, $65/$110 B&B
	Visa, MC, Amex, Diners, Discov
	16 Private, 2 Shared Baths
	Closed Christmas Eve & Day
	Appropriate for Children over 12; No Pets
R	Library, TV, Lawn Games, Golf, Swimming & Tennis nearby
	Breakfast, Dinner, Sun. Brunch; Wine & Liquor available
	Smoking Accepted
	Conference Facilities (60)

The Inn & Restaurant occupy the rural Lancaster County estate of Simon Cameron, Abraham Lincoln's first Secretary of War. Rooms at Cameron are furnished in grand style and are individually decorated; 7 have fireplaces. The restaurant offers a fine selection of American and classic foods as well as the appropriate wines. Groff's Farm Restaurant, the county's finest, is also nearby.

Rte. 283 to Rte. 772(S) to 1st light in Mt. Joy and R. on Main, 2nd light L. (S. Angle St.), R. on Donegal Springs Rd. at stop turn, L. on Colebrook, R. back onto Donegal Springs Rd., 1/4 mile on R.

TEL. 717-653-1773
FAX 717-653-9432
1895 Donegal Springs Rd.
Mount Joy, PA 17552
Stephanie Seitz, Larry Hershey, & Mindy Goodyear, Innkeepers

CENTURY INN

🛏	5 Rooms, $80/$85 EP 4 Rooms, $95/$135 EP
💳	No Credit Cards
🛁	All Private Baths
🏮	Open Year-round (lodging & parties)
🐕	Children Accepted No Pets
R	Tennis, Croquet, Volley-ball Court, Many Small Shops in Scenery Hill
🍷	Breakfast, Houseguests only; Lunch, Dinner (Dining rm. open Mar. 19–Dec. 30) ; Wine & Liquor Available
🚬	Smoking accepted
👥	Conference Facilities (175)
♿	

From I-70, Bentleyville Exit. Rte. 917(S) to Rte. 40. 1 mi.(E) to the inn.
TEL. 412-945-6600
Scenery Hill, PA 15360

Megin Harrington, Innkeeper

 It's not hard to believe this is the oldest operating inn (1794) on the National Pike (U. S. 40) when you see the hand-forged crane in the original kitchen and the vast array of rare antiques adorning this intriguing inn. Called one of the dining super stars in the Pittsburgh area, the inn, now celebrating its 200th year in operation, is a favorite destination for both country inn buffs and gourmands.

CLIFF PARK INN & GOLF COURSE

🛏	18 rooms, $100/$145 B&B
💳	Visa, MC, Amex, Diners, Discov
🛁	All Private Baths
🏮	Open Year-round
🐕	Children Accepted with Parents; No Pets
R	9-hole Golf Course, Hiking Trails, XC Skiing, Delaware River for Swimming, Fishing, Rafting, Canoeing
🍷	Breakfast, Lunch & Dinner; MAP rates available; Wine & Liquor Available
🚬	Smoking Permitted
👥	Conference Facilities (60 day, 36 overnight)
♿	Wheelchair access (5 rms., dining rm. & conf. fac.)

I-80 to Ex. 34B; Rte. 15N becomes 206N, into Milford, PA. Thru traffic light, 2 blks. L. onto 7th & go 1.5 mi. to inn. From I-84, Ex. 10, Milford, (E) on Rte. 6 for 2 mi. R. on 7th St. for 1.5 mi. to inn.
TEL. 717-296-6491
800-225-6535
FAX 717-296-3982
RR4, Box 7200
Milford, PA 18337-9708
Harry W. Buchanan III, Innkp.

 Historic Country Inn (1820) on secluded 600-acre estate, surrounded by long-established golf course (1913). Spacious rooms, some with fireplaces. This historic inn offers old-fashioned hospitality, heirlooms reflecting the life and times of the Buchanan family. Antiques and lace grace the guest rooms and the maple-shaded veranda overlooks the golf course. Their master chef specializes in American, French and Cajun cuisine. Golf, Honeymoon and Country wedding packages.

PENNSYLVANIA
CRESTMONT INN

	15 Rooms, $148/$155 MAP
	3 Suites/Apt., $178 MAP 1 Apt., $695 for 6 nights, EP Visa, MC
	All Private Baths
	Open Year-round exc. Dec. 24–25
	Children Welcome; Pets by Prior Arrangement
	Swimming pool, 6 Har-Tru Tennis crts., Golf, Lake, Hiking trails, Ice Skating, XC Skiing, Tobogganing, Cultural activities, summer
	Country Breakfast & Dinner; to the public by res. Wine & Liquor available No Smoking exc. outdoors
	Conference Facilities (30) Wheelchair Access (9

Situated atop the highest mountain in Sullivan County, Crestmont Inn is a perfect place to relax, unwind and enjoy the peaceful quietude of our natural woodland setting, beautiful gardens and gourmet dining. Enjoy skiing or hiking through some of the most spectacular scenery in the state. Try sailing or canoeing on the crystal-clear, Eagles Mere Lake. Classical music, fireplaces, candlelit dinners, hammocks, fresh mountain air and warm hospitality beckon you to a special place that has kept people returning for almost a century.

rms., dining rm. & conf. fac.)
From I-80, Exit 34 to 42 (N) for 33 mi. to Eagles Mere village. Continue thru town & follow signs to Crestmont Inn.

TEL. 717-525-3519
800-522-8767
Crestmont Dr.
Eagles Mere, PA 17731

John & Jane Wiley, Innkeepers

EAGLES MERE INN

	13 Rooms, $125/$175 MAP
	2 Suites, $135/$195 MAP Visa, MC
	All Private Baths
	Open Year-round
	Children Welcome No Pets
	Antiquing, Hiking, Swimming, Boating, Golf, Tennis, Winter Sports
	Full Breakfast & 5 course dinner; Wine and Liquor
	Smoking very limited
	Conference Facilities (30)

This Mountain top Resort offers Ultimate Stress relief! Peace & quiet with a private, pristine, crystal clear, lake and acres of Forest. Incredible Waterfalls & Vistas! Guests enjoy warm Hospitality, exceptional meals, outstanding wines and peaceful relaxation. Featured as a special vacation spot in numerous Travel Writer articles. The "Last Unspoiled Resort!"

From I-80, Exit 34 to Rt. 42 (N) 33 miles to Eagles Mere, turn on Mary Ave. & go 1 block to Inn

TEL. 717-525-3273
800-426-3273
Mary & Sullivan Avenues
Eagles Mere, PA 17731

Susan & Peter Glaubitz, Innkeepers

THE FRENCH MANOR

6 Rooms, $110/$160 B&B
3 suites, $160/$200 B&B

Visa, MC, Amex, Discov

All Private Baths

Open Year-round

Not suitable for Children
No Pets

Hiking, Croquet,
Beautiful scenery,
Swimming, Tennis, XC
Skiing, Ice Skating nearby

Breakfast, Lunch, Dinner;
French restaurant; MAP
rates available; Wine &
Liquor available
Non-smoking Dining

Conference Facilities (18)

Wheelchair Access (2 rms.)

From NYC: I-80(W), PA Exit 52 to Rte.
447(N) to Rte. 191(N) to S. Sterling.
Turn L. on Huckleberry Rd. From
Phila. NE extension of PA Tpke. to
Pocono Exit 35. Follow Rtes. 940(E),
423(N) to 191(N) 2.5 mi. to Huckle-
berry Rd.
TEL. 717-676-3244
RES. 800-523-8200
Box 39, Huckleberry Rd.
South Sterling, PA 18460
Ron & Mary Kay Logan, Innkps.

 The French Manor is an elegant country inn, secluded and private, like a secret lookout separate from the populace. You may choose from four spacious guest rooms in the Manor, three suites (one with jacuzzi and fireplace) or two comfortable rooms in the Carriage House. Enjoy a hearty breakfast with a view of the mountains from our dining room or in your room by request. Dinner is a celebration of authentic French cuisine in an atmosphere of elegance and refinement unmatched in the area.

GATEWAY LODGE

8 Rooms, $90/$100 EP,
$105/$115 B&B, $155/$165
MAP; 8 Cottages, $95/
$125 EP w/Fireplaces; 6%
Sales Tax, 15% Serv. Grat.
Visa, MC, Amex, Discov
11 Private Baths
Open Year-round exc.
Thanksgiving & Dec. 24–25
Children 8 & over
No Pets
X-ctry Skiing, Hiking, Bik-
ing, Horsebk. Riding, Ca-
noeing, Tubing, Hunting,
Fishing, Sum. Theater, Nat.
Walking, Antiqueing
Breakfast daily; Sack
Lunch Available; Dinner
except Mon. Aftnoon. tea.
Full Bar Service.
Smoking on porch
Meeting Facilities (50)
Wheelchair Access (2 rms.,
dining rm. & conf. fac.)

From E.: I-80, Exit 13 to Rte. 36 (N) to
Cook Forest. Inn is on Rte. 36, 1/4 mi.
(S) of Cooksburg Br. From W.: off I-
80, Exit 8 (Shippenville) to Rte. 66 to
Leeper (13 mi.) to Rte. 36 (S) (7 mi.).
Inn is on Rte. 36 1/4 mi. (S) of
Cooksburg Br.
TEL. 814-744-8017
800-843-6862 (PA/MD)
FAX 814-744-8017
Route 36, Box 125
Cooksburg, PA 16217
The Burney Family, Innkps.

 Amid some of the most magnificent forest scenery east of the Rocky Mountains, this rustic log cabin inn has been called one of the ten best country inns in the U.S. Guests gather around the large stone fireplace in the living room and savor wonderful home-cooked meals by kerosene light. Main inn guests may enjoy the indoor swimming pool, sauna, tea time, and turn-down service.

GLASBERN

🛏	10 Rooms, $100/$115 B&B
	13 Suites, $115/$230 B&B
💳	Visa, MC
🛁	All Private Baths, 16 Whirlpools
🏮	Open Year-round
🐕	Children Accepted No Pets
⒭	Swimming pool, Trails thru 100 acres, Bicycling, Hot air ballooning, Fishing, Carriage Rides
🍷	Breakfast; Dinner Daily, Wine & Liquor Available
🚬	Smoking Allowed
♨	Conference Facilities (16)
♿	Wheelchair Access (4 rms, dining rm. & conf. fac.)

🔥 Fireplaces and whirlpools embellish this farm established in the early-1800's, contemporized as an inn in 1985. contemporary American cuisine is served under the Barn's timbered cathedral ceiling. Flower and vegetable gardens flourish where a farm family once labored for basic provisions. Pastoral landscape, complemented by streams, ponds and paths, provides illusions of the past mingled with present-day comforts—private phones, TV's and VCR's. AAA & Mobil 3 stars; ABBA 4 crowns.

From I-78 take Rte. 100(N) for .2 mi. to L. at light (W) for .3 mi. to R. on Church St. (N) for .6 mi. to R. on Pack House Rd. for .8 mi. to the inn.

TEL. 215-285-4723
FAX 215-285-2862
2141 Pack House Rd.
Fogelsville, PA 18051-9743

Beth & Al Granger,
Owners

HICKORY BRIDGE FARM

🛏	6 Rooms, $79/$89 B&B
💳	Visa, MC
🛁	All Private Baths
🏮	Closed Christmas week
🐕	Children and Pets Accepted
⒭	Gettysburg touring, Fishing, Swimming, Hiking, Bicycling, Golf, Skiing
🍷	Breakfast (Houseguests), Dinner, Fri., Sat., Sun.
🚭	No Smoking
♨	Conference facilities (125)
♿	Wheelchair Access (conf. fac.)

🏠 A quaint country inn, offering 3-bedroom farmhouse accommodations and four private cottages and a delightful restaurant in a restored barn, filled with antiques, located 8 miles west of Gettysburg on a family operated farm. Fine, family-style dining Friday, Saturday and Sunday. Inn open seven days a week with bountiful morning meals. A quiet, rural setting with a country store museum, gift shop . . . a wonderful "country place!"

Gettysburg, Rte. 116(W) to Fairfield and R. 3 mi.(N) to Orrtanna. Or Rte. 977 to Rte. 30(E) for 9 mi. Turn (S) at Cashtown for 3 mi. to inn.

TEL. 717-642-5261
96 Hickory Bridge Rd.
Orrtanna, PA 17353

Robert & Mary Lynn Martin,
Dr. & Mrs. James Hammett,
Innkeepers

THE INN AT STARLIGHT LAKE

26 Rooms, $110/$154 MAP
1 Suite, $170/$200 MAP
Visa, MC

Private and Shared Baths

Open Year-round

Children Accepted
No Pets

Swimming, Boating, Tennis, Ice Skating, XC Skiing, Lawn Sports, Fishing, Golf

Breakfast, Lunch, Dinner, Sunday Brunch
Wine & Liquor available

No Smoking in Dining Room

Conference facilities (60)

From N.Y. Rte. 17, Exit 87 (Hancock). On Rte. 191 (S) 1 mi. to Rte. 370 (W), turn R. 3 mi. to sign on R. take R. 1 mi. to inn. From I-81, Exit 62, local roads; map sent on request.
TEL. 717-798-2519
800-248-2519
FAX 717-798-2672
Starlight, PA 18461
Judy & Jack McMahon, Innkeepers

Since 1909, guests have been drawn to this classic country inn on a clear lake in the rolling hills of northeastern Pennsylvania. The atmosphere is warm, congenial, and informal. Twenty two Mainhouse and cottage rooms, (one w. fireplace), suite w. Jacuzzi, and a family house and conference center complete this delightful little universe. There are activities for all seasons: swimming, boating, fishing, tennis, cycling, hiking; in winter, x-c skiing and ice-skating. Lakeside dining offers outstanding cuisine with emphasis on fresh ingredients, baked goods, and homemade pastas.

THE PINE BARN INN

75 Rooms, $46/$68 EP

Visa, Amex, CB, Disc, MC, Diners

All Private Baths

Open Year-round

Children Accepted; Pets (ltd. accommodations)

Golf, Tennis, Swimming, Horseback riding, Racquetball nearby

Breakfast, Lunch, Dinner
Wine & Liquor available

Non-smoking dining area

Conference Facilities (50)

Wheelchair Access (1 rm.)

From I-80, Exit 33, Rte. 54 (E) 2 mi. to Danville. L. 1st traffic light, signs to Medical Ctr. Inn at entrance to Geisinger Med. Ctr.
TEL. 717-275-2071; 800-627-2276; FAX 717-275-3248
#1 Pine Barn Place
Danville, PA 17821

Martin & Barbara Walzer, Innkeepers

A part of the history and tradition of Danville for over 100 years, this inn began life first as a barn and then as a riding stable. Today, the restaurant and original rooms still occupy the original barn, with many additional rooms in more recently completed buildings. The restaurant has been renowned for decades for its fresh seafood and homemade pies and pastries.

PENNSYLVANIA
1740 HOUSE

🛏	23 Rooms, $70/$110 B&B 1 Suite, $70/$110 B&B
💳	Personal Checks Accepted
🛁	All Private Baths
🏡	Open Year-round
🐕	No Children No Pets
ℝ	Pool at inn, Canoeing, Riding, Golf, Individual A/C
🍷	Breakfast, Daily to houseguests; Dinner, Fr. & Sat., by res.; BYOB
🚭	Non-smoking Dining Room
👥	Conference facilities (22)

🏠 An intimate view of the river from a lovely room with a private terrace or balcony is only one of the pleasures at this 18th-century, restored farmhouse on the the banks of the Delaware River. *Newsweek, McCall's, Glamour, & Harper's Bazaar* have all listed The 1740 House as one of their 10 favorite inns. The excellent restaurant is open to the public.

From NY & NJ use 202 (S) to Rte. 32. From I-95 use New Hope/Yardley exit (N) to New Hope. Lumberville is 7 mi. (N) of New Hope on Rte. 32.

TEL. 215-297-5661
River Rd. (Hwy. 32)
Lumberville, PA 18933

Harry Nessler & Robert John Vris, Innkeepers

THE SETTLERS INN

🛏	16 Rooms, $75/$95 B&B 3 Suites, $110/$125 B&B
💳	Visa, MC, Amex
🛁	All Private Baths
🏡	Open Year-round
🐕	Appropriate for Children No Pets
ℝ	Lake Wallenpaupack, Upper Delaware River, Promised Land State Park, Golf, Skiing, Horseback, Canoeing, Fishing, Glass Museum, Antique Shops
🍷	Breakfast, Lunch, Dinner Wine & Liquor available
🚬	Smoking designated areas
👥	Conference Facilities (100)
♿	Wheelchair Access (dining rm.)

🏠 Reminiscent of a small European hotel, this Tudor Manor is in the small turn-of-the-century town of Hawley. Chestnut wood beams, a bluestone fireplace, leaded windows, outdoor patio & herb gardens add to the ambiance. The dining room is well known for a cuisine based on our region's food traditions highlighting products from local farms. Lake Wallenpaupack, the upper Delaware River, and Promised Land State Park are nearby providing many recreational activities. Antique shops and summer theatre in town.

I-84 Exit 7, Route 390N. to Route 507 N. to Rt. 6 W., then 2 1/2 miles to Inn

TEL. 717-226-2993
800-833-8527
FAX 717-226-1874
Four Main Avenue
Hawley, PA 18428

Jeanne & Grant Genzlinger, Innkeepers

SMITHTON INN

🛏	8 Rooms, $65/$115 B&B 1 Suite, $140/$170 B&B
💳	Visa, MC, Amex
🛁	Private Baths, some Whirlpools
🪴	Open Year-round
🐕	Children and Pets by prior arrangement
☀R	Library, Gardens, Touring, Antiques, Epharta Cloister, Farmers Country Markets, Golf, Craft Center, Museums, Art Galleries
◉	Breakfast
🚭	No Smoking
⊬⊣⊣⊢	
♿	Wheelchair Access (1 rm.)

From North, PA Tpke. Exit 21 & Rte. 222 (S). From South, Hwy. 30 to Rte. 222 (N). From North or South, Exit Rte. 222 at Rte. 322 (W) for 2.5 mi. to inn.

TEL. 717-733-6094

900 W. Main St.
Ephrata, PA 17522

Dorothy Graybill, Innkeeper

17 A romantic 1763 stone inn located in Lancaster County among the Pennsylvania Dutch. Rooms are large, bright and cheerful with working fireplaces, canopy beds, desks, leather upholstered furniture, Penn. Dutch quilts, candles, chamber music, refrigeration, feather beds (by prior arrangement), books, and reading lamps. Common rooms are warm and inviting with fireplaces. Fresh flowers, night shirts and some of the best farmland of Amish, Mennonite, Brethren, etc. families.

THE STERLING INN

🛏	40 Rooms, $130/$160 MAP 16 Suites, $170/220 MAP
💳	Visa, MC, Amex, Discov
🛁	All Private Baths
🪴	Open Year-round
🐕	Children Accepted No Pets
☀R	Indoor Pool, Lake, Tennis, Hiking, Horseback Riding, Golf, XC Skiing, Sleigh Rides, Antiquing
◉	Breakfast, Lunch, Dinner. B&B rates on request Wine & Liquor available
🚭	No Smoking in Dining area
⊬⊣⊣⊢	Conference facilities (100)
♿	Wheelchair Access (3 rm., dining rm. & conf. fac.)

I-84, Exit 6, Rte. 507 (S), 3 mi. to Rte. 191 (S), 3 mi. to inn. I-80 (W) Exit 50, Rte. 191 (N) 25 mi. to inn. I-80 (E) Rte. 380 to Rte. 423 (N), to 191 (N), .5 mi. to inn.

TEL. 717-676-3311
RES: 800-523-8200

Rte. 191
South Sterling, PA 18460

Ron & Mary Kay Logan, Innkeepers

12 The country inn you've always looked for, but never thought you'd find. A friendly, romantic atmosphere with beautiful gardens, crystal clear streams, a waterfall, Victorian suites with fireplaces, & horse-drawn sleigh rides. Attractive rooms, indoor pool & spa, & outstanding meals make this family operated, 130-year-old inn everything you thought a country inn should be. Honeymooners may enjoy the "Innkeeping with Romance" Package. Social groups and family reunions can be accommodated in the lodge or guest house.

PENNSYLVANIA
SWISS WOODS

🛏	7 Rooms, $70/$120 B&B 1 Suite, $105/115
💳	Visa, MC, Discov
🛁	All Private Baths
🛋	Open Year-round
🐕	No Pets, Children Welcome ($15 add. per person)
ℝ	Canoe at lake, Hiking and Birdwatching
🍷	Breakfast
🚭	No Smoking
⌂	
♿	

🏠 Surrounded by meadows and gardens, Swiss Woods is a quiet retreat on 30 acres in Lancaster's Amish Country. All rooms here feature patios or balconies, some with views of the Speedwell Forge Lake, and decorated with light furnishings so popular in Europe. Fabulous breakfasts in a sunlight common room highlight your stay. Take a hike, watch the birds and relax! German spoken.

From PA Tpk Exit 21 to 222 S. to 322 W. Follow to Rt. 501. Take 501 S. 1 mi. to first crossroads. Turn R. on Brubaker Valley Rd. Go 1 mi. to the lake. Turn R. on Blantz Rd. The Inn is on your left.
TEL. 717-627-3358; 800-594-8018; FAX 717-627-3483
500 Blantz Rd.
Lititz, PA 17543
Werner & Debrah Mosimann, Innkeepers

TARA — A COUNTRY INN

🛏	25 Rooms $250/$350 MAP 2 Suites $430/430 MAP
💳	Visa, MC, Amex, Discov
🛁	All Private Baths
🛋	Open Year-round
🐕	Not appropriate for Children Kennels nearby for Pets
ℝ	Bocci, Croquet, Boating, Golf, Biking, Pool Table, Antiquing, XC Skiing, Swim Pools, Sauna, Steam
🍷	Breakfast, Lunch, Dinner, B&B rates available Wine & Liquor available
🚭	Smoking in designated areas
⌂	Conference Facilities (60)
♿	Wheelchair Access (dining rm. & conf. fac.)

🏠 If you loved the movie *Gone With the Wind*, you will love Tara. Built in 1854, this magnificent mansion reflects the golden days of the antebellum South, with rooms charmingly decorated to recall the grace and grandeur of yesteryear. Delightfully different cuisine, from gourmet to family-style, is served in the three totally different restaurants. Mobil 4-star and AAA 4-diamond.

From I-80, exit 1N, Rte. 18 (N) for 8 mi. Inn is located on (E) side overlooking Lake Shenango.
TEL. 412-962-3535
800-782-2803
3665 Valley View, Box 475
Clark, PA 16113

Jim & Donna Winner, Innkeepers

THE TAVERN AND LODGE

🛏	5 Rooms, $49/$60, B&B
💳	Tavern—No Credit Cards; Lodge—Visa, MC
🛁	All Private Baths
🛎	Tavern Closed July 4, Dec. 25, Thanksgiving & Tues., Lodge All Year
🐕	Children Accepted Pets Accepted
☀R	Golf, Canoeing, Fishing
🍷	Continental Breakfast, Houseguests (Buffet—Sat. & Sun.); Lunch, Dinner
🚬	Smoking Accepted
⊢🛏⊣	Conference Facilities (50)
♿	

I-80 E; Exit 1S onto Rte. 60 (S), to Rte. 18 (S). (E) on Rte. 208, 1 mi. to inn. I-80 W to Exit 2 (Mercer) south on Rte. 19 to West on 208, 8 miles to Inn.

TEL. 412-946-2020
Lodge: 412-946-2091
101 N. Market St.
New Wilmington, PA 16142

Mary Ellen Durrast,
Innkeeper

Turn back the clock & escape the rush of today. Awaken the clip-clop of horse-drawn buggies, visit the nearby mills & covered bridges, explore the many unique shops featuring local handcrafted items, see a simpler way of life in the Amish country of western Pennsylvania. Enjoy our legendary sticky rolls as your server calls the menu of our bounteous homestyle cooking which has kept guests returning for over 60 years. After dinner retire to one of our comfortable guest rooms for a relaxing evening.

THE WHITEHALL INN

🛏	6 Rooms, $170/$180 B&B
💳	Visa, MC, Amex, CB, Diners, Discov.
🛁	4 Private, 1 Shared Bath
🛎	Open Year-round
🐕	Appropriate for Children over 12; No Pets
☀R	Swimming Pool, Horseback Riding, XC Skiing, Public & Private Golfing, Tennis, Hiking, Delaware River Water Sports
🍷	4-Course Breakfast, Afternoon Tea; Wine Available
🚬	No Smoking on Property
⊢🛏⊣	Conference Facilities (15)
♿	

Hwy. 202 (S) from New Hope to Lahaska. L. on to Street Rd. to 2nd intersection, bear R. on Pineville Rd. Continue 1.5 mi. to inn on R.

TEL. 215-598-7945
RD2, Box 250
1370 Pineville Rd.
New Hope, PA 18938

Mike and Suella Wass,
Innkeepers

Experience the 4-course candlelight breakfast and afternoon high tea called "sumptuous" by *Bon Appetit*. Classical music is everywhere, fireplaces add a romantic touch, and family antiques provide a hint of home. Enjoy the rose garden and pool in the warmer months. Feed the dressage horses a carrot. Relax and do nothing. Mike and Suella extend a special welcome to their guests.

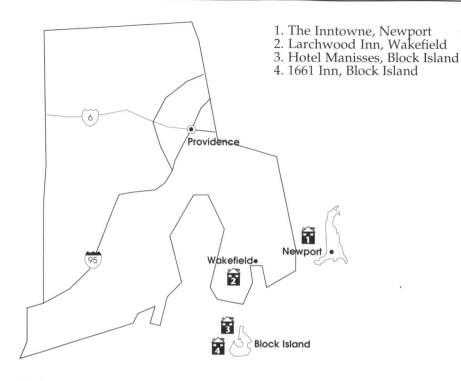

1. The Inntowne, Newport
2. Larchwood Inn, Wakefield
3. Hotel Manisses, Block Island
4. 1661 Inn, Block Island

HOTEL MANISSES

	17 Rooms, $75/$325 B&B
	Visa, MC, Amex
	All Private Baths; 4 Jacuzzis
	Open year-round; Dining Room open daily mid-May–Nov. 3; Wkends only Nov.–mid-May
	Appropriate for Children over 10; No Pets
	Swimming, Boating, Fishing, Hiking, Biking
	Buffet Breakfast, Lunch, Complimentary Wine & Nibble hour; Dinner Wine & Liquor available
	No Smoking in dining rm.
	Conference Facilities (80) Wheelchair Access (3 rms., dining rm. & conf. fac.)

Step into 19th Century yesteryear with a stay at this Romantic Victorian hotel featuring 17 meticulously appointed rooms with private baths and authentic Victorian furniture; some rooms with jacuzzis. The award-winning dining room serves dinner every evening. Sample delicious selections from our varied menu as featured in *Gourmet* magazine. Tableside flaming Coffees, Afterdinner drinks & Desserts served nightly in the upstairs parlour.

By ferry: Providence, Pt. Judith, Newport, RI & New London, CT. By air: Newport, Westerly, Providence, RI & New London, Waterford, CT. Contact inn for schedules.

TEL. 401-466-2421
FAX 401-466-2858
Spring St.
Block Island, RI 02807
The Abrams Family,
Innkeepers

THE INNTOWNE

21 Rooms, $110/$200 B&B
5 Suites, $195/$250 B&B

Visa, MC, Amex

All Private Baths

Open Year-round

Appropriate for Children over 12; No Pets

Beaches, Tennis Boating, Mansion touring

Continental Breakfast, Afternoon Tea

Smoking Accepted

Conference Facilities (15)

Cross Newport bridge, R. at 1st exit sign. R. at bottom of ramp, straight to Thames St. Inn is on corner of Thames and Mary Sts. across from Brick Marketplace.

TEL. 401-846-9200; 800-457-7803; FAX 401-846-1534
6 Mary St.
Newport, RI 02840

Carmella Gardner, Innkeeper

This in-town Colonial inn with a garrison roof is right in the center of bustling Newport, just a block from the water. Rooms are bright and cheerful with elegant antiques, good reproductions, and paintings. A few steps from the door are beautiful sunsets, towering sailboat masts, quaint and fashionable shops, and many restaurants.

LARCHWOOD INN

19 Rooms, $40/$90 EP

Visa, MC, Amex, Discov, CB, DC

Private and Shared Baths

Open Year-round

Children Accepted ($10) Pets Allowed ($5)

Ocean Swimming, Fishing, Golf, Tennis, Historic Touring, Bicycling, Boating

Breakfast, Lunch, Dinner Wine and Liquor available

Non-smoking dining area

Conference Facilities (125)
Wheelchair Access (dining rm. & conf. fac.)

NYC and S.; I-95 (N) to Exit 3A(Rte. 138E) to Kingston, 108 to Wakefield; R. on Main St., follow to inn on R. From Boston and N.; I-95(S) to Exit 9(Rte. 4) which becomes Rte.1. Exit at 1st sign for Wakefield, follow Main St. to inn on R.

TEL. 401-783-5454; 1-800-275-5450; FAX 401-783-1800
521 Main St.
Wakefield, RI 02879
Francis & Diann Browning, Innkeepers.

Watching over the main street of this quaint New England town for 160 years, this grand old house, surrounded by lawns and shaded by stately trees, dispenses hospitality along with good food and spirits from early morning to late night. Historic Newport, picturesque Mystic Seaport, and salty Block Island are a short ride away. Conveniences such as telephones, computers, and fax are available within the confines of this country inn with Scottish flavor. If you've never stayed at the Larchwood Inn, you're in for a real treat!

RHODE ISLAND
THE 1661 INN

	19 Rooms, $75/$325 B&B (3 w/fireplaces)
	Visa, MC, Amex
	17 Private Baths; 5 Jacuzzis
	Open Year-round
	Children of All Ages No Pets
	Swimming, Boating, Fishing, Hiking, Biking
	Breakfast, Lunch, Dinner (available at Hotel Manisses); Comp. Wine & Nibble hr.; Wine & Liquor Available Smoking Accepted
	Conference Facilities (80) Wheelchair Access (6 rms., dining rm. & conf. fac.)

Enjoy the Spectacular ocean views & authentic New England decor of The 1661 Inn. Most rooms feature an ocean view, private deck & jacuzzi; some rooms feature fireplaces. Marvel at the spectacular views of the Atlantic from our canopy covered deck while enjoying our full buffet breakfast and lunch menu.

By Ferry: Providence, Pt. Judith, Newport, RI, and New London, CT. By air: Newport, Westerly, Providence, RI and New London, Waterford, CT. Contact inn for schedules.
TEL.401-466-2421
FAX 401-466-2858
Spring Street
Block Island, RI 02807
The Abrams Family
Innkeepers

A SHORT HISTORY OF THE AMERICAN COUNTRY INN

Often a hotbed of political activity, where plots were hatched and plans were made, American inns in Colonial days were more than simply hostelries providing bed and board. Along with the church and the New England town meeting, the American inn ranks as one of the oldest continuing institutions in our country. In the 17th century some communities were required by law to provide accommodations and provender for travelers. They were called variously taverns or inns or ordinaries. The center of village activity, those early inns sometimes served as churches, gaols, courtrooms, political campaign headquarters, theaters, runaway slave stations, smuggler's hideaways, and even bordellos and mortuaries. In the seaport cities of the South, Spanish Main pirates had their favorite tavern haunts with secret tunnels, through which unwilling sailors could be shanghaied onto waiting ships.

During the Revolution, inns served as way stations between military posts, storing arms and ammunition and passing along intelligence on the movements of British troops. General Washington's New York headquarters were in the now-famous Fraunces Tavern.

As roads began to thread the colonies, stagecoach stops sprang up, and with westward expansion, the tradition of finding food and refuge in ranches and cabins on the prairie and in the mountains later turned many a farm and ranch into an inn.

Railroads made the stagecoach obsolete and often the once-bustling towns and inns on the stagecoach routes became irrelevant and sank into oblivion. Other towns grew up beside the railroads, and "commercial travelers" patronized the new "commercial hotels." Trains carried families to the mountains, seashore, and mineral springs resorts for summer vacations. Tremendous hotels with huge staffs became a significant part of the American vacation scene and remained popular destinations for 75 years. Lodgings included 3 meals daily, hence the term "American Plan."— **by Virginia Rowe**

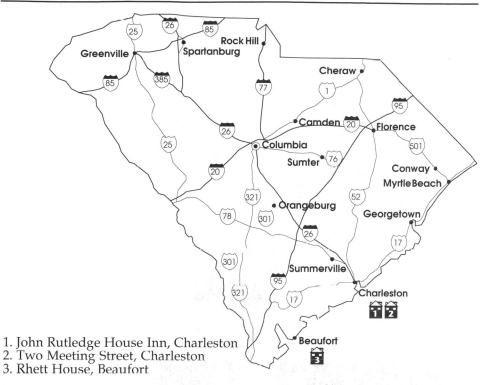

1. John Rutledge House Inn, Charleston
2. Two Meeting Street, Charleston
3. Rhett House, Beaufort

JOHN RUTLEDGE HOUSE INN

16 Rooms $130/$225 B&B
3 Suites, $235/$285 B&B

Visa, MC, Amex

All Private Baths

Open Year-round

Appropriate for Children
No Pets

Historic District, Homes
& Garden Tours, Market
area within walking distance

Continental Bfkfast. incl.,
Full Brkfast. available

Walking distance to
many restaurants for
lunch and dinner. Afternoon tea w/ light refresh.
Evening wine and sherry.

Smoking Restrictions

Conference Facilities (20)

Wheelchair Access (2
rms., conf. fac.)

From the Charleston Visitor's Center
turn R. onto John St. then L. onto King
St. Go one mi. to the Broad St. intersection. Turn R. onto Broad St. The
John Rutledge House is the 4th house
on the right.
TEL. 803-723-7999; 800-476-9741; FAX 803-720-2615
116 Broad St.
Charleston, SC 29401
Richard Widman, Innkeeper

Built in 1763 by John Rutledge, a signer of the United States Constitution, this elegant home is now a bed and breakfast inn. All guests receive wine and sherry in the ballroom, evening turndown with chocolate at bedside and continental breakfast and newspaper delivered to the room each morning. Free on-site parking. AAA Four Diamond. Historic Hotels of America.

THE RHETT HOUSE

🛏	10 Rooms, $125/$200 B&B/SC only 4-star B&B
💳	Visa, MC, Personal Checks
🛁	All Private Baths
🛋	Open Year-round Appropriate for Children over 5; No Pets
🐕	Antiques, Historic Antibellum Mansions, Moss-draped Live Oaks, Fabulous Barrier Island Beaches, Tennis, Carriage and Sailboat Tours, Lovely Gardens
☕	Breakfast, Afternoon tea; Picnic Lunch & Candlelit Dinners by Reservation, Wine & Liquor
🚬	Smoking–Verandas Only
🏨	Conference Facilities (40)
♿	Wheelchair Access (3 rms., dining rm. & conf. fac.)

Located in historic Beaufort by the bay, The Rhett House Inn is a beautifully restored 1820 plantation house. Furnished with English and American antiques, oriental rugs, fresh flowers, fireplaces and spacious verandahs. Romantic candlelit dinners featuring gourmet regional cuisine are graciously served with an extensive California wine list. Film site for *The Big Chill, Prince of Tides, The Great Santini*, and several upcoming productions. History laden Beaufort, Charleston and Savannah offer rich exploring.

I-95, Exit 33 & follow signs to Beaufort, R. on Craven St. for 4 blks. Off street parking in back. From the South, Exit 8 and follow signs to Beaufort.

TEL 803-524-9030
FAX 803-524-1310
1009 Craven St.
Beaufort, SC 29902

Steve & Marianne Harrison,
Innkeepers

TWO MEETING STREET INN

🛏	9 Rooms $115/$195 B&B
💳	No Credit Cards
🛁	All Private Baths
🛋	Closed Christmas (3 days)
🐕	Appropriate for Children over 8 years; No Pets Easy access to Shopping, Antiquing, World-class Golf, Tennis, Beaches, Plantations, Historic Houses, Museums, and Fine Dining
☕	Continental Breakfast; Afternoon Tea and Sherry
🚬	No Smoking
🏨	
♿	

Given as a wedding gift by a bride's loving father, this Queen Anne mansion welcomes all who are romantic at heart. From Southern rockers on the beautiful arched piazza, guests overlook White Point Gardens at Charleston's historic Battery. Family antiques, oriental rugs, Tiffany windows, and four-poster canopy beds create a most charming atmosphere. Share Texas size homemade muffins in the courtyard and enjoy a relaxing afternoon with sherry and tea on the wide veranda. For 55 years, the Spell family has graciously welcomed guests.

From 26E, exit Meeting Street. Travel south - Located on corner of Meeting and South Battery at White Point Garden.

TEL. 803-723-7322
2 Meeting Street
Charleston, SC 29401

Pete and Jean Spell,
Karen Spell Shaw
Innkeepers

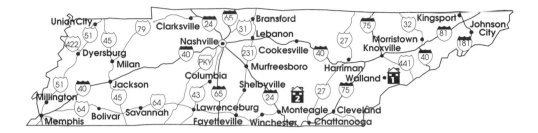

1. Inn at Blackberry Farm, Walland
2. Adams Edgeworth Inn, Monteagle

ADAMS EDGEWORTH INN

13 Rooms $60/$100 B&B
1 Suites, $135/$150 B&B

Visa, MC

All Private Baths

Open Year-round

Children welcome by prior arrangement; No Pets, kennel nearby

TN Aquarium, Sewanne University, Sauna, Music, Theatre, Hike, Tennis, Swim, Bike, Chautauqua

Breakfast, picnics on request, Candlelight Dinners by reservation; BYOB

Smoking Restricted

Conference Facilities (20)

Wheelchair Access (1 rm., dining rm. & conf. fac.)

I-24, Exit #134, R. 1/2 mi., L. under "Monteagle Assembly" archway. Thru stone gateway. Follow signs.

TEL. (615) 924-2669
FAX (615) 924-3236
Monteagle Assembly
Monteagle, TN 37356

Wendy & David Adams, Innkeepers

Nestled in a wilderness atop the Cumberland Mtns., Adams Edgeworth is an 1896 "Camelot" in a forest garden of brooks & tall trestle foot bridges. Come enjoy this National Register Inn featuring English manor decor, fine art, antiques, collector quilts, fireplaces and handmade mattresses on beautiful beds. Tour on bikes or our electric cart around the 150 Victorian cottages in our gated 96-acre private village. Fine candlelight dining by advance reservation. Musical & cultural events. Gift shop. Air conditioned.

INN AT BLACKBERRY FARM

27 rooms, $350/$450 AP
1 gate house, $495/$695

Visa, MC, Amex

All Private Baths

Open Year-round

Children welcome during holidays; No pets

Hiking, Flyfishing, Canoeing, Biking, Tennis, Swimming, Shuffle board, Scenic mountain drives, Rocking on the 155-foot veranda

Breakfast, Lunch, Dinner BYOB

Smoking restrictions

Conference Facilities (50) Wheelchair Access (1 rm., dining rm. & conf. fac.)

The Inn not only was recently accepted as a member of Relais & Chateaux (fewer than 20 luxury United States establishments are selected into this prestigious association), but it has been praised by Andrew Harper's *Hideway Report*, a connoisseur's guide to peaceful and unspoiled places. The Inn is the only property in the South to be included as one of the top 15 "little gems" in America in Harper's annual survey of the world's intimate hideaways. Staying at Blackberry is like having your own fully staffed country home.

From Knoxville, Tennessee, airport follow Highway 321 N. 16 miles to West Millers Cove Road (1/4 mi. past Foothills Parkway entrance on right). Turn R. on West Millers Cove Road and go 3.5 mi. to Blackberry Farm.
TEL. 615-984-8166
1-800-862-7610 (res.)
FAX. 615-983-5708
1471 West Millers Cove Road
Walland, Tennessee 37886
Kreis B. Beall, Innkeeper

MATTERS OF SOME MOMENT

Significant to the architectural heritage of our country, to communities, and to the public in general, is the reclamation of many historic and beautiful old buildings that have been brought back to life as country inns. Many of them are now listed on the National Register of Historic Places.

It was a slow process at first, but as interest in country inns grew, many wonderful things began to happen. For example, some of the inns of the 18th and 19th centuries that had been converted to other uses came back into their own. False ceilings were ripped away to find beautiful, heavy beams. Walls were removed to disclose handsome fireplaces. Layers of wallpaper were carefully peeled away to reveal beautiful 18th-century stenciling. Several inns in New England were discovered to have on their walls in remarkably preserved condition, the works of the famous itinerant artists, Rufus Porter and Moses Eaton. Porter was known for his murals and Eaton for his stencils.

Other valuable materials which have been (and are still being) saved and preserved are carved marble mantelpieces, beautiful glazed tiles, pressed tin ceilings, stained-glass windows, intricately carved moldings and balustrades, and various kinds of inlaid woods. Numerous previously lost or forgotten arts and crafts of construction and interior decoration have been recovered in the process.

Many buildings were saved from being torn down literally in the nick of time. In addition to the reclamation of former inns, buildings of all descriptions and former uses have been pressed into service. Former mansions and private residences are the most frequent beneficiaries of these conversions, but country inns may be found today in structures which were originally used as gristmills, barns, riding stables, log cabins, poorhouses, boarding houses, hospitals, schools, private clubs, and mountain lodges, to name a few.

Perhaps best of all, many American communities without village inns or small hotels since the late Victorian days find a new vigor and pride in their own restored inns and historic buildings, and the public is able to appreciate our architectural heritage and is enriched by having these beautiful old buildings available and accessible. — **by Virginia Rowe**

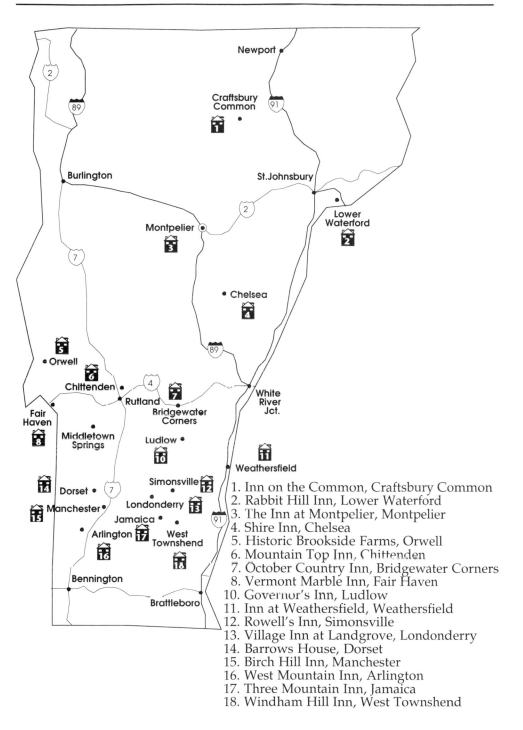

1. Inn on the Common, Craftsbury Common
2. Rabbit Hill Inn, Lower Waterford
3. The Inn at Montpelier, Montpelier
4. Shire Inn, Chelsea
5. Historic Brookside Farms, Orwell
6. Mountain Top Inn, Chittenden
7. October Country Inn, Bridgewater Corners
8. Vermont Marble Inn, Fair Haven
10. Governor's Inn, Ludlow
11. Inn at Weathersfield, Weathersfield
12. Rowell's Inn, Simonsville
13. Village Inn at Landgrove, Londonderry
14. Barrows House, Dorset
15. Birch Hill Inn, Manchester
16. West Mountain Inn, Arlington
17. Three Mountain Inn, Jamaica
18. Windham Hill Inn, West Townshend

BARROWS HOUSE

	17 Rooms, $170/$195 MAP 11 Suites, $190/$230 MAP
	Visa, MC, Amex, Discov
	All Private Baths
	Open Year-round
	Children Welcome Pets in 3 Cottages only
	Heated Pool, Sauna, Tennis Courts, Bike, Skiing, Hiking, Historic & Fine Arts centers, Shopping, Game & Puzzle Room
	Breakfast, Dinner, Brown bag Lunch on request; B&B available, Liquor & Wine available
	Smoking Restrictions
	Conference Facilities (25)
	Wheelchair Access (1 rm., dining rm. & conf. fac.)

The Barrows House is a collection of white clapboard buildings situated on 11 acres in the heart of a small picturebook Vermont town. Guests have a choice of 28 accommodations in eight different buildings, each with a history and style of its own. Dining at the Barrows House is an informal and delicious adventure in American regional cuisine. Whether with iced tea in the gazebo and English garden or mulled cider in front of a warm fire and historic stenciling, the Barrows House extends its welcome.

Manchester, Rte. 30 (N) 6 mi. to inn on R. Accessible from Vt. Rtes. 7, 4, 11, 30 and I-91 & 87.

TEL. 802-867-4455
800-639-1620 (Outside VT)
FAX 802-867-0132
Route 30
Dorset, VT 05251
Linda & Jim McGinnis, Innkeepers

BIRCH HILL INN

	5 Rooms, $105/$130 B&B 1 Cottage, $115 B&B
	Visa, MC, Amex
	All Private Baths
	Closed Nov. 1 - Dec. 26 Apr. 10 - May 30
	Appropriate for Children over 6; No Pets
	Pool, Trout Pond, Walking & XC Ski Trails, Antiquing, Summer Theatre
	Breakfast & Tea; Dinner for house guests weekends only; BYOB
	No Smoking

This inn has a spectacular location. On a back road away from busy village streets, among fabulous white birches, the inn has the feeling of a gracious home and quiet, peaceful retreat. Each cheerfully decorated room has views of surrounding mountains, farm and gardens. Hearty breakfasts and fine country dinners are among the pleasures to be found here.

In Manchester Center, Junction of Rtes. 7A & 30, take Rte. 30 (N) for 2.7 mi. to Manchester West Rd. go L. (S) for 3/4 of mi.

TEL. 802-362-2761
Res. 800-372-2761
West Road, P.O. Box 346
Manchester, VT 05254

Pat & Jim Lee, Innkeepers

VERMONT
THE GOVERNOR'S INN

🛏 8 Rooms, $170/$220 MAP

💳 Visa, MC, Pers Checks

🛁 All Private Baths

🛋 Open Year-round

🐩 Not appropriate for young Children; No Pets

⛷ Downhill & XC Skiing, Antiquing, Golf, Boating, Fishing, Hiking, Winery, Summer Theater, Priory

🍽 Full Breakfast, Picnic Baskets, Dinner, Afternoon Tea, Wine & Liquor available

🚭 No Smoking

Conference Facilities (16)

♿

Ludlow is located at junction of Rtes. 100 & 103. Inn is (S) on Rte. 103, just off village green.

TEL. 802-228-8830; 800-GOVERNOR (468-3766)

86 Main Street
Ludlow, VT 05149

Charlie & Deedy Marble,
Innkeepers

🏠 Three times judged one of the Nation's Ten Best Inns and awarded ★★★★ by Mobil, this may be the ultimate experience at a Victorian country inn. From potpourri scented air to soft strains of classical music, to beautifully kept heirlooms, attention is given to every detail insuring pleasure and comfort. Fifteen culinary awards, including "Vermont's Best Apple Pie," and recognition for excellence in innkeeping, service, and ambiance only add to the warm and generous hospitality intended to delight and surprise.

HISTORIC BROOKSIDE FARMS

🛏 5 Rooms, $85/$150 B&B
1 Suite, $150/$185 B&B

💳 No Credit Cards

🛁 Private & Shared Baths

🛋 Open Year-round

🐩 Children Welcome No Pets

⛷ Hiking, XC Skiing, Boating, Fishing, Golf, Tennis, Horseback riding

🍽 Breakfast, Dinner including wine; Lunch by request

🚭 Smoking Restricted

Conference Facilities (50)

♿ Wheelchair Access 1 Km.

From I-87 (N), exit 20 (Glen Falls). L. on Rte. 9 to Rte. 149 (E) to Rte. 4 (E) to Rte. 22A (N) on 22A for 13 mi. From I-89 (N) exit White River Junction, Rte. 4 (W) to 22A (N).

TEL. 802-948-2727
FAX 802-948-2015

Route 22A
Orwell, VT 05760

Joan & Murray Korda,
Innkeepers

🏠 This magnificent 200-year-old Greek Revival mansion is an architect's dream, where antique furnishings, paintings, and music abound. Skiers have only to step out the door to enjoy 300 acres of trails and meadow skiing. The farm provides wholesome food for the table, with beef, lamb and vegetable gardens. Three generations of innkeepers welcome guests to this homey setting.

VERMONT
THE INN AT MONTPELIER

🛏	19 Rooms, $99/$147 B&B (7 Deluxe)
💳	Visa, MC, Amex, Diners, CB
🛁	All Private Baths
🛋	Open Year-round
🐾	Children Welcome No Pets Downhill Skiing, 25 miles. State Capitol,
R	Shops, & 100 acre park a short walk.
🍷	Generous Continental Breakfast; Dinner daily; Restaurant closed Monday eves.
🚭	Wine & Liquor available Smoking Accepted
🏠	Conference Facilities (16)
♿	Wheelchair Access (dining rm. & conf. fac.)

An elegant, comfortable historic inn where fine dining and caring service are our specialties. Enjoy fireside dining or relax on Vermont's grandest porch. Each guest room is uniquely decorated with antiques, reproductions, fine art and many have fireplaces. Guest pantries offer at-home convenience and warmth with refreshments at any time. TV, telephone and air-conditioning.

I-89 to exit 8 Montpelier. Go to 4th light, turn L onto Main St. Inn approximately 3 blocks on right.

TEL. (802) 223-2727
FAX (802) 223-0722
147 Main St.
Montpelier, VT 05602

Maureen & Bill Russell,
Innkeepers

THE INN AT WEATHERSFIELD

🛏	9 Rooms, $175/$200 MAP 3 Suites, $200/$210 MAP
💳	Visa, MC, Amex, Discov, CB, Diners
🛁	All Private Baths
🛋	Open Year-round
🐾	Appropriate for children over 8; Pets Accepted with Prior Notice
R	Golf, Skiing, Hiking, Biking, Fishing, Sleigh & Carriage Rides, Sauna, Aerobics Equipment
🍷	High Tea, Dinner & Breakfast; Wine & Liquor Available
🚭	Smoking Restricted
🏠	Conference Facilities (40)
♿	Wheelchair Access (1 rm.)

Congeniality and caring have made this gracious "Colonial Sampler," woven with romance, tradition, music and poetry, one of America's "Ten Best Inns." The 21-acre Country Inn is nestled in the lap of Vermont history with skiing, golf, biking, swimming and horse-draw sleigh/carriage rides. Many of the twelve individually decorated suites and guest rooms feature canopy beds, fireplaces, and all have private baths. Award Winning Wine List, English high tea, five-course dinners with duo grand piano entertainment and bountiful breakfast buffet round out the ultimate inn experience.

From I-91 (N), Exit 7 (Springfield), Rte. 11 (W) to Rte. 106 (N). Inn 5 mi. on left. From I-91 (S), Exit 8, Rte. 131 (W) to Rte. 106 (S). Inn is 4 mi. on right.

TEL. 802-263-9217; 800-477-4828; FAX 802-263-9219
Rt 106 (Nr Perkinsville), Bx 165
Weathersfield, VT 05151

Mary Louise & Ron Thorburn,
Innkeepers

INN ON THE COMMON

16 Rooms, $190/$260
MAP

Visa, MC

All Private Baths

Open Year-round

Children Accepted
Pets Accepted

Pool, Tennis Court,
Gardens, XC Skiing, Golf,
Lake, Trails

Breakfast & Dinner
Wine & Liquor available

No Smoking in Dining
Room

Conference Facilities (20)

From I-91 (N), Exit 21, Rte. 2 (W) to
Rte. 15 (W),. In Hardwick, Rte. 14 (N)
7 mi. turn R., 3 mi. to inn. From I-91 (S)
Exit 26, Rte. 58 (W) Rte. 14 (S) 12 mi.
to marked L. turn.
**TEL. 802-586-9619; RES. 800
521-2233; FAX 802-586-2249**
Main Street
Craftsbury Common, VT 05827
Michael & Penny Schmitt,
Innkeepers

With the ambiance of a sophisticated country house hotel, this inn offers outstanding cuisine and an award-winning wine cellar. With beautiful gardens and wonderful views, the lovely and comfortable guest rooms elegantly decorated with antiques and artworks, some with fireplaces, are spread among a compound of 3 meticulously restored Federal houses. (AAA◆◆◆◆)

The IIA Gift Certificate

A Lovely Gift for Someone Special

The gift of an overnight stay or a weekend at a country inn can be one of the most thoughtful and appreciated gifts you can give your parents or children, dear friends, or valued employees for Christmas, a birthday, an anniversary, or any special occasion. Innkeepers and other employers are discovering this is an excellent way of rewarding their employees, while at the same time giving them some much needed rest and relaxation.

An IIA gift certificate means that you can give the gift of a stay at any one of over 250 member inns from Kennebunkport, Maine to Southern California; from Quebec, Canada to Key West, Florida; from Martha's Vineyard, Massachusetts to Seaview, Washington. We have inns in the Blue Ridge Mountains, on ranches in the western desert, near state parks and forests and nature preserves, in restored villages in historic districts, on lakes and by the sea. Choose your pleasure.

An IIA gift certificate is good for two years and may be purchased through the IIA office by personal check or Mastercard or Visa. With each gift certificate we send along a brand new copy of the *Innkeepers' Register*. For further information call **800-344-5244**.

A five dollar ($5) postage and handling fee will be added to all gift certificate purchases.

VERMONT
MOUNTAIN TOP INN AND RESORT

	35 Rooms $104/$242 B&B 22 Chalets $134/$316 B&B
	Visa, MC, Amex
	All Private Baths
	Open Year-round
	Children Welcome No Pets—Kennels nearby
	Full resort — XC Skiing, Skating, Horseback & Sleigh Rides, Swimming, Sailing, Golf, Tennis
	Breakfast, Lunch, Dinner Wine & Liquor available
	No Smoking in dining room
	Conference Facilities (180)

Commanding a spectacular lake & mountain view on a 1,000-acre estate, this inn offers a complete resort experience. Included in the rates are tennis, heated pool, pitch 'n' putt golf, sailing, fishing, trap shooting, mountain biking, and fly fishing. Special horseback riding vacations with instructions in riding, jumping, dressage and introductory polo and golf school are available. In winter cross country skiing, horsedrawn sleigh rides, sledding, ice skating and winter horseback riding. Attractive, congenial surroundings, and fine dining complete the picture.

Chittenden is 10 mi. (NE) of Rutland. (N) on Rte. 7 or (E) on Rte. 4 from Rutland. Follow state signs to "Mountain Top Inn."

**TEL 802-483-2311
or 800-445-2100**
Mountain Top Rd.
Chittenden, VT 05737

William Wolfe, Innkeeper

OCTOBER COUNTRY INN

	10 Rooms, $117/$145 MAP
	Visa, MC, Amex
	Private and Shared Baths
	Closed early Nov., Re-opening for Thanksgiving, Closed April
	Children Accepted No Pets
	Skiing, Tennis, Golf, Summer Theater, Coolidge Homestead, Swimming Pool, Games, Books
	Full Breakfasts; Family-style Dinners; Wine & Liquor Available
	No-smoking Inn
	Conference Facility (18)

Relaxed and comfortable, this converted 19th century farmhouse on five acres near Woodstock offers warmth and intimacy in the finest innkeeping tradition. The scents of baking breads, fresh herbs and homemade desserts fill the inn as Chef Patrick works magic in Mexican, Italian, French Country, Greek and American motifs. Swim in the pool, bicycle, hike, ski, shop, sightsee or simply relax by the fire—then dine by candlelight. Away from the crowds, yet close to Killington, Woodstock and Dartmouth.

From Woodstock continue 8 miles west on Rte 4 to junction of Rte 100A. Continue on 4 for 200 yards. Take 1st rt. then rt. again.

**TEL. 802-672-3412;
800-648-8421**
Upper Road, P.O. Box 66
Bridgewater Corners, VT 05035

Richard Sims & Patrick Runkel, Innkeepers

138

RABBIT HILL INN

	16 Rooms $169/$239 MAP 4 Suites $209/$239 MAP
	Visa, MC
	All Private Baths
	Closed April & Nov. 1-15
	Appropriate for Children over 12; No Pets
	Downhill & XC Skiing, Hiking, Canoeing, Iceskating, Swimming, Golf, Antiquing, Fishing, Lawn Games.
	Full Breakfast, Dinner, Teatime, Picnics Wine & Liquor available
	No Smoking
	Conference Facilities (20) Wheelchair Access (1 rm , 1 dining rm. & conf. fac.)

From I-91 (N or S), Exit 19 to I-93 (S).
Exit 1 R. on Rte. 18 (S), 7 mi. to inn.
From I 93 (N), Exit 44, L. on Rte. 18
(N), 2 mi. to inn.

TEL. 802-748-5168
Reserv. 800-76-BUNNY
FAX 802-748-8342
Route 18
Lower Waterford, VT 05848
John & Maureen Magee,
Innkeepers

 Full of whimsical and charming surprises, this 1795 Federal-period inn has been lavished with love and attention. Many rooms with fireplaces, canopy beds, jacuzzis for 2. Candlelit 4-Diamond dining, unique turn-down service and a sense of pampered relaxation make this an enchanting hideaway. Set in a tiny hamlet that is an Historic District overlooking mountains, the Inn is elegantly stylish and romantic, renowned for exceptional service and detail; personal, caring touches above all! On of the nation's "10 Best Inns" 3 years in a row. AAA ◆◆◆◆ Inn.

ROWELL'S INN

	5 Rooms, $140/$160 MAP
	Visa, MC, Personal Checks preferred
	All Private Baths
	Closed Apr. & 1st 2 weeks of Nov.
	Appropriate for Children over 12; No Pets
	Skiing, Golf, Tennis, Fishing, Bicycling, Hiking
	Breakfast & Dinner for houseguests only; Wine & Beer available
	Smoking Restricted

The inn is on Rte. 11 (an east/west
rte.) connecting Rtes. 7 & I-91. The inn
is 7 mi. (W) of Chester and 7 mi. (E) of
Londonderry.

TEL. 802-875-3658
RR #1, Box 267-D
Simonsville, VT 05143

Beth & Lee Davis
Innkeepers

 This 1820 stagecoach stop (National Register of Historic Places) continues to welcome weary travelers with a brand of hospitality those early guests never enjoyed. With antiques & memorabilia, cozy fireplaces, an English-style pub, & a kitchen overflowing with enticing aromas, this inn offers guests hearty, scrumptious dishes, & casual, homey comfort in authentic period surroundings.

VERMONT
SHIRE INN

🛏	6 Rooms, $90/$120 B&B $150/$195 MAP
💳	Visa, MC, Amex
🛁	All Private Baths
🌳	Open Year-round
🐕	Appropriate for Children over 6; No Pets
R	XC & downhill Skiing, Skating, Sleigh Rides, Bicycling, Swimming, Canoeing, Antiquing
🍷	Breakfast & Dinner Wine & Beer available
🚭	No Smoking
♿	

Centrally located for easy day trips to the best of rural and historic attractions in both Vermont and New Hampshire, this Inn and Chelsea Village (National Register) provide "just the kind of withdrawn New England atmosphere you hoped to find." (Norman Simpson) The elegant 1832 Adams-style brick and granite home on 25 acres offers large guest rooms with high ceilings, tall windows, canopied queen-sized beds and fireplaces. The antique laden parlor is well stocked with books, puzzles and games. Exceptional meals start and end a day of genial relaxation.

I-89, Vt. Exit 2 (Sharon) L. for 300 yds., R. on Rte. 14 (N). R. onto Rte. 110 (N). 13 mi. to Chelsea. From I-91 Exit 14, L. onto Rte. 113 (N/W) to Chelsea.

TEL. 802-685-3031
800-441-6908
Main Street, Box 37
Chelsea, VT 05038

Jay & Karen Keller, Innkeepers

THREE MOUNTAIN INN

🛏	14 Rooms, $80/$110 B&B $130/$170 MAP 1 Suite, $200/$230 MAP
💳	Amex, Visa, MC, Discov
🛁	All Private Baths
🌳	Closed April 1 — Mid May
🐕	Children over 6 welcome; No Pets
R	Swimming pool, Hiking, Biking on premises, Tennis, Golf, Horseback riding, XC and Downhill Skiing nearby—10 minutes away
🍷	Breakfast & Dinner Wine & Liquor available
🚭	Smoking restricted
♿	Conference Facilities (40)

Capture the feeling of Vermont's past in this authentic 1790's inn where the innkeepers make the guests feel welcome. Relax, surrounded by mountain views in an unspoiled village. Rooms with canopied beds and fireplaces. Casual dining with a choice of the menu. Fireplaces in two romantic dining rooms with excellent reputation for pridefully prepared gourmet fare. Featured in *Gourmet*. Hike, bike, or x-ct ski to Jamaica State Park. Storage barn for bikes. Backroads maps available. Pub lounge. Specializing in small weddings, family gatherings and group functions.

Jamaica is located on Rte. 30, 1/2 hr. (NW) of Brattleboro (I-91) Exit 2 and 1/2 hr. (E) of Manchester (Rte. 7N to Rt. 30/11).

TEL. 802-874-4140
FAX 802-874-4745
P.O. Box 180R
Jamaica, VT 05343

Charles & Elaine Murray,
Innkeepers

VERMONT MARBLE INN

	8 Rooms, $145/$185 MAP 4 Suites, $210/$225 MAP
	Visa, MC, Amex
	All Private Baths
	Open Year-round
	Children over 12 No Pets
	Water sports, Skiing, Golf, Tennis, Bicycling, Horseback Riding, Hiking
	Breakfast, Dinner, Afternoon Tea; Wine & Liquor available
	Smoking accepted
	Conference Facilities (25)

I-87, Exit 20, Rte. 149 (W) to Rte. 4 (N).
Exit 2 in Vt., follow sign to Fair Haven. Straight down street to town green.
TEL. 802-265-8383
800-535-2814
FAX 802-265-4226
On the Town Green
Fair Haven, VT 05743
Bea & Richard Taube, Shirley Stein, Innkeepers

This totally restored Victorian marble mansion with its hand-carved, working fireplaces and high ceilings offers an elegant and romantic intimacy. The candlelit breakfast is truly a banquet, and the award-winning cuisine has earned rave reviews. The warm hospitality of the innkeepers is legend. Judged one of the nation's "10 Best Inns." Rated sublimely romantic, Vermont's only AAA ◆◆◆◆ and MOBIL ★★★★ country inn, with a AAA ◆◆◆◆ restaurant.

THE VILLAGE INN AT LANDGROVE

	16 Rooms, $65/$105 B&B
	Visa, MC, Amex, Discov
	Private and Shared Baths
	Closed Apr. 1-May 15 Nov. 1-Dec. 15
	Children Welcome No Pets
	Tennis Courts, Heated Pool, Platform Tennis, Hay & Sleigh Rides, Golf, XC & Downhill Skiing, Stocked Pond
	Breakfast & Dinner Wine & Liquor available
	No Smoking in Dining or Sleeping Rooms
	Conference Facilities (40)

I-91 (N), Exit 2 (Brattleboro). Rte. 30 (N), R. onto Rte. 11. L. at signs for Village Inn, bear L. in village of Peru. From Rte. 7 (N), (E) in Manchester on Rte. 11. Continue as above.
TEL. 802-824-6673
800-669-8466
R.D. 1, Box 215, Landgrove
Londonderry, VT 05148
Jay & Kathy Snyder
Innkeepers

The principle of "Vermont continous architecture" extended this original 1840 farmhouse into the rambling inn it is today. It is in a true country inn setting, tucked into a valley in the mountains, with gravel roads and a town population of 200. There's candlelit, fireside dining, and a mix of activities and fun for all ages at this informal, engaging country inn. Three generations of the Snyder family define the meaning of "family run country inn." The kind of place where relaxation and recreation come together in a most idyllic and secluded setting.

WEST MOUNTAIN INN

🛏	12 Rooms $144/$160 MAP 6 Suites, $181 MAP
💳	Visa, MC, Amex, Discov
🛁	All Private Baths
🕯	Open Year-round
🐕	Families Welcome No Pets
R	Hiking, Canoeing, Tubing, Flyfishing, Wilderness X-Country Skiing, Sledding, Skating and Golf and Tennis nearby.
☕	Downhill Skiing also nearby. Breakfast & Dinner
🚬	Wine & Liquor available No Smoking
👥	Conference Facilities (40)
♿	Wheelchair Access (1 rm., dining rm. & conf. fac.)

Llamas and African violets are only two of the delightful surprises at this happy, relaxed country inn, nestled on a mountainside overlooking the Battenkill River. In addition to Wes Carlson's herd of treking llamas and the custom of presenting guests with a lovely African violet, there are cheerful rooms and a rich outdoor world to explore. Miles of trails for hiking or wilderness x-country skiing, and river sport opportunities abound. Guests dine on exceptional New England country cuisine in an atmosphere filled with a spirit of genuine warmth and hospitality.

Rt. 7 (N), Exit 3. Take access road to end, R. on Rte. 7A into Arlington. L. on Rte. 313 for .5 mi. L. on River Rd. to inn.

TEL. 802-375-6516
FAX 802-375-????
Box 481, Rte. 313 & River Rd.
Arlington, VT 05250

Mary Ann & Wes Carlson,
Innkeepers

WINDHAM HILL INN

🛏	15 Rooms, $160/$210 MAP
💳	Visa, MC, Amex
🛁	All Private Baths
🕯	Closed Apr. to mid-May, early Nov.
🐕	Appropriate for Children over 12; No Pets
R	XC Ski Learning Center, floodlit Skating pond, Downhill Skiing, Hiking, Day Tripping, nearby
☕	Tennis, Swimming & Golf. Breakfast & Dinner
🚬	Non-smoking Inn
👥	Conference Facilities (30)
♿	

On 160 acres at the end of a country road, threaded by rock walls and magnificent views across the hills. Friendly innkeepers and staff welcome guests to this peaceful, secluded retreat with its sparkling rooms, memorable six-course gourmet meals, award-winning ambiance, and closeness to nature. Extensive onsite trail network for hiking and cross country skiing. Designated an "Inn of Distinction" having been judged one of the nation's ten best inns for a third year.

I-91 (N). Exit 2 (Brattleboro Rte. 30 (N) for 21.5 mi. R. on Windham Rd. 1.5 mi. to inn.

TEL. 802-874-4080
800-944-4080
R.R. 1, Box 44
West Townshend, VT 05359

Grigs & Pat Markham
Innkeepers

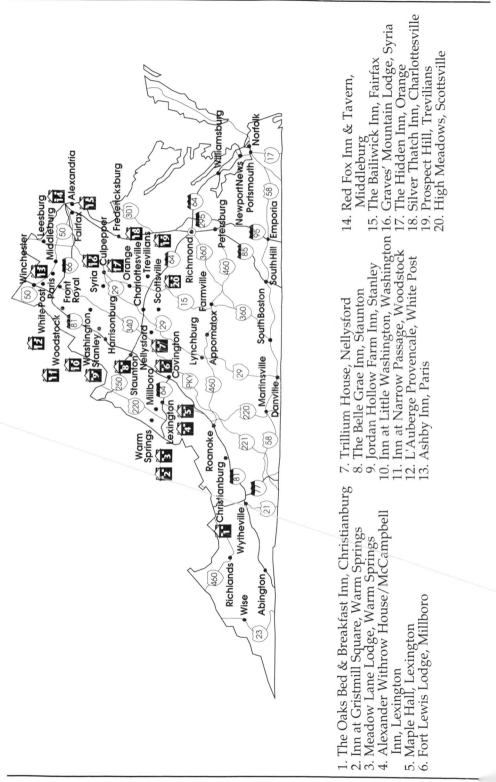

1. The Oaks Bed & Breakfast Inn, Christianburg
2. Inn at Gristmill Square, Warm Springs
3. Meadow Lane Lodge, Warm Springs
4. Alexander Withrow House/McCampbell Inn, Lexington
5. Maple Hall, Lexington
6. Fort Lewis Lodge, Millboro
7. Trillium House, Nellysford
8. The Belle Grae Inn, Staunton
9. Jordan Hollow Farm Inn, Stanley
10. Inn at Little Washington, Washington
11. Inn at Narrow Passage, Woodstock
12. L'Auberge Provencale, White Post
13. Ashby Inn, Paris
14. Red Fox Inn & Tavern, Middleburg
15. The Bailiwick Inn, Fairfax
16. Graves' Mountain Lodge, Syria
17. The Hidden Inn, Orange
18. Silver Thatch Inn, Charlottesville
19. Prospect Hill, Trevilians
20. High Meadows, Scottsville

ALEXANDER-WITHROW HOUSE/ McCAMPBELL INN

🛏	14 Rooms, $95/$110 B&B 8 Suites, $130/$150 B&B
💳	MC, Visa, Discov
🛁	All Private Baths
🏛	Open Year-round
🐑	Children Welcome No Pets - Kennels available
Ⓡ	Historic Buildings, Museums, Fishing, Canoeing, Tennis, Pool, Croquet
☕	Breakfast for houseguests Dinner at Maple Hall nightly
🚬	Limited Smoking
⌗	Conference Facilities (15)
♿	

In southwest Virginia, replete with impressive history and scenery, is the town of Lexington and two gracious and graceful inns, the Alexander-Withrow House, (ca. 1789) and McCampbell Inn (ca. 1809) of Historic Country Inns. Parents of VMI or W&L students as well as business or holiday travelers enjoy the comforts of these inns, within easy walking distance of all attractions. Each room interestingly furnished offers individual heating and cooling controls, TVs, phones & refreshment centers. Your needs and comfort are our main concern.

I-81 or I-64, take either exit for Lexington and continue to town center, Main & Washington Sts. Inns across from Court House.
TEL. 703-463-2044
FAX 703-463-7262
11 No. Main Street
Lexington, VA 24450
The Peter Meredith
Family, Owners;
Don Fredenburg, Innkeeper

THE ASHBY INN

🛏	10 Rooms, $80/$175 B&B
💳	Visa, MC
🛁	8 Private, 1/2 shared baths
🏛	Closed Jan. 1, July 4, Dec. 24 & 25
🐑	Appropriate for Children over 10; No Pets
Ⓡ	Antiquing, Vineyards, Bocci, Horseshoes, Horseback Riding, Golf, Tennis, Hiking
☕	Breakfast, Dinner Wed.—Sat.; Sun. Brunch Wine & Liquor available
🚬	No Smoking in guest rms.
⌗	Conference Facilities (20)
♿	

This 1829 inn finds its character in the small village of Paris and its heart in the kitchen. The views from guest rooms or dining patio are wonderful in every direction. The menu changes daily, ranging from home-cured salmon gravlaks or local wild mushrooms on toast to jumbo lump crabcakes or duckling with turnips.

From Wash. D.C. Rte 66 (W) to Exit 23 — Rte. 17 (N), 7.5 mi. L. on Rte. 701 for .5 mi. Or Rte. 50 (W) thru Middleburg; 3 mi. beyond Upperville. L. just after traffic light (Rte. 759).
TEL. 703-592-3900
FAX 703-592-3781
Rte. 1, Box 2A
Paris, VA 22130
John & Roma Sherman,
Innkeepers

THE BAILIWICK INN

13 Rooms, $130/$180 B&B
1 Suite $250 B&B
Bridal Suite, $275 B&B

Visa, MC, Amex

All Private Baths, 2 with Jacuzzis

Open Year round

Children Welcome
No Pets

Mt. Vernon, Gunston Hall, & Woodlawn Plantations. Convenient to Washington, D.C. by metro. Civil War battlefields. Vineyard tours and Antiquing.

Full Breakfast; Afternoon Tea; Candlelight Dinner

Wine & Beer available
No Smoking

Conference Facilities (20)

♿

Route 123 (Chain Bridge Rd.) 1 mi. (S) of I-66, or via Rte. 50 from I-495 and I-95 to the (E) and (S). Midway National and Dulles International Airports.
TEL. 703-691-2266
800-366-7666
FAX 703-934-2112
4023 Chain Bridge Road
Fairfax, VA 22030

Holly Snyder, Manager

This luxurious National Historic Register Inn is located 15 miles from Washington, D.C. with convenient access by metrorail. The rooms are patterned after those of famous Virginians featuring antiques, queen size feather beds, fireplaces and jacuzzis. Candlelight dinners are available by reservation. The inn has monthly Winemaster Dinners and Murder Mystery Weekends.

THE BELLE GRAE INN

9 rooms, $69/$109 B&B
5 suites, $99/$150 B&B

Visa, MC, Amex

All Private Baths

Open Year-round

Well-behaved young adults 12 and above are welcome; No Pets

Full service Athletic Club, Golf, Tennis, Swimming in/out, Theater, Antiquing, Museums, Historic homes

Breakfast daily; Dinner Wed.-Sun., 6-9 P.M.; MAP Rates Available

Wine & Liquor Available
Smoking in Some Rooms

Conference Facilities (50)

♿ Wheelchair Access (2 rms., dining rm. & conf. fac.)

Exit 222 off I-81. Follow 250 west to center of Staunton. Left on Frederick St. to 515 W. Frederick St. Circle block for off-street parking.
TEL. 703-886-5151
FAX 703-886-6641
515 W. Frederick St.
Staunton, VA 24401

Michael Organ, Innkeeper

With a wide veranda and wicker rockers for chatting and sipping, and graciously furnished rooms with fireplaces, canopied and 4-poster beds and antiques, this group of restored Victorian mansions is in the center of Historic Staunton, near the homes of 4 presidents and numerous museums. Southern-flavored Continental cuisine is served in the Old Inn or in the courtyard cafe.

FORT LEWIS LODGE

9 Rooms, $120/$140 MAP
3 Family Suites, $150 MAP
2 Log Cabins, $180 MAP
Visa, MC

All Private Baths

Closed Jan. - Mar.

Children Welcome
Prior Approval for Pets

3 mi. private River Fishing,
Hiking, Mtn. Biking,
Horseback Riding, Swimming, Golf, Deer Watching

Breakfast, Dinner, Picnic
Lunch available
Beer & Wine available

No Smoking in Guest Rooms

Conference Facilities (35)

It's not just getting away, it's getting back. To a 3200-acre mountain farm where your companions are the earth, the sky, and the river. At the heart of it all is a truly unique country inn, decorated with wildlife art and locally hand-crafted furniture. A silo with 3 bedrooms "in the round" and two historic hand-hewn log cabins with stone fireplaces are ideal for a romantic getaway. Meals served in the restored Lewis Mill reflect a rare devotion to home cooking.

From Staunton, Rte. 254 (W) to Buffalo Gap; Rte. 42 to Millboro Sprgs.; Rte. 39 (W) for 0.7 mi to R. onto Rte. 678, 10.8 mi. to L. onto Rte. 625, 0.2 mi. to lodge on L.

TEL. 703-925-2314
FAX 703-925-2352
HCR 3, Box 21A
Millboro, VA 24460
John & Caryl Cowden,
Innkeepers

GRAVES' MOUNTAIN LODGE

53 Rooms/Cottages
Hotel Rooms $70/$80 AP
Cottages, $95/$175 AB
Visa, MC

Private & Shared Baths

Open March 18, 1994 to
Nov. 27, 1994

Children Accepted; Pets
Accepted in some rooms

Swimming, Tennis, Nature Walks, Hiking, Fishing, Basketball,
Horseback riding

Breakfast, Lunch, Dinner
Wine & Beer available

Smoking allowed in
Designated areas

Conference Facilities (100)

Wheelchair Access (38
rooms)

This Blue Ridge Mountain rustic paradise offers complete resort facilities as well as gracious Southern hospitality and good home-cooked food, like country-fried chicken, corn pudding, and hot fudge cake. Many fun things to do, from experiencing great natural beauty to sightseeing and touring or just relax and enjoy the rustic serenity.

From Madison, VA. U.S. Rt. 29, take Rt. 231 (N) for 7 mi. to L. at Greystone Service Sta. Turn L. on Rt. 670. Go 4 mi. to Syria Merchandise Store. Lodge 200 yds. past Syria on L.

TEL. (703) 923-4231
FAX 703-723-4312
General Delivery
Syria, VA 22743
Jim & Rachel Graves,
Innkeepers

THE HIDDEN INN

	6 Rooms $79/$129 B&B 4 Cottages $139/$159 B&B
	Visa, MC
	All Private Baths 4 Jacuzzis
	Closed Christmas
	Children Accepted No Pets
R	Lawn games, Wineries, Antiquing, Historic Sites, Biking, Fishing, Boating
	Full Breakfast & Afternoon Tea; Optional candlelight Picnic; Tues.-Sat. fixed price Dinner; Wine & Beer available
	No Smoking
	Conference Facilities (20)

From Wash., DC, I-66 (W) to Rte. 29 (S) at Gainesville to Rte. 15 (S), Orange exit, to Orange; inn on L. From Richmond, I-64 (W) to Rte. 15 (N), through Gordonsville to Orange; inn on R.
TEL. 703-672-3625; 800-841-1253; FAX 703-672-5029
249 Caroline St.
Orange, VA 22960
Ray & Barbara Lonick, Innkprs.

Lace and fresh-cut flowers accent this romantic Victorian farmhouse, surrounded by seven wooded acres and gardens in the heart of historic Virginia's wine country. Enjoy a cup of tea before a crackling living room fire or sip lemonade on the veranda porch swing. A full country breakfast in the sunlit dining room starts the day, packed with fascinating things to do. Guests can visit Monticello, Montpelier, tour several wineries, shop at local shops & antique stores. Bicycling, horseback riding, golf and hiking are nearby.

HIGH MEADOWS

	7 Rooms, $95/$145 B&B 5 Suites, $105/$145 B&B
	Visa, MC, Pers. Checks
	All Private Baths
	Closed Dec. 24 & 25
	Appropriate for Children over 8; Prior Approval for Pets
R	Hiking, Wine-tasting, Croquet, Vineyard, Canoeing, Tubing, Fishing, History, Antiquing, Horseshoes, Monticello
	Breakfast & Dinner; Twilight Wine-tasting; Sat. rates MAP, add $35 pp
	Smoking restricted
	Conference Facilities (20)

I-64 in Charlottesville, Exit 121 to Rte. 20 (S) for 17 mi. After intersection with Rte. 726, continue .3 mi. to L. at inn sign
TEL. 804-286-2218
800-232-1832
Route 20 S., Rte. 4, Box 6
Scottsville, VA 24590

Peter Sushka and Mary Jae Abbitt, Innkeepers

Choice accommodations and diversions as individual as you. Spacious and comfortable rooms & suites with fireplaces, porches, soaking and whirlpool tubs. Romantic flower gardens, relaxing walks on 50 tranquil acres of rolling meadows; spectacular mountain sunsets; European supper baskets at the pond, in the gazebo or the vineyard; Full country breakfasts on the terrace or by the fire; Fine candlelight dining after a twilight tradition of Virginia wine-tasting are a few of the pleasures that await you at this 19th-century inn (National Register of Historic Places).

VIRGINIA
THE INN AT GRISTMILL SQUARE

8 Rooms, $80/$95 B&B
7 Suites, $85/$150 B&B

Visa, MC, Discov

All Private Baths

Open Year-round

Children Welcome; Pets not allowed

Swimming Pool, Tennis, Sauna, Golf, Horseback Riding, Hiking, Fishing, Skiing, Ice Skating

Continental Breakfast & Dinner; Sun. Brunch; MAP Available

Wine & Liquor available

Smoking Allowed

Conference Facilities (45)

On a designated historic site, a 1771 gristmill and a blacksmith's shop are among the cluster of restored 19th-century buildings comprising this handsome inn. Guest rooms are tastefully furnished in both traditional and contemporary decor; many have working fireplaces. Exceptional dining and the many attractions of the Allegheny Mountains & spa country draw visitors from afar.

From (N) on Rte. U.S. 220 turn R. (W) on Rte. 619 (Small state marker) for .3 mi. to inn on R. From (S) on Rte. 220, L. (W) on Rte. 619.

TEL. (703) 839-2231
P.O. Box 359
Warm Springs, VA 24484

The McWilliams Family, Innkeepers

THE INN AT LITTLE WASHINGTON

9 Rooms, $240/$450 B&B
3 Suites, $390/$580 B&B

MC, Visa

All Private Baths

Open Year-round

Children by special arrangement

Blue Ridge Mtns., Shenandoah Natl. Park, Luray Caverns, 1 1/2 hr. from Washington, D.C.

Breakfast for inn guests Dinner; Wine & Liquor available

Conference Facilities (20)

Wheelchair Access

In a sleepy village, America's 1st and only 5★ 5♦ inn offers luxurious guest rooms, lavishly furnished in imported English antiques and lush fabrics, some with balcony views of town and countryside. Chef Patrick O'Connell has captured international acclaim with his creative regional cuisine, which, along with the impeccable service, makes a visit here a memorable experience. The Inn At Little Washington has been named the nation's Restaurant of the Year by The James Beard Foundation.

From Wash., D.C., (1.5) hrs.) to I-66 (W) to Exit 43A (Gainesville) to Rte. 29 (S) to R. on Rte. 211 (W) (Warrenton). Continue 23 mi. to R. on Bus. Rte. 211 to Washington (W) for 0.5 mi. to inn on R.

TEL. 703-675-3800
FAX 703-675-3100
Middle and Main Streets,
Washington, VA 22747
Patrick O'Connell and
Reinhardt Lynch, Innkeepers

148

INN AT NARROW PASSAGE

- 12 Rooms, $55/$95
- Visa, MC
- 10 Private Baths
- Closed Dec. 24 & 25
- Well-behaved Children welcome; No Pets
- Fishing, Canoeing, Vineyards, Antiquing, Hiking, Skiing, Historic Sites, Caverns
- Full Breakfast
  BYOB
- No Smoking in guest rooms
- Conference Facilities (20)

From Wash., D.C.; I-66 (W) to I-81 (S) to Exit 283 (Woodstock) and U.S. Rte. 11 (S) for 2 mi. The inn is at the corner of Rte. 11 and Rte. 672.

TEL. 703-459-8000
FAX 703-459-8001
U.S. 11 South,
Woodstock, VA 22664

Ellen & Ed Markel, Innkeepers

This historic 1740 log inn with five acres on the Shenandoah River is a convenient place to relax and enjoy the beauty and history of the valley. In a country setting along the old Valley Pike, the inn's newer guest rooms open onto porches with views of the river and Massanutten Mountain. Early American antiques and reproductions, working fireplaces, queen-sized beds, original beams, exposed log walls, and pine floors create a comfortable Colonial atmosphere. Fine restaurants for lunch and dinner are nearby.

JORDAN HOLLOW FARM INN

- 21 Rooms $140/$180*
  MAP
- Visa, MC, Diners, CB, Discov
- All Private Baths
  4 Whirlpools
- Open Year-round
- Well-behaved Children Welcome; No Pets
- Horseback Riding, Pub/game rooms, Walking Trails, Hiking, Swimming, Canoeing
- Full Breakfast, Dinner and Box Lunches
  Wine & Liquor available
- Smoking allowed
- Conference Facilities (34)
  Wheelchair Access (1 rm., dining rm. & conf. fac.)

Luray, Va. Rte. 340 Business (S) for 6 mi. to L. onto Rte. 624 L. on Rte. 689 over bridge & R. on Rte. 626 for .4 mi. to inn on R.

TEL. 703-778-2285
FAX 703-778-1759
Route 2, Box 375
Stanley, VA 22851

Marley & Jetze Beers,
Innkeepers

A cozy 200-year-old restored Colonial horse farm with walking trails and spectacular views, located in the beautiful Shenandoah Valley. Guest rooms have sun porches, rocking chairs, and whirlpool baths. The restaurant serves a "country continental" menu. The stable offers trail rides daily and carriage lessons by appointment. Guests can bring their own horses. Located near Luray Caverns, Skyline Drive, New Market Battlefield Museum, antiquing. Two hours west of Washington, D.C.

149

L'AUBERGE PROVENÇALE

🛏	10 Rooms, $145/$190 B&B; 1 Suite, $165/$190 B&B
💳	Visa, MC, Amex, Diners
🛁	All Private Baths
🕯	Open Year-round
🐕	Appropriate for Children over 10; No Pets
℞	Biking, Hiking, Horseback Riding, Antiquing, Canoeing, Skiing, Tennis, Museums, Golfing, Vineyard Tours, Outlet Shopping, Theatre
🍷	Breakfast & Dinner; Sunday Brunch; Wine & Liquor available
🚭	Smoking not allowed in guest rms. or dining rms.
🏨	Conference Facilities (30)
♿	Wheelchair Access (dining rm. & conf. fac.)

A warm, "south of France" breath blows over this eclectic and sophisticated country inn, with its renowned "cuisine moderne Provençale" by French master- chef/ owner Alain Borel, who grows his own vegetables, herbs and spices. Charming guest rooms and the bucolic setting in the hunt country of northern Virginia offer a special experience for discerning guests. 4 ◆◆◆◆ rated.

On Rte. 340 (S). 1 mi. (S) of Rte. 50; 20 mi. (W) of Middleburg, 9 mi. (E) of Winchester, VA

TEL. 703-837-1375
800-638-1702
FAX 703-837-2004
Route 340, P.O. Box 119
White Post, VA 22663

Celeste & Alain Borel,
Innkeepers

MAPLE HALL

🛏	16 Rooms, $95/ $110 B&B; 5 Suites, $130/$150 B&B
💳	Visa, MC, Discov
🛁	All Private Baths
🕯	Open Year-round
🐕	Children Welcome; No Pets—Kennel 1/4 mile
℞	Tennis, Pool, Croquet, Fishing, Walking Paths, Canoeing, Hiking, Museums, Historic Sites
🍷	Breakfast, Houseguests Dinner daily; Wine & Liquor available
🚭	Smoking somewhat restricted
🏨	Conference Facilities (20)
♿	Wheelchair Access (1 Room)

A member of the Historic Inns of Lexington, this 1850 plantation home on 56 rolling acres offers guests a lovely place for recreation, exploring historic sites, or just relaxing. There are walking trails, a swimming pool, tennis and fishing. The new Pond House has lovely suites and many of the attractive guest rooms have fireplaces. Historic Lexington is just a short drive away. Convenience, comfort, quiet and service attract many private and corporate groups to select Maple Hall for their small business conferences from 4 to 40.

I-81 Exit 195 to Rte. 11 (N). Inn is (E) of the Interstate.

TEL. 703-463-2044
FAX 703-463-6693
11 No. Main St.
Lexington, VA 24450

Peter Meredith Family, Owners
Don Fredenburg, Innkeeper

VIRGINIA
MEADOW LANE LODGE

11 Rooms, $85/$105 B&B
3 Suites, $95/$115 B&B
3 Cottages, $100/$130 B&B

Visa, MC, Amex

All Private Baths

Open Year-round

Children over 5 accepted in some rooms; No Pets

Tennis, Fishing, Hiking, Swimming, Mtn. Biking, Birding, Croquet, Camping, Golf, Horseback Riding, Sporting Clays, Skiing, Ice Skating

Full Breakfast daily; Picnic lunches available; Dinner Fri. & Sat. (Apr.— Oct.); Beer & Wine available; BYOB

No smoking

Conference Facilities (18)

From Staunton, Rte. 254 (W) to Buffalo Gap, Rte. 42 S. to Millboro Springs; Rte. 39 (W) to Rte. 220, continue Rte. 39 (W), 4.5 mi. to lodge on right.

TEL. 703-839-5959

Star Route A, Box 110
Warm Springs, VA 24484

Cheryl & Steve Hooley, Innkeepers

With miles of hiking trails and two miles of scenic private trout and bass stream rippling through its 1,600 acres of mountain forests and meadows, this is one of the most unusual inns to be found anywhere. Guests enjoy working fireplaces, sunny porches, and roosters crowing wakeup calls to an unforgettable country breakfast. Wildflowers, wildlife, birdlife, and domestic animals galore add to the enjoyment of this beautiful, peaceful estate, a rarity in today's rapidly expanding world.

THE OAKS BED & BREAKFAST INN

5 rooms, $75/$130 B&B

Visa, Mc, Amex, Disc

All Private Baths

Open Year-round

No Pets; Children over 12

Garden hot tub, Sauna for two, croquet court, library, TV/VCR, etc.

English-style breakfast

Smoking outside only

Conference Facilities (15–20)

I-81 (exit 114) 2 miles. From Blue Ridge Parkway, (MP165) Route 8 west 24 miles to The Oaks.

TEL. 703-381-1500

311 East Main Street
Christiansburg, VA 24073

Margaret & Tom Ray, Owners/Innkeepers

Warm hospitality, comfortable, relaxed elegance and memorable breakfasts are the hallmark of The Oaks, a century-old Queen Anne Victorian; National Register of Historic Places. Set on Christiansburg's highest hill and located in the beautiful mountain highlands of southwest Virginia, The Oaks delights and welcomes leisure and business travelers from around the world. Surrounded by lawn, perennial gardens and 300-year-old oak trees, the inn faces Main Street, once part of the Wilderness Trail blazed by Daniel Boone and Davey Crockett. Mobil 3-star; AAA 3-diamond.

PROSPECT HILL PLANTATION INN

🛏	10 Rooms, $200/$260 MAP
🛏	3 Suites, $270/$290 MAP Visa, MC
🛁	All Private Baths 8 Jacuzzi tubs
💡🍸	Closed Dec. 24 & 25
🐕	Children Accepted in some Rooms; No Pets
⚡R⚡	Swimming Pool, Walking Paths, Hiking, Biking, Golf, Carriage Rides, Antiquing, Ballooning, Peace & quiet
🍽🍷	Breakfast & Dinner daily Wine & Beer available
🚭	Smoking not allowed in dining room
🏢	Conference Facilities (26)
♿	Wheelchair Access (2 rms., dining rm.)

🏠 Prospect Hill is a 1732 plantation just 15 miles east of Charlottesville, Virginia. Lodgings are in the manor house and renovated outbuildings featuring working fireplaces, verandahs, Jacuzzis, and breakfast-in-bed. Continental candlelight dinners served daily by reservation. Please accept our invitation to arrive early enough to enjoy afternoon tea and relax before dinner. AAA four-diamond; Winner Uncle Ben's Best Inn of the Year 1992–93.

Rte. 29 (S) to Rte. 15 (S) to Zion Crossroads & Rte. 250 (E) 1 mi. to L. on Hwy. 613 for 3 mi. to inn. (Inn is 15 mi. (E) of Charlottesville via Rte. 250; 98 mi. (SW) of D.C.)

TEL. 800-277-0844
703-967-0844
FAX 703-967-0102
Route 3 (Hwy. 613) Box 430
Trevilians, VA 23093
Bill, Mireille, Michael Sheehan,
Innkeepers

RED FOX INN & MOSBY'S TAVERN

🛏	15 Rooms, $135/$145 B&B 8 Suites, $155/$225 B&B
💳	Visa, MC, Amex, Diners, Discov
🛁	All Private Baths
💡🍸	Open Year-round
🐕	Children Accepted No Pets
⚡R⚡	Manassas Battlefield, Polo, Upperville Horse Show, Nat'l Beagle Trials, Steeplechasing, Wineries
🍽🍷	Breakfast, Lunch, Dinner Wine & Liquor available
🚭	Non-smoking rooms available
🏢	Conference Facilities (250)
♿	Wheelchair Access (4 rms.)

🏠 In one of the oldest incorporated towns in America, Joseph Chinn built his tavern in 1728 and called it Chinn's Ordinary. It has continued, through many changes and reincarnations, to be a popular destination for Washingtonians. Deep in hunt country, this historic inn preserves the feeling of the past along with all the modern amenities and outstanding cuisine. (AAA◆◆◆◆)

From Washington, D.C. * Rte. 66 (W) to Rte. 50 (W) exit for 25 mi. to Middleburg & inn on right.

TEL. 703-687-6301
800-223-1728
FAX 703-687-6187
2 E. Washington St.
P.O. Box 385
Middleburg, VA 22117

The Reuter Family, Innkeepers

SILVER THATCH INN

7 Rooms, $110/$125 B&B

Visa, MC

All Private Baths

Open Year-round exc. Dec. 24–25

Well-behaved Children over 5 welcome; No Pets

Swimming, Tennis. Nearby—Golf, Horseback Riding, Jogging, Hiking, Biking, Blue Ridge Mtns., Monticello, U. of Va.

Breakfast, houseguests Dinner Tues.-Sat. Wine & Liquor available

No Smoking

Conference Facilities (20)

From (N); U.S. Rte. 29 (S) 1 mi. (S) of Airport Rd. to L. on Rte. 1520 to inn. From(S): U.S. 250 (W) Bypass to U.S. Rte. 29 (N) 5 mi. to R. on Rte. 1520 to inn.

TEL. 804-978-4686
3001 Hollymead Dr.
Charlottesville, VA 22901

Rita & Vince Scoffone, Innkeepers

This historic inn began life as a barracks built by captured Hessian soldiers during the Revolutionary War. It now provides gracious accommodations in antique-filled guest rooms and elegant candlelit dining. The restaurant features modern American cuisine, which changes with the seasons, and a wine list that won the Wine Spectator Award of Excellence.

TRILLIUM HOUSE

10 Rooms, $85/$105 B&B
2 Suites, $120/$150 B&B

Visa, MC

All Private Baths

Closed Dec. 24 & 25

Well-behaved Children with Responsible Parents Welcome; No Pets

Skiing, Golf, Tennis, Swimming, Hiking, Fishing, Horseback Riding, Canoeing, Antiquing

Breakfast; single entree fixed-price Dinner Fri. & Sat.; Reservation required Wine & Liquor available

Non-smoking Dining Room, discouraged in bedrooms

Conference Facilities (25)

Wheelchair access (8 rms., dining rm. & conf. fac.)

(S) of I-64; (E) of I-81; (W) of Rte. 29. On Rte. 664, which connects Rte. 151 with Blue Ridge Pkwy, between Mile Posts 13 & 14.

TEL. 804-325-9126
RES. 800-325-9126
FAX 804-325-1099

Wintergreen Dr., Box 280
Nellysford, VA 22958

Ed & Betty Dinwiddie, Innkeepers

One of the newer country inns, designed and built in 1983 to meet today's standards while retaining the charm of yesteryear. Outstanding common areas, library and sunroom. In the heart of Wintergreen's Devil's Knob Village, a year-round 11,000-acre resort, with an assortment of recreational activities available to guests at preferred rates, includes indoor swimming across the road. Mountain country, with trees, birds and a golf course seen from the dining room.

1. Turtleback Farm Inn, Eastsound
2. Captain Whidbey Inn, Coupeville
3. Willcox House Country Inn, Bremerton
4. Shelburne Inn, Seaview
5. Birchfield Manor, Yakima

BIRCHFIELD MANOR

5 rooms, $70/$100 EP

Visa, MC, Amex, Diners

All Private Baths

Open Year-round

Children older than 8
No pets

Pool (in season)
Spa (year-round)

Breakfast, Dinners,
Banquets (including
luncheons)

No smoking

Conference Facility (50)
Wheelchair Access (restaurant only)

This award-winning restaurant and country inn is in the casual, relaxed atmosphere of a gracious home. Parklike grounds surround the outdoor swimming pool, and there is also an indoor spa open year-round. On the edge of sunny Washington Wine Country. We can personalize a wine tour just for you! Mobile ★★★

Call for directions.
TEL. 509-452-1960
2018 Birchfield Road
Yakima, WA 98901

Wil & Sandy Massett,
Innkeepers

THE CAPTAIN WHIDBEY INN

23 Rooms, $85/$125;
2 Suites & 7 other, $145/
$195 B&B (Full)

Visa, MC, Amex, Discov,
Diners

Private & Shared Baths

Open Year-round

Children Welcome in
some Rooms; No pets (off-
premises boarding avail.)

Beach, Library, Boats,
Bikes, Horseshoes, Walk-
ing Trails, Historic Town,
Sailing, Charters avail.

Breakfast (Full), Lunch
(avail. daily July-Sept;
wknds. Oct-June); Din-
ner daily; Wine &
Liquor available

Non-Smoking areas

Conference Facilities (30,
Lagoon Lib.; 40, Cove
Cottage)

From north: I-5 (S) Exit 230 & Hwy. 20
to Coupeville. Turn on Madrona.
From (S): I-5 (N) Exit 189, Mukilteo
Ferry, Hwy. 525. Hwy. 20. From west:
Keystone Ferry, Hwy. 20.
TEL. 206-678-4097
800-366-4097
FAX 206-678-4110
2072 W. Captain Whidbey Inn Rd.
Coupeville, WA 98239
Capt. John Colby Stone, Innkeeper

This romantic, rustic log inn dates from 1907 and over-looks the waters of Penn Cove. Feather beds, antiques and artwork in every room and superb Northwest coastal cuisine and wines are enjoyed by guests. Spot eagles and herons, or sail the cove on a day-cruise available with our innkeeper. A gracious welcome and profound relaxation await you.

SHELBURNE INN

13 Rooms, $89/$125 B&B
2 Suites, $160/$165 B&B

Visa, MC, Amex

All Private Baths

Open Year-round

Quiet, well-supervised
Children; No Pets

Beachcombing, Bicycling,
Golf, Horseback Riding

Breakfast, Lunch, Dinner
Wine & Liquor available

Smoking restricted

Conference Facilities (35)

Wheelchair Access
(1 Room)

From Seattle, I-5 (S) to Olympia Hwy.
8 & 12 to Montesano & Hwy. 101 (S)
to Seaview. From OR coast, U.S. 101
across Astoria Bridge L. to Liwaco (N)
2 mi. to Seaview.
TEL. 206-642-2442
FAX 206-642-8904
Box 250, 4415 Pacific Way
Seaview, WA 98644
David Campiche & Laurie
Anderson, Innkeepers

An unspoiled 28-mile stretch of wild Pacific seacoast is just a 10-minute walk through rolling sand dunes from this inviting country inn, built in 1896. Restoration and refurbishing of the award-winning inn has included the addition of Art Nouveau stained glass windows, along with antique furnishings and fine art. A sumptuous breakfast featuring the best of the northwest is complimentary with your room. Innovative cuisine has brought national recognition to the outstanding restaurant and pub, where lunch and dinner are served. The Shelburne has been named one of the "Top 25 inns worldwide."

WASHINGTON
TURTLEBACK FARM INN

	7 Rooms, $75/$150 B&B
	Visa, MC
	All Private Baths
	Open Year-round
	Appropriate for children over 8; Pets not allowed
	Hiking, Salt & Fresh-water Fishing, Sea Kayaking, Golf, Bicycling, Boating, Local Crafts
	Full Breakfast, Beverages any time, Sherry and Fruit BYOB
	No Smoking
	Conference Facilities (15)
	Wheelchair Access (3 Rooms)

A country farmhouse located on Orcas Island, the loveliest of the San Juan Islands which dot Puget Sound. This graceful and comfortable inn is considered one of the most romantic places in the country (*L.A. Times, USA Today*). Turtleback is noted for its spectacular setting, detail-perfect restoration and expansion, spotless maintenance & award-winning breakfasts. A haven for those who enjoy breathtaking scenery, varied outdoor activities, unique shopping and superb food, Turtleback Farm Inn provides a perfect destination for the discriminating traveler.

From Orcas ferry landing, follow Horseshoe Hwy. (N) to first intersection (2.9 mi.). Turn L. to first R. (0.9 mi.). Continue on Crow Valley Rd. 2.4 mi. (N) to inn.
TEL 206-376-4914
Crow Valley Rd., Route 1
Box 650, Eastsound,
Orcas Island, WA 98245
William & Susan C. Fletcher, Innkeepers

WILLCOX HOUSE COUNTRY INN

	4 rooms, $110/$165 B&B 1 suite, $110 B&B
	Visa, MC
	All Private Baths (2 with Jacuzzi)
	Open year-round
	Children over 15; No pets
	Private beach & pier, Floating dock, Row boat & Peddle boat, Hiking, Golf courses in area, Antiquing
	Breakfast, Lunch, Dinner Afternoon wine & cheese hour; breakfast included; prix fixe; lunch and dinner by reservation; wine list; Wine available
	Smoking outdoors only
	Conference Facilities (10)
	Wheelchair access (1 rm., dining rm.)

Overlooking Hood Canal, this historic 1930's Country House Inn is situated in a forest setting between Seattle and the Olympic peninsula. The mansion estate offers park-like grounds, private saltwater beach and spectacular views. Comfortable period pieces and antiques are featured in guest rooms and the great room, billiard room, pub, library, and view dining room. *Country Inns Magazine* award: one of the top twelve inns in North America in 1993.

17 mi. east of Bremerton on Hood Canal, near Holly. Call for directions.
TEL. 206-830-4492
FAX 206-830-0506
(call first)
2390 Tekiu Rd.
Bremerton, WA 98312

Cecilia & Phillip Hughes, Innkeepers

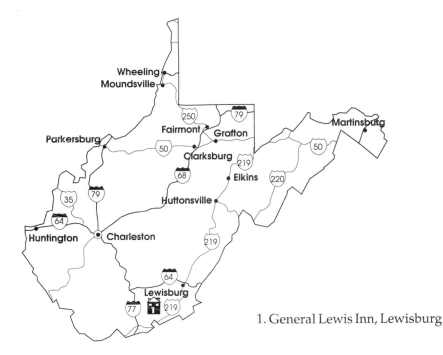

1. General Lewis Inn, Lewisburg

THE GENERAL LEWIS

23 Rooms, $55/$80 EP
2 Suite, $80/$120 EP

Visa, MC, Amex

All Private Baths

Open Year-round
Children Welcome
Pets Allowed
Garden, National Historic
District, Golf, Tennis (all
seasons), Hiking Trails,
Biking, Horseback Riding,
Carriage Ride, Swimming
(all seasons), Fishing, Ca-
noeing, White Water
Rafting, Antiquing, The-
ater, Caverns
Breakfast, Lunch, Dinner
Wine & Liquor available
Smoke-free Dining Room

I-64, Lewisburg Exit 169 & Rte. 219 (S)
for 1.5 mi. to Rte. 60 (E) for .3 mi. to inn
on R.

TEL. 304-645-2600
800-628-4454

301 E. Washington St.
Lewisburg, WV 24901

Mary Noel Hock &
Jim Morgan, Innkeepers

Come rock in a chair on the veranda of the General Lewis Inn. See passengers alight from a horse-drawn carriage. On chilly days dream by the fireplace, solve one of the puzzles, or play a fascinating game. Don't miss Memory Hall's display of old tools for home and farm. Antiques furnish every room, including comfortable canopy, spool and poster beds. The dining room in the 1834 wing features Southern cooking. Nestled in beautiful Greenbrier Valley, the Inn offers nearby walking tours. Explore the Lewisburg district and browse the antique shops. AAA ◆◆◆ Mobil ★★★

1. Old Rittenhouse Inn, Bayfield
2. White Gull Inn, Fish Creek
3. Inn at Cedar Crossing, Sturgeon Bay
4. White Lace Inn, Sturgeon Bay
5. The Creamery, Downsville

THE CREAMERY RESTAURANT & INN

3 Rooms, $75/$105 B&B
1 Suite, $105 B&B

No Credit Cards

All Private Baths

Closed Jan.-March

Children - Yes
Pets Discouraged

Dunn Co. Pottery & Gallery, Red Cedar St. Park, Hiking, Biking, Skiing Historical Museums

Breakfast daily for guests; Lunch, Dinner Tues.- Sun., Sun. Brunch; Wine & Liquor available

Smoking not encouraged

This remodeled turn-of-the-century creamery in the hills of western Wisconsin contains four large guest quarters with cherry woodwork, handmade tiles, pottery lamps and concealed TVs. Its sweeping views of the Red Cedar River Valley and hills along with a reputation for exceptional cuisine and fine wines has made this family-run inn well known from Chicago to Minneapolis. Dunn County Pottery studio and showrooms adjacent to the restaurant.

From I-94, Exit 41 at Menomonie; Hwy. 25(S) 10 mi., L. at CTH "C," 1/3 mi. on R. (75 mi. E. of St. Paul, MN.)

TEL.715-664-8354
P.O. Box 22
Downsville, WI 54735

Richard, David, John Thomas; Jane Thomas De Florin, Innkeepers

INN AT CEDAR CROSSING

9 Rooms, $79/$135 B&B

Visa, MC, Discov

All Private Baths
5 Whirlpools

Open Year-round exc. Dec. 25

Older Children Welcome
No Pets

Sailing, Hiking, Skiing, Beaches, 5 State Parks, Galleries, Shops, Summer Theater, Golf, Tennis

Breakfast, Lunch, Dinner, Evening Refreshments
Wine & Liquor available

Smoking Restricted

Conference Facilities (26–off season)

Wheelchair access (dining rm. & conf. fac.)

Hwy. 42 or 57 (N) to Sturgeon Bay. Bus. Rte. 42/57 into town across old bridge. L. on 4th Ave. 1 blk., then L. on Louisiana St. to inn.

TEL. 414-743-4200 (lodg.)
414-743-4249 (dining)
336 Louisiana St.
Sturgeon Bay, WI 54235

Terry Wulf, Innkeeper

 Warm hospitality, elegant antique-filled guestrooms, and creative regional cuisine are tradition at this most intimate Door County inn (National Register of Historic Places). Lovingly restored, you'll find cozy fireplaces, room service, and evening refreshments await pampered travelers. Guestrooms are exceptionally furnished—oversized canopied beds, double whirlpool tubs, private porches, inviting fireplaces. Exquisite dining features fresh ingredients, enticingly prepared entrees, sinful desserts, and casual pub, set in the beauty and culture of Wisconsin's Door Peninsula.

OLD RITTENHOUSE INN

17 Rooms, $99/$139 B&B
4 Suites, $129/$189 B&B

Visa, MC

All Private Baths
5 Whirlpools

Open Year-round; inquire for Winter weekdays

Children Accepted

Sailing, Biking, Skiing, Tennis, Swimming (indoor year-round)

Breakfast houseguests
Dinner & Sun Brunch, public; Wine available

No Smoking in Dinning Rooms

Conference Facilities (15)

Wheelchair Access (2 rms., dining rm.)

Duluth Hwy. 2 (E) for 60 mi. to L. on Hwy. 13 (N) (just outside Ashland) for 20 mi. to Bayfield

TEL. 715-779-5111

301 Rittenhouse Ave.,
P.O. Box 584
Bayfield, WI 54814

Jerry & Mary Phillips,
Innkeepers

 Three turn-of-the-century homes make up this Victorian inn where hospitality, superior dining, and music blend into a joyous whole. Mary and Jerry Phillips share in the creation of wonderful meals, lovely dinner concerts and other events. Guest rooms are handsomely outfitted with antiques, working fireplaces and the entire inn offers a delightful sojourn.

THE WHITE GULL INN

13 Rooms, $64/$121 EP
5 Cottages, $133/$205 EP

Visa, MC, Amex, Discov, Diners

13 Private Baths

Open Year-round exc. Thanksgiving Day, Dec. 24–25

Children Welcome in suitable rooms; No Pets

Golf, Tennis, Swimming, Sailing, Hiking, Biking, XC Skiing, Summer Stock Theatre, Music Festival, Antique Shops, Art Galleries

Breakfast, Lunch, Dinner, Wine & Beer available

No Smoking

Wheelchair Access (dining room)

Established in 1896, this white clapboard inn is tucked away in the scenic bayside village of Fish Creek, on Wisconsin's Door Peninsula. The turn-of-the-century antiques and fireplaces give the inn rooms and surrounding cottages a warm, comfortably hospitable atmosphere. Famous for hearty breakfasts and lunches and quiet candlelight dinners, the inn is renowned for the unique, traditional Door County fish boils, featuring locally caught whitefish cooked outside over an open fire.

Milwaukee I-43 for 98 mi. to Green Bay, then R. on Rte. 57 (N) for 39 mi. to Sturgeon Bay; (N) on Rte. 42 for 25 mi. to Fish Creek. L. at stop sign for 3 blks. to inn.

TEL. 414-868-3517
FAX 414-868-2367
4225 Main St., P.O. Box 160
Fish Creek, WI 54212

Andy & Jan Coulson, Innkeepers

WHITE LACE INN

14 Rooms (10 with fireplaces), $45/$128 B&B
1 Suite, $130/$150 B&B

Visa, MC, Discover

All Private Baths
7 Whirlpools

Open Year-round

Older Children welcome
No Pets

Gardens, Beaches, Sailing, Shopping, XC Skiing, Hiking, Golf

Breakfast & Snacks

10 No-smoking Guest Rooms

Wheelchair Access (1 Room)

Romance begins as you follow a winding garden pathway that links this charming inn's 3 historic homes. Guest rooms are furnished with exceptional comforts, period antiques, oversized whirlpool tubs, and inviting fireplaces. A warm welcome awaits as guests are greeted with lemonade or hot chocolate. Located in the resort area of Door County, the inn is close to many delights.

Hwy. 57 (N) to Sturgeon Bay & Bus. Rte. 42-57 into town. Cross downtown bridge to L. on 5th Ave.

TEL. 414-743-1105
16 No. 5th Ave.
Sturgeon Bay, WI 54235

Dennis & Bonnie Statz,
Innkeepers

INTERNATIONAL HOSPITALITY

We are proud to feature in this *Register* a fine array of accommodations in Canada and Great Britain. The increase in number over those listed in previous editions reflects our recent Association emphasis in assisting the international traveler.

Now, more than ever before, guests who enjoy IIA Inns in the United States are also traveling across the borders and across the oceans seeking similar kinds of hospitality there. Certainly international travelers who are accustomed to depending on the quality of the Independent Innkeepers' Association in the continental United States will be looking for assurance of corresponding hospitality experiences wherever they travel in other countries. Conversely, IIA member Inns in the United States would like very much to show the foreign traveler our place in the world of hospitality.

Whether in the United States, Canada, England, Scotland, or Wales, the Independent Innkeepers' Association includes hospitality establishments of the finest quality. These select establishments include country house hotels, manor houses, historic homes, traditional inns, farmhouses, and small hotels. They are located in the countryside, in towns, along seashores, on mountain tops, and in other locations, all worth a visit.

To stay with any of our international number is to discover the finest innkeeper care and hospitality in comfortable, unique and well maintained facilities which you will want to brag about when you return home.

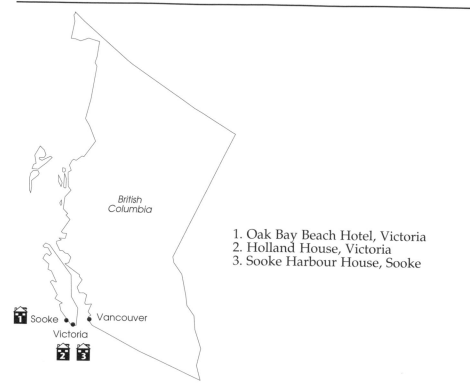

British
Columbia

1. Oak Bay Beach Hotel, Victoria
2. Holland House, Victoria
3. Sooke Harbour House, Sooke

Sooke   Vancouver

Victoria

HOLLAND HOUSE INN

10 Rooms, $80/$210 Can.
B&B
$80/$145 Can. Off Season
$115/$210 Can. On Season
Visa, MC, Amex, Diners
All Private Baths

Open Year-round

Children Accepted;
No Pets

Golf, Fishing, Cycling,
British High Tea,
Butchart Gardens, Royal
B.C. Mus-eum, Antiques,
Beacon Hill Park

Full Gourmet Breakfast
Beverages at any time.
Wine Available; BYOB

Non-Smoking Environ-
ment

Conference Facilities (20)
Wheelchair Access (1
Room)

This unique small hotel, where fine art and unequalled comfort are combined, creates an atmosphere of casual elegance — luxurious rooms, some fireplaces, queen-size beds, goose-down duvets, antique furnishings and delightful small balconies. The Gallery Lounge, where you may relax by the fire or browse in the art library, showcases original works by premier artists of Victoria.

From Hwy. 17; (S) to Belleville St., L.
on Government St. for 2 blocks (S) to
corner of Government & Michigan.

TEL. 604-384-6644
595 Michigan St.
Victoria, B.C. Canada
V8V1S7

Lance Austin-Olsen & Robin
Birsner, Innkeepers

OAK BAY BEACH HOTEL

46 Rooms, $78/$218 Can. B&B; 5 Suites, $238/$345 Can. B&B

Visa, MC, Amex

All Private Baths

Open Year-round

Children Welcome
No Pets

Yacht Excursions, Fishing, Whale Watching, Lunch/ Dinner Cruises, Jogging. Also: Golf, Tennis, Pool. Recreation Center nearby.

High Tea or Lunch Cruise Included; Dinner, High Tea Daily; Wine & Liquor avail.
Some Non-smoking rms.

Conference Facilities (150)

Wheelchair Access (3 rms., dining rm. & conf. fac.)

South on Hwy. 17. Left on Hillside (E), which becomes Lansdowne. Right on Beach Dr. to Hotel.
TEL. 604-598-4556
800-668-7758
FAX 604-598-4556
1175 Beach Dr.
Victoria, B.C. Canada
V8S 2N2
Bruce R. Walker & Kevin Walker, Innkeepers

Beautiful seaside location, warm and gracious hospitality, crackling fireplaces, first-class accommodations in an atmosphere of old world charm. This prestigious family-owned hotel in the residential area of Oak Bay is a significant part of the history and heritage of the city of Victoria. Magnificent lawns and gardens rolling to the ocean, islands, mountains in the distance, provide wonderful views. The Tudor-style architecture is complemented by antiques and period pieces. Meals, service and hospitality are the best. Rates incl. lunch cruise or High Tea. AAA◆◆◆◆ award.

SOOKE HARBOUR HOUSE INN

13 Rooms, $100/$223 B&BL (includes lunch)

Visa, MC, Amex

All Private Baths
7 Jacuzzis

Open Year-round

Children Welcome; Well-behaved Pets Accepted

Botanical & Garden Tours, Wind Surfing, Scuba Diving, Salmon & Steelhead Trout Fishing, Hiking

Breakfast & Lunch for Houseguests; Dinner for Public; Wine & Liquor Available
Non-smoking Areas

Conference Facilities (50)

Wheelchair Access (1 Room)

Victoria, B.C., Hwy. 1 (W) to Hwy. 14 & Sooke Village. Through Stoplights, 1 mi. to L. on Whiffen Spit Rd. for .5 mi. to inn.
TEL. 604-642-3421
1528 Whiffen Spit Rd.
R.R. #4, Sooke, B.C. Canada
V0S 1N0
Fredrica & Sinclair Philip, Innkeepers

Cozy and homelike, consistently rated one of Canada's top ten restaurants which has become known as a leader in West Coast Canadian cuisine. The restaurant uses only fresh, organic ingredients which are grown in the inn's gardens, by nearby organic farms or harvested in the wilds from around Sooke. The inn offers secluded, romantic rooms with fabulous views of the ocean and mountains. Each room features fireplaces, jacuzzi and antique furnishings and art pieces.

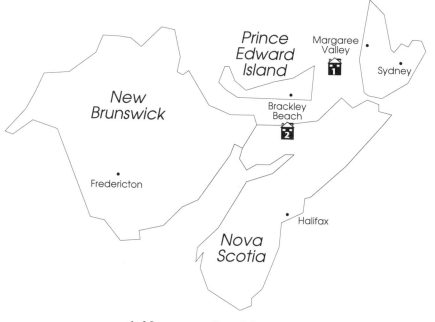

1. Normaway Inn, Margaree Valley
2. Shaw's Hotel, Brackley Beach

NORMAWAY INN

9 Rooms, $159/$199*
Can. MAP (1 pers., $117)

19 Cabins, $184/$199*
Can. MAP

Visa, MC

All Private Baths

Open June 17 to Oct. 15

Children Accepted; Pets
by prior Arrangement

Tennis, Hiking, Biking,
Lawn Games, Fiddle
Concerts/Barn Dances,
Canoeing, Salmon Fish-
ing, Whale Cruises

Breakfast & Dinner;
Packed Lunches; Wine &
Liquor Available

No Smoking in Dining
Room

Conference Facilities (50)

Wheelchair Access
(2 Rooms)

Nestled in the hills of the Cape Breton Highlands, near the beginning of the spectacular Cabot Trail, this 250-acre property offers a 1920's inn and cabins, most with woodstove fireplaces and some with jacuzzis. Enjoy superb food and sincere service in a classic setting. After dinner relax by the fireside in the living room and enjoy traditional entertainment or films.

Trans Canada Hwy. Jct. 7 at Nyanza (N) on Cabot Trail. 17 mi. Between Lake O'Law and N.E. Margaree turn at Egypt Rd. 2 mi. to inn.

**TEL. 800-565-9463
or 902-248-2987
FAX 902-248-2600**
Box 138, Margaree Valley
N.S. Canada B0E 2C0
David M. MacDonald,
Innkeeper

SHAW'S HOTEL

17 Rms. (5 Suites), $140/$190 Can. MAP; 18 Cott., $185/$230 Can. MAP

Visa, MC, Amex

All Private Baths
2 Jacuzzis

Open May 27–Oct. 2
Cottages open year-round

Children Welcome
Pets in Cottages only

Sailing, Canoeing,
Walking Paths, Golf,
Ocean Swimming, Tennis

Breakfast, Dinner
Wine & Liquor available

Smoking allowed

Conference facilities (60)
Wheelchair Access (1 rm.,
dining rm.)

Take ferry or plane to P.E.I. Trans Canada Hwy. (Rte.1) to Charlottetown. Follow signs to airport and Rte. 15 for 10 mi. to Brackley Beach.
TEL. 902-672-2022
FAX 902-672-3000
Brackley Beach
Prince Edward Island,
Canada C1E 1Z3
Robbie and Pam Shaw, Innkps.

We are the oldest family operated Inn in Canada. The Shaw's family continues the tradition which began in 1860. Shaw's Hotel is located on a 75 acre pennisula overlooking glistening Brackley Bay. It provides an ideal setting for its 17 antique furnished rooms and suites plus its 18 charming cottages ranging in size from 1 to 4 bedrooms. Our 7 deluxe chalets featuring sauna & whirlpools are open yearly. Shaw's Hotel provides superb meals in their rates. We provide many recreational activities and are located 600 yards from Brackley Beach.

WHO ARE THE INNKEEPERS?

Innkeepers who can lay claim to being the third or fourth generation of an innkeeping family are a rare breed, indeed. They have had the advantage of growing up in an inn and becoming thoroughly conversant and comfortable with the intricacies of innkeeping. There are only a very few of these younger innkeepers who are able to draw on a wealth of past experience.

Since the mid-1970s, more and more people have followed their dream of owning a lovely country inn, enjoying a slower-paced lifestyle and the opportunity to be creative and independent far away from urban pressures and the "fast track."

This dream has brought into the world of innkeeping such diverse types as advertising executives, bankers, school teachers, airline stewardesses, management consultants, engineers, interior decorators, social workers, architects, political speech writers, and many others who have left successful careers.

Some innkeepers came out of training in large hotel chains, many are graduates of hotel management schools and culinary institutes. A few are master chefs.

As is so often the case, the reality does not live up to the dream in all respects. Innkeeping is a hard taskmaster — the hours are long, the demands on time, energy, patience, perseverance, humor, and cash are great. However, the rewards, too, are great. There is the pride of accomplishment in creating an independent way of life, and in seeing the results of hard work, ingenuity, and creativity paying off.

Beyond the satisfaction of operating a successful inn is the sense of the personal pleasure in knowing that guests truly enjoy themselves and appreciate the atmosphere of the inn.

Innkeepers sometimes develop long-standing friendships with guests who return for visits over many years. In fact, just as there are a few third- and fourth-generation innkeepers, so there are a few third- and fourth-generation guests. This is more likely to happen at resort-type inns, where families spend their vacations year after year.

Innkeepers or their assistants have many kinds of personal interactions with guests, sometimes sharing a recipe for a particularly favored dish, tracking down a baby sitter or the location of some esoteric antiques dealer, finding lost eyeglasses, mapping out a scenic drive, verifying a quotation in a book, recommending a doctor, a mechanic, a jeweler, or . . . Making reservations at restaurants, reserving tickets for concerts and the theater, and calling taxis are among the more usual services in metropolitan areas.

This is just a glimpse at the kind of dedicated, intelligent and friendly people who are keepers of country inns. — **by Virginia Rowe**

1. Auberge Handfield,
    St. Marc-sur-le-Richelieu
2. Hovey Manor, North Hatley
3. Rosemount Inn, Kingston
4. Ste. Anne's, Grafton
5. Elora Mill Inn, Elora
6. Eganridge Inn, Fenelon Falls
7. Sherwood Inn, Port Carling
8. The Briars, Jackson Point
9. Chantry House Inn,
    Southampton
10. Little Inn of Bayfield,
    Bayfield
11. Stone Maiden Inn, Stratford

THE BRIARS

78 Rooms, $95/$140 U.S. B&B; 14 Suites & Cott., $120/$175 U.S. B&B
Visa, MC, Amex

All Private Baths

Open Year-round
Fun-filled Children's program (in season)
Pet Kennels nearby
Golf, Tennis, Swimming, Boating, Summer Theatre, Nature Trails, Fireplaces, Solarium Pool, Whirlpool, Sauna & Game Rooms.
Breakfast, Lunch, Dinner
Wine & Liquor available

No pipes/cigars in dining room

Conference Facilities (75)

Wheelchair access (14 rms.)

This enchanting, historic inn is an oasis of traditional hospitality in acres of lush lawns, gardens & trees beside sparkling Lake Simcoe. 1840 Regency manor has newer wings, lakeside cottages. Challenging Scottish Woodlands golf course, tennis, nature walks, year-round recreation. Social and children's programs in season. Country-fresh gourmet fare. AAA Four-Diamond Award. Area attractions: Canada's Wonderland, McMichael Canadian Art Collection, world famous Lift Locks, year-round fishing, Sharon Temple and Museum, Toronto's many attractions.

Toronto Hwy 404 (N) to Davis; R (E) to Woodbine; L (N) 20 mi. on hwy to Sutton; L (N) on Dalton to Jackson's Pt; R (E) on Lake Drive .6 mi to Hedge Rd & Briars.

TEL 800-465-2376
FAX 905-722-9688
55 Hedge Rd., R.R. #1
Jackson's Point, Ontario, Can.
LOE 1LO
John & Barbara Sibbald
& family, Innkeepers

CHANTRY HOUSE INN

- 4 Rooms, $75/$95 Can. B&B; 4 Suites, $95/$150 Can. B&B
- All Major Credit Cards
- All Private Baths
- Open Year-round
- Well-supervised Children Kennel for Pets nearby
- Boardwalk, Beaches, Lake Huron, Golf, Tennis XC Skiing, Bird Sanctuary, Historic Lighthouses
- Breakfast for houseguests Dinner by reservation Wine & Liquor Available
- No Smoking
- Conference Facilities (20)

Turn West off Hwy 21 (scenic Bluewater Rte.) 2 blks. toward Lake Huron at the only stoplight in Southhampton.
TEL. 519-797-2646
FAX 519-797-5538
Res. 800-461-INNS
118 High Street
Southampton, Ontario,
Canada NOH 2LO
David & Diane Snyder, Innkps.

This restored, award-winning inn (1859-1885) is in the lake port of Southampton (pop. 2,000). The Snyders are descendants of Joseph Schneider from Lancaster, PA, founder of Kitchener, Ontario. Historic family recipes from 1563 to the present time influence their menu. Enjoy modern comforts, warm hearts and food that *Schmecks*.

EGANRIDGE INN & COUNTRY CLUB

- 5 Cotts., $140/$175 Can. B&B; 6 Suites, $120/$140 Can. B&B
- Visa, MC, Amex
- All Private Baths
- Closed Nov. - Apr.
- Children Accepted No Pets – Kennels nearby
- Private Golf, Tennis, Beach, Boating, Theater, Antiquing, Galleries, Shopping
- Lunch, Dinner, Room Service; MAP Rates available Wine & Liquor available
- Some Non-smoking areas
- Conference Facilities (45)
- Wheelchair Access (4 Rooms)

From Toronto, (E) on Hwy. 401 to Exit 436. Hwy. 35. R. on Hwy. 121 to Fenelon Falls. R. on County Rd. 8 for 9 km to inn signs.
TEL. 705-738-5111
RR#3, Fenelon Falls
Ontario, Canada, K0M IN0

John & Patricia Egan, Innkeepers

Overlooking a spectacular vista across Sturgeon Lake, in a setting of pine and stone, this inn includes Dunsford House, one of North America's finest preserved examples of 2-story, hand-hewn log home architecture, built in 1837. Challenging golf, award-winning continental cuisine, and the ultimate in luxurious accommodations fulfill guests' highest expectations.

ELORA MILL INN

29 Rooms, $90/$150 Can. B&B; 3 Suites, $170/$200 Can. B&B

Visa, MC, Amex, En Route

All Private Baths

Open Year-round

Children Welcome
No Pets

Golf, Tennis, Squash, Hiking, XC Skiing, Canoeing, Crafts & Antiques Shopping, Mennonite tours, Music & Highland Fest.

All Meals
MAP Rates available
Wine & Liquor available
Non-smoking Dining Room

Conference Facilities (120)

Wheelchair Access (Public Rooms)

This converted 19th-century grist mill is perched on the spectacular Grand River Falls in the quaint village of Elora. With heritage guest rooms and a fireside dining room and lounge, the historic country inn serves Canadian specialties with a Continental flair. Guests can enjoy the diversions of Ontario festival country or while away the hours in the inn's out-of-the-way nooks.

From Hwy. 401, Exit 295 (N) on Hwy. 6 (Guelph Bypass) for 2 mi. (N) of Guelph. Turn L. on Elora Rd. for 9 mi. to flashing light. Turn R. & follow signs to Elora center.

TEL. 519-846-5356
FAX 519-846-9180
77 Mill St. West,
**Elora, Ontario, Canada
N0B 1S0**
Timothy & Kathy Taylor,
Innkeepers

THE LITTLE INN OF BAYFIELD

19 Rms, $99/$160 Can. EP; 12 Sts, $160/$190 Can. EP; 10% disc. w/ theatre fest. tickets

Visa, MC, Amex, EnRoute

All Private Baths

Open Year-round

Children Welcome

Pets by prior arrangement

Beaches, Boating, Fishing, Cycling, Golfing, Hiking, XC Skiing, Museums, Stratford and Blyth Festivals, Winetastings, Cooking Weekend, Oktoberfest

All Meals, afternoon Tea; Sun. Brunch; MAP avail.; Wine & Liquor available

Non-smoking dining area

Conference Facilities (65)

Wheelchair Access (5 rms., dining rm. & conf. fac.)

Originally a stagecoach stop, the Inn has been welcoming guests to the picturesque lakeside village of Bayfield since the 1830's. This designated heritage Inn is replete with fireplaces, ensuite whirlpools, sauna, games and books. Fine dining has long been a tradition with superb meals and imaginative menus. Guests have a perfect base to explore the countryside and attend the Stratford and Blyth Festivals. There is much to do any time of the year.

From Port Huron, MI. Hwy. 402(E) to Hwy. 21(N) to Bayfield. From Toronto, Hwy. 401(W) to Hwy. 8(W) to Seaforth; follow signs to Bayfield.

TEL 519-565-2611
FAX 519-565-5474
Main Street, Bayfield,
Ontario, Canada N0M1G0

Patrick & Gayle Waters,
Innkeepers

ROSEMOUNT INN

8 rooms, $75/$135 Can.
B&B

Visa, MC

All Private Baths

Open mid-Jan.–mid-Dec.
Not suitable for children
under 13; No pets
4-block walk to water-
front (Swimming,
Sailboarding, Sailing,
Boardwalk), Hiking
trails, Historic Walking
Tours, Antiquing, Stage
Productions, Fine Dining,
Farmers' Market
Full Gourmet Breakfast

No smoking

Take Hwy. 401 to exit #615 (Sir John
A. MacDonald Blvd.); South 5 km. to
Johnson St.; Turn left; 2 km. to
Sydenham St. S.; Turn right; 2 blocks.

TEL. 613-531-8844
FAX. Available
46 Sydenham St. South
Kingston, Ontario K7L 3H1

Holly Doughty & John
Edwards, Innkeepers

Step through the old iron gates into the quiet charm of an 1850 limestone Tuscany Villa in the heart of historic Kingston. Let us pamper you . . . your room is exquisitely appointed with Victorian antiques, fine linens and down duvets. In the morning, be awakened by the aroma of Holly's "just baked" muffins or perhaps by John's "Welsh Toast" with a s-c-r-u-m-m-y berry sauce and local maple syrup. A short stroll will take you to the historic sites, antique market, fine dining and specialty boutiques.

STONE MAIDEN INN

14 rooms, $85/$160 Can.
B&B

Visa, MC, Personal checks

All Private Baths

Open mid-April–late Dec.
Not suitable for young
children; No pets
Tennis, Swimming
nearby; Lots of Local Gal-
leries, Bookstores and
Antique Shops; Historic
Walking Tours;
Shakespearean Theatre
Festival May through
mid-November.
Breakfast (full breakfast
buffet)
Smoking restricted

Conference Facilities (25)

From Detroit: Hwy. 401 E., Exit 222
N. to Stratford.From Toronto: Hwy
401 to Hwy. 8 W. to Stratford. From
Buffalo: Hwy. Q.E.W. to Hwy. 403 at
Hamilton; W. to Hwy. 2 at Brantford;
Hwy. 403 W. to Hwy. 401 W. to Exit
222; N. to Stratford.
TEL. 519-271-7129
123 Church Street
Stratford, Ontario N5A 2R3
Barb & Len Woodward, Innkps.

Named after the stone maiden-heads which grace our front hallway, we offer quiet Victorian elegance with superior accommodations and the utmost in personal service. Hand-made quilts, ensuite bathrooms and handsome antiques grace our 14 air-conditioned rooms. Some rooms have canopy beds, fireplaces and whirlpool tubs. Afternoon refreshments and our generous breakfasts are complimentary. Visit Stratford during May to October for our world-renown Shakesperean Festival. Located close to city-centre and our 3 theatres. Call for theatre info.

SHERWOOD INN

🛏	26 Rooms, $139/$207* MAP - $99 B&B 2 Suites, $176/$207* MAP
💳	Visa, MC, Amex, Diners, Enroute
🛁	Private & Shared Baths
🛋	Open year-round
🐕	Children Welcome: No Pets
☀R☀	Tennis, Hiking, Mountain Bikes, Health Spa, Water Sports, XC Skiing (16 kms. of trails on site), Golf and Horseback Riding nearby.
🍽	Breakfast & Lunch, Dinner available
🚬	Wine & Liquor available Smoking Restricted
♿	Conference Facilities (90)

Set amongst towering pines on the edge of Lake Joseph, tranquil Sherwood Inn offers atmosphere, impeccable service and gastronomic excellence, complimented by an outstanding wine cellar. Attentive staff anticipate guests' needs with quiet efficiency and genuine friendliness. Most of all, Sherwood is a place where guests may relax and rediscover the finer qualities of life. Received the Four Diamond Award from AAA for the past 16 years.

2 Hrs from Toronto, via hwy. 400 N, to hwy. 69 N to Foot's Bay. Turn R. to 169 S & travel 10 kms. to the Sherwood Rd; turn L. just before the junc. of hwy 118.

TEL. 705-765-3131
800-461-4233
FAX 705-765-6668
PO Box 400, Lake Joseph
Port Carling, ONT P0B IJ0
John & Eva Heineck, Innkps.

STE. ANNE'S COUNTRY INN & SPA

🛏	10 Rooms, $120/$180 B&B $180/$220 AP
💳	Visa, MC, Amex, Enroute
🛁	All Private Baths
🛋	Open Year-round
🐕	Not suitable for Children No Pets
☀R☀	Tennis, Swimming Pool, Hot Tub, Walking Trails, Victoria Hall, The Northumberland Players, Antique Hunting, Full Spa
🍽	Breakfast, Lunch & Dinner available for guests; BYOB
🚬	No Smoking Throughout
♿	Conference Facilities (10)

Rest, relax, rejuvenate . . . savor the sweet smell of fresh country air, drink pure spring water, enjoy a candle lit dinner. Pamper yourself with a massage, or maybe a facial. All this can be found in this English style "Castle" nestled on 560 acres in the hills of Northumberland County, one hour from Toronto. Exclusive spa packages mix the finest elements of a country inn ambiance with pampering and/or invigorating treatments to ensure the ultimate in relaxation and rest. Come for the day by train on the "Stress Express" from Toronto or Kingston.

Hwy. 401 to Grafton. Exit @ 487. N towards Centreton on Aird St. for 1.5 km, to Academy Hill Rd. 1.5 km, L. to stone wall.

TEL. 800-263-2663
FAX 905-349-3106
Massey Road, R.R. 1
Grafton, Ontario, Canada
K0K 2G0
Jim Corcoran and Ann Harris,
Innkeepers

AUBERGE HANDFIELD

50 Rooms, $55/$115 Can. EP; 3 Suites, $145/$205 Can. EP

Visa, MC, Amex, EnRte, Disc

All Private Baths, 11 Jacuzzis

Open Year-round

Children Accepted

No Pets; Kennel nearby

Swimming Pool, Skating, Theater, Sugaring-off parties, Bicycle Ride, Boating, Golf, Tennis, Health Club

Breakfast, Lunch, Dinner

Wine & Liquor available

Smoking Allowed

Conference Facilities (130)

From Hwy. 20 Exit 112 (Beloeil/St.Marc) turn L. on Rte. 223 (N) for about 10 km. to inn.

TEL. 514-584-2226
FAX 514-584-3650

555 Chemin du Prince
St. Marc-sur-Richelieu
Quebec, Canada J0L 2E0

M. & Mme. Conrad Handfield, Innkeepers

 Quintessentially French is this inn on the Richelieu River in an ancient French-Canadian village, where French is universally spoken. The rustic decor of this venerable 160-year-old mansion is complemented with antiques and crafted furnishings. A marina and resort facilities, including a health club, along with outstanding cuisine make this a most enjoyable experience.

HOVEY MANOR

40 Rooms, $145/$265 US MAP (no serv. chg.)

Visa, MC, Amex, Diners, EnRoute

All Private Baths, 14 Jacuzzis; 24 Fireplaces

Open Year-round

Young Children and Babies Discouraged; No Pets

On site: Beaches, All Water Sports, Tennis, Touring Bikes, XC-Ski Trails, Skating Rink, Snowshoes, Ice-Fishing, Games Room on Site. Alpine Skiing, Golf, Riding nearby.

Breakfast, Lunch, Dinner

Wine & Liquor available

Non-smoking Dining area

Conference Facilities (2–75)

Wheelchair Access (2 rms. & dining rm. & conf. fac.)

VT. I-91 (N) to border. Continue on Rte. 55N for 29 kms. to No. Hatley Exit 29 & Rte. 108 (E) for 9 kms. to No. Hatley & Hovey Manor signs.

TEL. 819-842-2421
FAX 819-842-2248

Hovey Rd., P.O. Box 60,
No. Hatley, Quebec, Canada
J0B 2CO

Steve & Kathryn Stafford, Innkeepers

Formerly a private estate modeled on Mt. Vernon, this gracious manor abounds with antiques and flowers in a romantic, lakeside setting. Most of the individually decorated rooms offer combinations of fireplaces, jacuzzis, canopy beds and private balconies with superb views of the lake and English gardens. Acclaimed contemporary French cuisine and a full range of year-round recreational facilities on site and included in our rates make Hovey Manor a destination in itself, only 20 minutes from Vermont.

HOSTING YOUR SMALL GROUP

Meeting planners responsible for arranging and hosting small meetings and conferences have found that many country inns offer a new and exciting opportunity. The traditional impersonal and somewhat sterile atmosphere of many larger Conference Centers has forced the astute planner to turn to the many pleasantries found at country inns. Usually, the size of the facility ensures privacy and personal hospitality. Many larger Conference Centers must book several groups at a time to efficiently utilize their facility. Small group meetings, on the other hand, are frequently the only guests enjoying the comfortable, nicely appointed ambiance of a country inn facility.

State of the art audio-visual and facsimile equipment is now commonplace in meeting rooms at IIA inns. The only thing missing is the often exorbitant surcharge assessed for this equipment by larger establishments. Innkeepers happily work with meeting planners to arrange local entertainment and visits to special area attractions as well as fitness and exercising opportunities for their conferee-guests. A small group meeting and personalized hospitality are a natural combination at country inns.

Food service for small group meetings is another natural for innkeepers and their chefs. The usual non-commercial orientation of inn kitchens ensures specialized menus and many "from scratch" dishes to please the appetites of business people after a full schedule of meetings. Innkeepers often tell of conferees who make arrangements to return to the inn with friends for a non-meeting visit because they wanted to share their special gastronomic discoveries.

This *1994 Innkeepers' Register* includes information about the conference facilities available at each inn. A phone call to the inn can quickly provide answers to your specific questions and access to brochures and conference information packets. As astute meeting planners have found, personal contact with an IIA innkeeper can take the work and worry out of planning meetings.

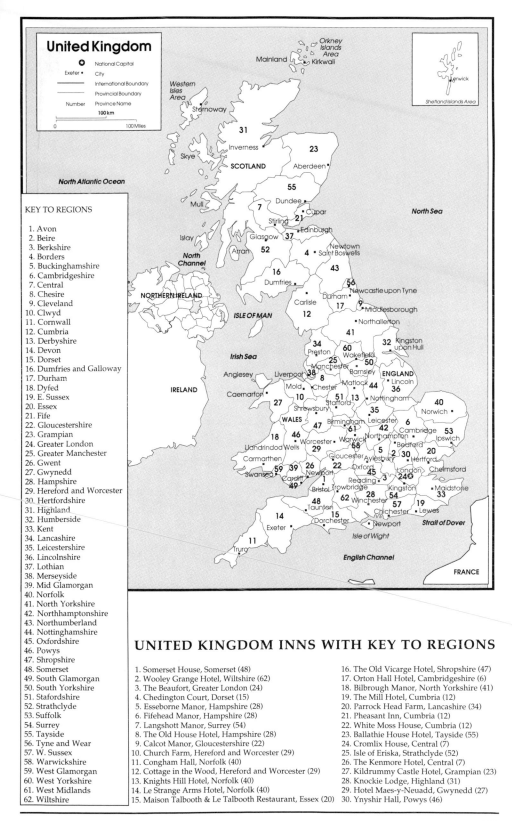

United Kingdom

- ✪ National Capital
- Exeter • City
- International Boundary
- Provincial Boundary
- Number Province Name

100 km

0   100 Miles

KEY TO REGIONS

1. Avon
2. Beire
3. Berkshire
4. Borders
5. Buckinghamshire
6. Cambridgeshire
7. Central
8. Chesire
9. Cleveland
10. Clwyd
11. Cornwall
12. Cumbria
13. Derbyshire
14. Devon
15. Dorset
16. Dumfries and Galloway
17. Durham
18. Dyfed
19. E. Sussex
20. Essex
21. Fife
22. Gloucestershire
23. Grampian
24. Greater London
25. Greater Manchester
26. Gwent
27. Gwynedd
28. Hampshire
29. Hereford and Worcester
30. Hertfordshire
31. Highland
32. Humberside
33. Kent
34. Lancashire
35. Leicestershire
36. Lincolnshire
37. Lothian
38. Merseyside
39. Mid Glamorgan
40. Norfolk
41. North Yorkshire
42. Northhamptonshire
43. Northumberland
44. Nottinghamshire
45. Oxfordshire
46. Powys
47. Shropshire
48. Somerset
49. South Glamorgan
50. South Yorkshire
51. Staffordshire
52. Strathclyde
53. Suffolk
54. Surrey
55. Tayside
56. Tyne and Wear
57. W. Sussex
58. Warwickshire
59. West Glamorgan
60. West Yorkshire
61. West Midlands
62. Wiltshire

UNITED KINGDOM INNS WITH KEY TO REGIONS

1. Somerset House, Somerset (48)
2. Wooley Grange Hotel, Wiltshire (62)
3. The Beaufort, Greater London (24)
4. Chedington Court, Dorset (15)
5. Esseborne Manor, Hampshire (28)
6. Fifehead Manor, Hampshire (28)
7. Langshott Manor, Surrey (54)
8. The Old House Hotel, Hampshire (28)
9. Calcot Manor, Gloucestershire (22)
10. Church Farm, Hereford and Worcester (29)
11. Congham Hall, Norfolk (40)
12. Cottage in the Wood, Hereford and Worcester (29)
13. Knights Hill Hotel, Norfolk (40)
14. Le Strange Arms Hotel, Norfolk (40)
15. Maison Talbooth & Le Talbooth Restaurant, Essex (20)
16. The Old Vicarge Hotel, Shropshire (47)
17. Orton Hall Hotel, Cambridgeshire (6)
18. Bilbrough Manor, North Yorkshire (41)
19. The Mill Hotel, Cumbria (12)
20. Parrock Head Farm, Lancashire (34)
21. Pheasant Inn, Cumbria (12)
22. White Moss House, Cumbria (12)
23. Ballathie House Hotel, Tayside (55)
24. Cromlix House, Central (7)
25. Isle of Eriska, Strathclyde (52)
26. The Kenmore Hotel, Central (7)
27. Kildrummy Castle Hotel, Grampian (23)
28. Knockie Lodge, Highland (31)
29. Hotel Maes-y-Neuadd, Gwynedd (27)
30. Ynyshir Hall, Powys (46)

SOMERSET HOUSE

🛏	10 Rooms, £45/£60 B&B £40/£48 MAP, 1 person
💳	Visa, MC, Amex
🛁	All Private Baths
🛋	Open Year-round
🐕	Children and Small Pets Welcome (2/3 rate for children 10–13)
☀	Large Garden (over 1 acre), Miniature Railway (not always in operation), Parlor Games, Piano
🍽	Breakfast & Dinner daily Wine & Beer available
🚭	No Smoking
♨	Conference Facilities (25-30 if non-residential)
♿	

Somerset House is an elegant Georgian town house from which guests may enjoy views across the city of Bath as well as walks into the adjacent National Trust fields. The city centre (Abbey and Roman Baths) is only twelve minutes walk away (3/4 of a mile). To convey the emphasis we place on the food, we describe Somerset House as a restaurant with rooms. We want our guests to enjoy the freshness of the best of local produce.

WEST COUNTRY

Off A36 (Pulteney Road) at St. Mary-the-Virgin Church on road to Bath University.

TEL. 0225 466451
35 Bathwick Hill,
Bath BA2 6LD

Malcolm & Jean Seymour

WOOLLEY GRANGE HOTEL

🛏	18 Rooms, £90/£165 B&B 2 Suites, £135/£185 B&B
💳	Visa, Amex, Access, Diners
🛁	All Private Baths
🛋	Open Year-round
🐕	Children and Dogs
☀	Grass Tennis Courts, Croquet, Badminton, Heated Outdoor Swimming Pool, Children's Garden, Indoor Games Room, Large Victorian Vegetable Garden (walled).
🍽	All meals daily Wine & Liquor available Smoking except in dining room
♨	Conference Facilities (35)
♿	Wheelchair Access (1 rm. & dining rm.)

The home of the Baskerville family for two centuries, Woolley Grange is a stone manor house built in 1610 on the rural fringe of the Saxon Hillside Woolen town of Bradford-on-Avon. The hotel is renowned for the warmth of our welcome, the stylish but relaxed atmosphere, the quality of our food, much of which we grow or comes from local farms, and our genuine welcome for families. We offer the Woolley Bears Den, a manned nursery from 10 AM to 6 PM every day.

WEST COUNTRY

Eight miles from Bath on B3109, 1/2 mile NE of the town of Bradford-on-Avon.

TEL. 0225 864705
FAX 0225 864059

Woolley Green, Wiltshire
BA15 1TX England

Nigel Chapman

174

THE BEAUFORT

23 Rooms & 5 Junior Suites, 250 B&B

All Credit Cards

25 Private Baths

Open Dec. 28–Dec. 18

Children & Pets by arrangement

Complimentary health club membership, tennis nearby

Wine & Liquor available

Smoking restricted in some rooms

Conference facilities nearby

LONDON/SOUTH/SOUTHEAST
100 yards from Harrods.
TEL. 0715 845252
FAX 0715 892834
33 Beaufort Gardens,
London SW3 1PP

Diana Wallis

Owned by Diana Wallis, we're 150 yards from Harrods in a peaceful Knightsbridge Square, and have 28 bedrooms. The Beaufort is outstanding value—low room rates include *all* drinks, including champagne, all light snacks, a delicious continental breakfast, health club membership, service and VAT. All rooms are air-conditioned, personal Fax/answerphones are available (all calls are charged at cost), and we have a closed front door for additional security. Rated by Zagat as London's top hotel for service.

CHEDINGTON COURT

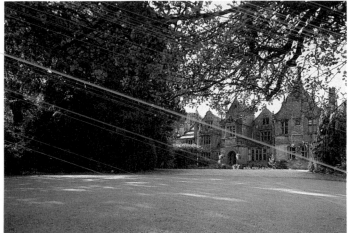

10 Rooms, £80/£120 B&B; £68/£88* MAP

Visa, MC, Access

All Private Baths

Closed Jan. 3–Feb. 3

Children & Pets accepted (with restrictions)

Own Golf Course, Billiards & Snooker, Croquet, Putting, Stately Homes & Gardens

Breakfast, Snacks, Dinner Wine & Liquor available

Some smoking restrictions

Conference Facilities (30)

Wheelchair Access (dining room)

WEST DORSET
Just off the A356. Crewkerne to Dorchester Road 4 1/2 miles SE of Crewkerne at Winyards Gap.
Tel. 0935 891265
FAX 0935 891442
Chedington, Nr. Beaminster,
Dorset DT8 3HY

Philip & Hilary Chapman

Jacobean style manor. Renowned for food and wine. One of the most spectacular views in Southern England. Splendid 10 acre gardens, massive sculptured yew hedge, grotto, water garden, ponds, lawns, terraces. Welcoming interior, fine Persian rugs, antiques, stone fireplaces, atmosphere of distinctive informality and relaxation. 9–Hole par 74 golf course on beautiful parkland. Excellent center for seeing Dorset, Devon, Somerset and many country houses and gardens, antique shops, and Thomas Hardy country.

ESSEBORNE MANOR

🛏	11 Rooms, 1 Suite, £47.50/£56.00* B&B
💳	Visa, MC, Amex, Diners
🛁	All Private Baths
🌳	Open Year-round
🐕	Children over 12 No pets
⅀R	Tennis, Croquet, Walking. Nearby: Golf, Riding, Swimming, Horse racing
◎	Breakfast, Lunch, Dinner Wine & Liquor available
🚭	Smoking restricted
⊢🏛⊣	Conference Facilities (10)
♿	Wheelchair Access (1 rm., dining rm. & conf. fac.)

5 The Hotel is a small, unpretentious yet stylish Country House perfectly placed for those who wish to visit and explore this enchanting area of England designated one of outstanding natural beauty. Aptly described as "invitingly snug," Esseborne has spacious and comfortable bedrooms, furnished to a very high standard, with views over the gardens and rich farmland beyond. The pretty dining room reflects the importance the owners place on their cuisine and service.

From London: M4 exit No. 13. A34 to Newbury. A343 toward Andover. (Hotel: 8 miles from Newbury).

TEL. 0264 736444
FAX 0264 736473
Hurstbourne Tarrant
NR Andover
Hants SP11 OER
Michael & Frieda Yeo

FIFEHEAD MANOR

🛏	16 Rooms, £80/£105 B&B
💳	Visa, Amex, Access
🛁	All Private Baths
🌳	Open Year-round
🐕	Children & Pets Welcome
⅀R	Croquet
◎	Breakfast, Lunch, Dinner Wine & Liquor available
🚬	Smoking permitted
⊢🏛⊣	Conference Facilities (20)
♿	Wheelchair Access (2 rms., dining rm. & conf. fac.)

6 A friendly family atmosphere attracts guests regularly to this convenient hotel managed by Margaret Van Veelen, who speaks French, German and Dutch. Our chef, Mark Robertson, creates some wonderful dishes. The oldest part of the house is 11th century but modern large bedrooms look out onto the attractive garden. Convenient, on main route west from London airports.

On A34S between Andover & Salisbury (after crossroads 5th house on left).

TEL. 0264 781565
FAX 0264 781400
Middle Wallop, Stockbridge,
Hampshire SO20 8EG

Mrs. Margaret Van Veelen

LANGSHOTT MANOR

7 Rooms, £90/£108 EP
Cont. Brkfst., £5 each;
Full Eng. Brkfst., £8 each

Visa, MC, Amex, Diners

All Private Baths

Open Year-round

Babes in arms & over 12
when possible; No pets

Croquet; Golf nearby

Breakfast, Lunch, Dinner
Wine & Liquor available

Smoking restricted

Conference Facilities (12)

SOUTH/SOUTHEAST

From A23 at Horley take Ladbroke
Rd. (Chequers Hotel roundabout) to
Langshottt. The Manor is 1/4 mile
down road.

TEL. 0293 786680
FAX 0293 783905

Gatwick (Horley)
Surrey, RH6 9LN

Geoff & Christopher Noble

A beautifully restored Grade II Elizabethan manor house, tucked away down a quiet country lane, offering the warmest welcome and old-fashioned hospitality. Log fires, excellent, hearty food . . . a resting place, a perfect stopover for Gatwick Airport, 8 minutes away. Jaguar courtesy car to airport and rental car depots, an ideal base from which to explore London and the southeast of England.

THE OLD HOUSE HOTEL

12 Rooms, £62/£69 B&B
(MAP from £65/person)

Visa, MC, Amex, Diners

All Private Baths

Open Year-round except
2 wks. in Aug. & 2 wks.
at Christmas

Children welcome
No pets

Golf, Tennis, Riding,
Fishing, Sailing,
Sightseeing (all nearby)

Breakfast, Lunch, Dinner

Smoking restrictions

Conference Facilities (10)

Wheelchair Access (dining
rm./conf. fac.)

SOUTH/SOUTHEAST

Exit 10 Motorway 27 (M27) then
2 1/2 N. to village. 9 mi. from Ports-
mouth; 10 mi. from Southampton; 11
mi. from Winchester.

TEL. 0329 833049
FAX 0329 833672

The Square, Wickham,
Hampshire PO17 5JG

Richard and Annie Skipwith

A beautifully restored Georgian town house dating from 1715, situated in a historic village near Winchester, the old capitol city. Personally run and supervised for over 23 years by Richard Skipwith and his French wife, Annie. Furnished and decorated as a private house with antiques but with modern hotel facilities and services throughout. The Restaurant, a converted barn, has an enviable reputation for the French style cooking, complemented by an interesting wine list.

CALCOT MANOR

	14 Rooms, £87/£135 B&B 4 Suites, £125 B&B
	Visa, MC, Amex, Diners
	All Private Baths
	Open Year-round
	Family suites available No pets
R	Outdoor heated swimming pool, Croquet, Golf (nearby), Horseriding
	Breakfast, Lunch, Dinner Wine & Liquor available
	Smoking not allowed in restaurant
	Conference Facilities (25)
	Wheelchair Access (7 rms., dining rm.)

This lovely Cotswold Manor House was originally a farmhouse, and its beautiful barns and stables, now converted into superb bedrooms, include a 14th-century tithe barn that is among the oldest in Britain. A recent conversion also provides 4 family suites. Located on the edge of the Cotswolds, Calcot is within 2 hours drive from Heathrow and makes an ideal base for visiting Bath, Cirencester, and Tetbury, famous for its antiques.

CENTRAL/EASTERN

From Junction 18 on M4: Travel north on A46. Turn right on A4135. Calcot on left. 4 miles west of Tetbury on A4135.

TEL. 0666 890391
FAX 0666 890394
Near Tetbury
Gloucestershire GL8 8YJ

Richard Ball

CHURCH FARM

	3 Suites £55/£60 B&B; £86 MAP; £100 AP
	All Private Baths
	Open Feb. 1–Dec. 1
R	Canal towpath for Jogging, Hiking, Biking, Sightseeing
	Breakfast, Lunch, Dinner Wine & Liquor available
	Smoking permitted

On 230 acres of rolling Worcestershire countryside, Church Farm offers visitors comfort and privacy with the enjoyment of a warm welcome. Spacious rooms give a good setting for fine family furniture and fresh flowers. The cathedral city of Worcester is 6 miles away and many attractions of the midlands are in easy reach.

CENTRAL/EASTERN

From MS Jct 6 (Worcester North) A4538 toward Droitwich for 400 yds. Turn R at sign for Smite. Follow past Pear Titee Inn and turn R. Soon after T Jct turn L and then R after 40 yds. Church Farm is 1/3 mi on R.

TEL. 0905 772387
FAX 0905 772387
Oddingley, Droitwich
Worcestershire, WR9 7NE
Anne Dean

CONGHAM HALL

- 12 Rooms, £99/£125 B&B
  2 Suites, £160/£180 B&B
- Visa, Amex, Diners, Access
- 13 Private Baths
- Open Year-round
- No children under 12
  No pets in hotel; outside dog kennels
- Sandringham Royal Estate, Historic & National Trust Properties, Coastal Beaches, Golf Courses, Bird Sanctuaries, Race Courses
- Breakfast, Lunch, Dinner Wine & Liquor available
  No smoking in restaurant
- Conference Facilities (12)
- Wheelchair Access (dining rm.)

CENTRAL/EASTERN

Go to the A149/A148 interchange NE of Kings Lynn. Follow the A148 to Sandringham Fakenham/Cromer for 100 yards then turn right to Grimston. Hotel is 2 1/2 miles on left-hand side.
TEL. 0485 600250
FAX 0485 601191
Lynn Rd., Grimston, Kings Lynn
Norfolk PE32 1AH
T.C. Forecast

In forty acres of parkland, yet only six miles from Kings Lynn, Congham Hall offers its guests complete relaxation. With its paddocks, orchards and gardens, visitors can unwind and enjoy their holiday in an atmosphere of complete tranquility. Built as a Georgian Manor House in the mid-eighteenth century, Congham Hall was converted into a luxury hotel in 1982. The owners have retained the family atmosphere and a welcoming warmth that is evident in all they and their staff do for you.

THE COTTAGE IN THE WOOD

- 20 Rooms, £97/£135 B&B (English)
- Visa, MC, Amex, Access, Barclay Card
- All Private Baths
- Open Year-round
- Children & pets accepted
- Walking on 9-mile Malvern Hill Range. 18-hole golf, 1 mi. Squash, 1/2 mi. Clay pigeon shooting can be arranged.
- Breakfast, Lunch, Dinner Wine & Liquor available
- No smoking in restaurant
- Conference Facilities (14)

CENTRAL/EASTERN

3 miles south of Great Malvern off A449 turning opposite Jet Gas Station. Signposted from main road.
TEL. 0684 573487
FAX 0684 560662
Holywell Road, Malvern Wells,
Worcester WR14 4LG

John Pattin, Proprietor

A family owned and run hotel, famed for both its magnificent position high on the Malvern Hills, commanding a 30-mile view to the Cotswold Hills, and for its cuisine for which an AA red rosette has been awarded. Small charming hotel guide also awarded a coveted Cèsar in 1992. The London Daily Mail entitled the view "the best view in England." An ideal touring base for the Cotswolds, Stratford upon Avon, Wye Valley, and the cathedral cities of Worcester, Gloucester, and Hereford.

KNIGHTS HILL HOTEL

52 Rooms, £75/£90

Visa, Amex, Access, Diners, Switch

All Private Baths

Open Year-round
Children free under 15 in parents' room (1/2 price in own room); meals as taken

Indoor Pool, 2 All-weather Tennis Courts, Spa Bath, Steam Room, Sauna, Solarium, Snooker, Fitness Studio.
Breakfast, Lunch, Dinner
Wine & Liquor Available
Smoking restricted

Conference Facilities (300)
Wheelchair Access (dining rm., conf. fac.)

With its origins firmly rooted in history—growing from a hunting lodge in the King's Chase to large working farm and hub of the local community—Knights Hill has evolved, through sympathetic renovation into a well-appointed, three-star hotel with a choice of bedroom styles, restaurants, a traditional country pub and extensive leisure center. Close to the royal estate at Sandringham, guests have a comfortable base from which to explore the coastal and rural beauty of West Norfolk.

CENTRAL/EASTERN

At junction of A148/A149 on King's Lynn ring road.
TEL. 0553 675566
FAX 0553 675568
South Wootton
Kings Lynn
Norfolk PE30 3HQ

Bernard Ducker &
Howard Darking

LE STRANGE ARMS HOTEL

37 Rooms, 1 Suite £65/£75 B&B

Visa, MC, Amex, Diners

All Private Baths

Open Year-round

Children Welcome
Pets at Management's Disgression

Tennis Court (grass), Children's Play Area, Snooker Room
Breakfast, Lunch, Dinner
Wine & Liquor Available

Smoking Restricted

Conference Facility (150)
Wheelchair Access (dining rm. & conf. fac.)

A Victorian building located on the North West Norfolk coastline with lawns sweeping down to the beach. Near to many wildlife reserves and places of historical interest, such as Royal Sandringham, Houghton and Holkham Halls. The hotel has a wide range of accommodations, including four-poster rooms and family suites. The hotel's Restaurant has a reputation for fine food and friendly, yet professional service.

CENTRAL/EASTERN

One mile north Hunstanton. Just off the A149 coastal road.
TEL. 0485 534411
FAX 0485 534 534724
Old Hunstanton
Norfolk PE36 6JJ

Robert & Anne Wyllie

MAISON TALBOOTH & LE TALBOOTH RESTAURANT

- 10 Rooms, £102.50/ £137.50 B&B
- Visa, MC, Amex
- All Private Baths
- Open Year-round
- Children Welcome No Pets
- Constable Country, Sailing by Arrangement
- Breakfast, Lunch, Dinner Wine & Liquor Available
- Smoking Permitted
- Conference Facility (60)
- Wheelchair Access (dining rm.)

CENTRAL/EASTERN

6 miles north of Colchester off A12.

TEL. 0206 322367
FAX 0206 322752
Dedham
Colchester, Essex C07 6HN

Gerald Milsom

15 John Constable country, with this unique combination of a hotel and restaurant 10 minutes walk apart. Gerald Milsom started this business nearly 40 years ago and has achieved fame with Pride of Britain Hotels, which he started. Maison Talbooth is elegant with luxurious bedrooms, some quite glamorous. Le Talbooth is very attractive with Tudor white and black half-timbers overlooking the garden and river Stour, with an appropriate high standard of food.

THE OLD VICARGE HOTEL

- 13 Rooms, £85/£100 B&B; £59.50 any 2 or more nights (supplement for luxury) MAP; 1 Suite, £100*
- Visa, MC, Amex, Diners, Access
- All Private Baths
- Open Year-round
- Children & dogs accepted
- Half-price golf available at nearby golf course. Croquet on lawn.
- Breakfast, Lunch, Dinner Wine & Liquor Available
- 6 no-smoking bedrooms; no-smoking bar; no-smoking dining room
- Conference Facilities
- Wheelchair Access (2 rms., dining rm. & conf. fac.)

CENTRAL/EASTERN

8 miles west of Wolverhampton, 1 mile off A454; 8 miles south of Junction 4 of M54.

TEL. 0746 716497
FAX 0746 716552
Worfield, Nr. Bridgnorth
Shropshire WV15 5JZ

Peter & Christine Iles

16 Standing in 2 acres of grounds on the edge of Worfield, The Old Vicarage offers its visitors an opportunity to enjoy a peaceful retreat in the Shropshire countryside. An imaginative menu features the best of local produce with a wide range of British cheeses. Over 200 fine wines are kept in the cellar and a good selection of malt whiskies is available. Local attractions include the Ironbridge Gorge Museum Complex and the Severn Valley Steam Railway. Close to Birmingham and Manchester airports.

ORTON HALL HOTEL

🛏	50 Rooms, £69/£112–£130
💳	Special Wknd F.S.S. £57 DBB PP
	Visa, MC, Amex, Diners
🛁	All Private Baths
🏺	
	Open Year-round
🐕	Children Yes; Pets by Arrangement
☀R	On site Croquet; within 1 mi. 2 Golf Courses, Sailing, Windsurfing, Front and Coarse Fishing, Swimming, Gym, Horse Riding, Nene Park, River Trips
🍷	Breakfast, Lunch, Dinner
	Wine & Liquor Available
🚭	Smoking Restricted
🏛	Conference Facilities (120)
♿	Wheelchair Access (4 rms., dining rm. & conf. fac.)

17   A former stately home, this magnificent 17th Century building is one of Peterborough's finest Hotel and Conference Centres, set in twenty acres of glorious mature parkland in the heart of the conservation village of Orton Longueville, Peterborough. Excellent base from which to visit the rich assortment of local culture and history, in Peterborough, Cambridge, Oundle and Stamford—the set for the BBC's acclaimed period drama of George Eliot's "Middlemarch," with Burghley House close-by.

CENTRAL/EASTERN

From the A1 take A1139; then follow Nene Park signs, then Orton Longueville signs or A605 from city centre.

TEL. 0733 391111
FAX 0733 231912

The Village, Orton Longueville
Peterborough PE2 0DN
Barry Harpham

BILBROUGH MANOR

🛏	12 Rooms, £42.50/£75 B&B & VAT; £62.50/£95* B&B, dinner, & VAT
💳	Visa, Amex, Diners, Access
🛁	
🏺	Closed Dec. 25–29
🐕	Children over 10 accepted; No pets
☀R	Croquet, Walking, Riding, Golf arranged
🍷	Breakfast, Lunch, Afternoon Tea, Dinner & Bar Lunches
🚭	No smoking in restaurant
🏛	Conference Facilities (30 theatre style; 12 boardroom style)
♿	Wheelchair Access (restaurant)

18   Bilbrough Manor is the ancestral home of the Fairfax family dating back to 1086 and was converted into a Country House Hotel in 1986 by the present owners. Situated in 100 acres of pasture land on the edge of the rustic conservation village of Bilbrough, the House exudes warmth, charm and roaring log fires in chilly weather. Renowned for its good food, friendly and excellent service, this little gem is already a firm favourite with American visitors. Recommended in all Main Guides and is the Best Yorkshire Hotel in 1993.

NORTH COUNTRY

Just off A64 York-Leeds road. Turn opposite Happy Eater.

TEL. 0937 834002
FAX 0937 834724
Bilbrough, York Y02 3PH

Colin & Sue Bell

THE MILL HOTEL

8 Rooms, £39/£55 MAP*
1 Suite, £48/£55 MAP*

None

7 Private Baths

Open Feb.–Nov.

Children and Dogs Welcome

Lake District National Park, Hiking, Fishing, Horseback Riding, Golf, Canoeing, Birding, Historic Sights, Bicycling

Breakfast & Dinner; Wine & Liquor Available

No smoking in restaurant

NORTH COUNTRY

Exit 40 on M6. A66 8 miles toward Keswick. Take sign right to Mungrisdale Village. Hotel next door to Inn.

TEL. 0768 779659

Mungrisdale, Penrith
Cumbria CA11 OXR

Richard & Eleanor Quinlan

19 At the foot of the Skiddaw Range in the Lake District is a charming white house by a stream. Here Richard & Eleanor Quinlan have established a good reputation for individual hospitality. Homemade bread and a mouth-watering range of puddings are featured alongside main courses which include vegetarian dishes as well as game, beef and lamb. Most people return again and again. The cluster of farms and the church nearby with the great fells towering around never cease to appeal.

PARROCK HEAD HOTEL

9 Rooms, £59/£64 B&B

Visa, MC, Amex, Diners

All Private Baths

Open Year-round

Yes to Children; Dog in garden rooms only

Fishing, Walking, Golf Nearby

Breakfast, Lunch, Dinner Wine & Liquor Available

No Smoking in restaurant

Conference Facilities (2-20)

Wheelchair Access (3 rms., dining rm.)

NORTH COUNTRY

TEL. 0200 446614

Slaidburn, Clitheroe
Lancashire BB7 3AH

Richard Umbers

20 Just an hour's drive from Manchester airport this 17th-century Dales farmhouse is in a world apart. Surrounded by rolling fells. Centrally placed for the lakes and dales of northern England; an ideal place to relax after your flight o visits to busy tourist centers. A warm welcome awaits U visitors from Richard and Vicky Umbers. All rooms en su lounge and library furnished with antiques, and a restau with a growing reputation.

PHEASANT INN

🛏	20 Rooms, £88/£92 B&B & VAT & service
💳	Visa, Access
🛁	All Private Baths
👪	Open Year-round Children 1/3 reduction if sharing a room; Dogs allowed in lounges; not in bedrooms
🐕	
☈	Hill walking; Motoring around Lakes and to Roman Wall; Enjoying peace and quiet of our gardens and grounds
☕	Breakfast, Lunch, Dinner Wine & liquor available
🚭	No smoking in dining room and 1 of 3 lounges
♿	Wheelchair Access (1 rm., dining rm.)

🏨 Tranquil, traditional Lake District inn close to Bassenthwaite Lake. Surrounding gardens and woodland provide a wealth of wildlife. Three lounges feature antiques, open fires, beams, and fresh flowers. Commended by Major Guides for high quality English food and service. 20 individually decorated bedrooms all with private facilities.

NORTH COUNTRY

Just off A66 7 miles west of Keswick; 23 miles from Motorway M6.

TEL. 0768 776234
FAX 0768 776002
Bassenthwaite Lake
Near Cockermouth
Cumbria CA13 9YE

W.E. Barrington & Mary Wilson

WHITE MOSS HOUSE

🛏	6 Rooms, £64/£86 MAP
💳	Visa, MC
🛁	All Private Baths
👪	Open Mar.–Nov.
🐕	Older Children Welcome No Pets
☈	Fell (mountain & lake) walking from doorstep, Dove Cottage & Rydal Manor 1 mi. away. Free Fishing. Free use of local leisure club.
☕	Breakfast, Dinner; Wine & Liquor Available
🚭	Smoking Restricted
♿	

🏨 Wordsworth once owned this attractive house overlooking Rydal Water. A very intimate atmosphere has been created by Susan and Peter Dixon, that has so many comforts and good food. The reputation of the restaurant is well served and one should stay for at least two nights in this central area of the Lake District, with so much to see and excellent walking in every direction.

NORTH COUNTRY

A 591 at Rydal Water halfway between Ambleside & Grasmere.

TEL. 0539 435295
Rydal Water, **Grasmere**
Cumbria LA229SE

Susan & Peter Dixon

BALLATHIE HOUSE HOTEL

27 Rooms, £110/£150 B&B
1 Suite, £140/£200 B&B

Visa, MC, Amex, Diners

All Private Baths

Open Year-round

No restrictions on children; dogs in rooms

Fishing (Salmon), Shooting, Golf, Tennis

Breakfast, Lunch, Dinner

No Smoking in Dining Room

Conference Facilites (10)
Wheelchair Access (2 rms., dining rm. & conf. fac.)

Take A9 N. of Perth to 1st exit (Stanley); take R. fork 1 mi. N. of Stanley. Hotel off B 9099.
TEL. 0250 883268
FAX 0250 883396
(Nr. Perth) Kinclaven, by Stanley
Perthshire PH1 4QN

Christopher J. Longden

23 Situated in its own estate overlooking the River Tay, Ballathie House offers Scottish hospitality in a house of character and distinction dating from 1850. The original public rooms are elegantly furnished and spacious premier bedrooms retain antique furniture and period bathrooms with all modern facilities. Standard rooms are cozy and charmingly decorated. On the ground floor there are rooms suitable for disabled guests and a suite opening out on to the lawns which incline to the river. Food is local with Tay Salmon, Beef, Lamb and West Coast seafood.

CROMLIX HOUSE

6 Rooms, £135/£150 B&B
8 Suites, £170/£220, B&B

Visa, MC, Amex, Diners

All Private Baths

Open March–Jan.

Children welcome if supervised

3 Trout Lochs: Salmon fishing: Sportings: Walking: Nearby: Golf, Horseriding, Stirling Castle, Scone Palace

Breakfast, Lunch, Dinner
Wine & Liquor Available

No smoking in dining rooms

Conference Facilities (30)
Wheelchair Access (dining room, 3 steps)

Off A9, 1 mile north of Dunblane, through Kinbuck village. 2nd left after narrow bridge or on B8033 from Crieff.
TEL. 0786 822125
FAX 0786 825450
Kinbuck, by Dunblane
NR. Stirling
Perthshire, Scotland
David & Ailsa Assenti

24 "To experience Crumlix is a taste of serenity." 1 hr. from Edinburgh. 40 mins. from Glasgow & Perth. Built in 1874 within its own 5,000-acre estate, Cromlix retains the feeling of a well-loved home where you are a most cherished guest. Original features. Antiques and fine furnishings throughout. Very spacious suites. Open fires. Peaceful & relaxed! A unique house!! Prestigious hospitality, quality & cuisine awards. Reduced rates October–March. Truly an excellent touring base.

ISLE OF ERISKA

🛏	16 Rooms, £155/£185 B&B 1 Suite, £155/£185 B&B
💳	Visa, MC
🛁	All Private Baths
🌳	Open March Nov.
🐕	1 family rm. for 2 adults & up to 2 children under 10; Dogs at our discretion
ⓡ	Tennis, Croquet, Put-Put Golf, Windsurfing, Water- skiing
🍷	Breakfast, Lunch, Dinner Wine & Liquor Available
🚬	Smoking accepted
Conference Facilities (17)	
♿	Wheelchair Access (2 rms., dining rm. & conf. fac.)

SCOTLAND
From Edinburgh/Glasgow: Drive to Crianlarich then A85 to Oban. At Connel proceed by bridge on A828. Follow signs from Benderloch.
TEL. 0631 72 371
FAX Toll Free from USA:
1-800-239-0197
Ledaig, Oban
Argyll PA37 1SD
Robin Buchanan-Smith

The Buchanan-Smith Family welcome you to their private West Highland Island. Cross by the vehicle bridge to your own 300-acre nature reserve. Enjoy the comfort of this internationally rated 5 Crown Deluxe Scottish Baronial House. Watch the seals and badgers or play tennis and walk on the Scottish hills. An ideal centre for visiting the island of Iona, Inverary Castle and Glencoe. Just 2 hours by car from Glasgow International Airport.

THE KENMORE HOTEL

🛏	35 Rooms, £44 B&B* 3 Family Rooms, £58* MAP
💳	Visa, Amex, Access, Switch
🛁	34 Private Baths
🌳	Open Year-round
🐕	Children of all ages wel- come; No dogs in hotel but in Sportsman's Lodge
ⓡ	Own 18-hole Taymouth Castle Golf Course; 69 par Parkland Course; own 2 1/2 mile stretch of the River Tay for salmon/trout fishing; green fees 50% dis- count to residents
🍷	Breakfast, Lunch, Supper (Bar lunches/suppers) Wine & Liquor Available
🚬	No smoking in restaurant
Conference Facilities (40)	
♿	Wheelchair Access (7 rms., dining rm. & conf. fac.)

SCOTLAND
Proceed west on the A827 off the A9 Perth to Inverness Road.
TEL. 0887 830205
FAX 0887 830262
Kenmore, by Aberfeldy
Perthshire PH15 2NU

Andrew McTaggert

Kenmore at the head of Loch Tay is designated as one of Scotland's prettiest villages. It also boasts Scotland's oldest inn. Build in 1572 the Kenmore Hotel is the focal point in the village, known for its excellent facilities and courteous good manners of an attentive staff. Modern conveniences, carefully combined while maintaining old traditional features ensure that visitors enjoy the experience of Kenmore as was once enjoyed by Robbie Burns.

KILDRUMMY CASTLE HOTEL

- 15 Rooms, £110/£130 B&B
- Visa, MC, Amex
- All Private Baths
- Open Feb.–Dec.
- Children & Dogs Welcome
- Fishing, Golf, Horse Riding
- Breakfast, Lunch, Dinner Wine & Liquor Available
- Non-smoking Restaurant

SCOTLAND

Off A97 Huntly/Ballater Rd. 35 miles west of Aberdeen.

TEL. 0975 571288
FAX 0975 571345
Kildrummy by Alford
Aberdeenshire AB33 8RA

Thomas & Mary Hanna

27 A converted country mansion house set amidst acres of planted gardens, in the heart of the Grampian Highlands, 35 miles west of Aberdeen and close to the royal family's Scottish retreat—Balmoral Castle. All the facilities of a modern first-class hotel with the original turn-of-the-century interior—carved oak paneling, wall tapestries, oak ceilings—the perfect base from which to explore Scotland's Castle Trail, discover the Malt Whiskey Trail, and enjoy the northeast's fine natural produce.

KNOCKIE LODGE

- 10 Rooms, £130/£190 MAP (4 dbl., 4 twin, 2 sgl.)
- Visa, MC, Amex, Diners
- All Private Baths
- Open May–October
- No children under 10 Dogs welcome
- Fishing, Deer stalking Hiking, Sailing, Bird watching, Golf nearby
- Breakfast, Dinner Wine & Liquor Available
- No smoking in dining room
- Conference Facilities (10–12)

SCOTLAND

Take A9N to Daviot or A82N to Fort Augustus. Then B862/851 to Whitebridge.

TEL. 0456 486276
FAX 0456 486389
Whitebridge
Inverness-shire IV1 2UP

Ian N. Milward

28 Situated 800 feet above Loch Ness few places can enjoy quite such a rare feeling of timelessness and perfect peace and quiet. The atmosphere at Knockie is cozy, friendly and extremely relaxed. It is essentially the home of Ian and Brenda Milward with its beautifully proportioned rooms filled with antique furniture, paintings and other personal belongings. Although remote, it is extremely accessible and provides an excellent base for exploring a wide area of the Northern Highlands.

WALES
HOTEL MAES-Y-NEUADD

🛏	16 Rooms, £113/£152 B&B
💳	Visa, MC, Amex, Diners
🛁	All Private Baths
🕯	Open Year-round
🐕	Children charged for meals only in parents' room; Dogs by arrangement
☀ R	Royal St. Davids Golf Club nearby; Walking, Mountains, Historic Castle, Lakes, Beaches
🍷	Breakfast, Lunch, Dinner Wine & Liquor Available
🚭	No smoking in dining room
⊢▦⊣	Conference Facilities (14)
♿	Wheelchair Access (3 rms., dining rm.)

WALES

3 miles north of Harlech off B4573.

TEL. 0766 780200
FAX 0766 780211
Talsarnau Nr. Harlech
Gwynedd, North Wales
LL476YA

June Slatter

29 Maes-y-Neuadd, an ancient, part 14th-century granite built manor house, nestling into the mountains of Snowdonia, surrounded by some of the most spectacular scenery in Britain. All modern comforts have been blended into the historic fabric of the old beamed bar, charming lounge and gracious Georgian dining room. Delicious local produce for which the area is famous form the basis of the restaurant menus.

YNYSHIR HALL

🛏	9 Rooms, £95/£130 B&B 3 Suites, £110/£130 B&B (dinner priced separately)
💳	Visa, MC, Amex, Diners, Access
🛁	All Private Baths
🕯	Open Year-round
🐕	Children over 9 welcome Pets by prior arrangement in some rooms
☀ R	Bird-watching, Golf, Walking, Fishing, Boating, Shooting, Riding, Castles & Museums
🍷	Breakfast, Lunch, Dinner Wine & Liquor Available
🚭	No smoking in restaurant & in certain bedrooms
⊢▦⊣	Conference Facilities (20)
♿	

WALES

About 3 hrs. from Manchester or Birmingham airport. Situated off the A487 6 miles from Macuynlletu & 11 miles from Aberystwyt.

TEL. 0654 781209
FAX 0654 781366
Eglwysfach, Machynlleth
Powys SY20 8TA, Wales

Rob & Joan Reen

30 Once owned by Queen Victoria and situated in 12 acres of glorious landscaped grounds on the edge of the Dyfi Estuary. Furnished with antiques and original paintings. Highly acclaimed cuisine and fine wines help make this one of Wales' best deluxe hotels. Ideally placed for exploring Wales and its beautiful countryside. An oasis of peace and tranquility.

TENNIS ANYONE?

There are usually places to go, things to do, and sights to see in the vicinity of most country inns, and the inns will have suggestions and maps for all sorts of activities, scenic drives, and sightseeing, from nature walks to nearby historic sites to the best outlet shopping. Tennis courts, swimming pools, and sometimes golf courses are standard at resort inns. Many other forms of diversion are offered at various inns. Here is an idea of the kinds of recreation or entertainment you might find on the grounds or under the auspices of a country inn.

Near water there could be fishing, sailing, rowboating, canoeing, kayaking, paddle boating, rafting, waterskiing, and tubing. A couple of innkeepers have Coast Guard captain's licenses and take guests out in their boats. Others have boats for the use of their guests for fishing, excursions, and sightseeing.

In ski country, sometimes there are groomed and marked ski and nature trails leading from front doors into woods, where deer, moose, fox, mink, bobcats, raccoons, or maybe even a bear might be glimpsed. Some inns have their own ski shops with lessons and rental equipment. These might also have tobogganing, sledding, and ice skating.

Western ranches have horses and trail rides, as do a few inns in the South and East. Farms have animals for petting, feeding, and watching; some guests like to flex their muscles at haying time, tossing and stacking bales of hay.

Guided or unguided wildflower, birdwatching, and nature walks might include a picnic beside a forest stream. Some inns provide a basket of goodies for a picnic lunch on a remote beach, by a waterfall, or to break a mountain hike or a bicycle ride on back roads. There are inn-to-inn programs for hikers and bikers.

A couple of inns feature hot-air balloon rides, either from the inn grounds or nearby.

Some on-premises activities include English croquet, shuffleboard, lawn bowling, paddle tennis, pitch 'n' putt golf, volleyball, horseshoes, ping-pong, pool or billiards, fitness centers for aerobic exercise, Nordic track exercisers, stationary bicycles, rowing machines, barre, weights, hot tubs, saunas, spas with mineral springs, massages, and facials.

For rainy days, some inns have VCR's and film libraries, puzzles, board games, and libraries of all sorts of books and magazines. Some inns offer evening entertainment with lovely music programs—musicians playing original instruments and tunes from the 1800s, or chamber music and soloists, or sometimes impromptu recitals by a talented guest who sits down at the baby grand or picks up a guitar. A few innkeepers are accomplished musicians in their own right. A Canadian inn offers local color with films about the area, storytellers, singers and fiddlers, and square dances. Another Canadian inn holds sugaring-off parties in March.

And then there is the inn that has created a sylvan glade where guests can sit and commune with nature. And there are lots of porches with rocking chairs— sometimes all the recreation or entertainment a guest desires is to sit and rock and watch the world go by.

— by Virginia Rowe

Canada

United States

Upper New England
Maritimes and Quebec

VERMONT
1. Inn on the Common, Craftsbury Common
2. Rabbit Hill Inn, Lower Waterford
3. The Inn at Montpelier, Montpelier
4. Shire Inn, Chelsea
5. Historic Brookside Farms, Orwell
6. Mountain Top Inn, Chittenden
7. October Country Inn, Bridgewater Corners
8. Vermont Marble Inn, Fair Haven
10. Governor's Inn, Ludlow
11. Inn at Weathersfield, Weathersfield
12. Rowell's Inn, Simonsville
13. Village Inn at Landgrove, Londonderry
14. Barrows House, Dorset
15. Birch Hill Inn, Manchester
16. West Mountain Inn, Arlington
17. Three Mountain Inn, Jamaica
18. Windham Hill Inn, West Townshend

CANADA—QUEBEC
1. Auberge Handfield, St. Marc-sur-le-Richelieu
2. Hovey Manor, North Hatley

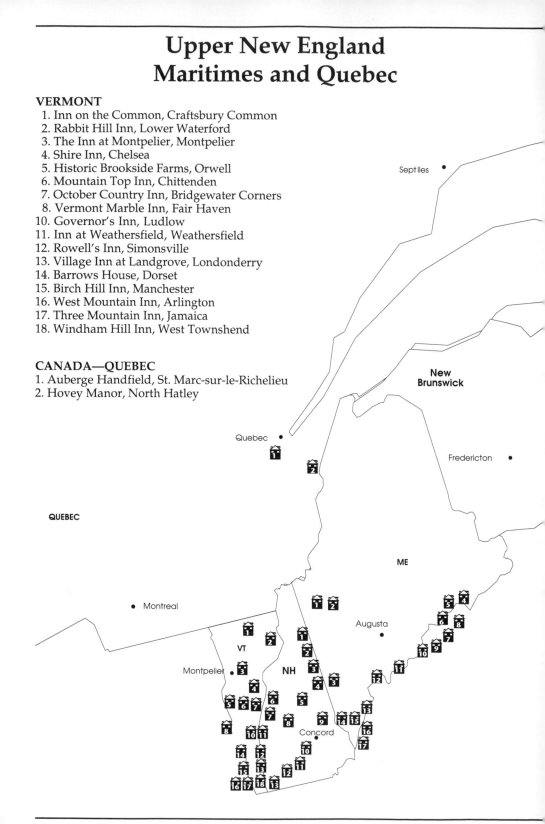

NEW HAMPSHIRE

1. Philbrook Farm Inn, Shelburne
2. Christmas Farm Inn, Jackson
3. Darby Field Inn, Conway
4. Stafford's in the Field, Chocorua
5. Corner House Inn, Center Sandwich
6. Lyme Inn, Lyme
7. Moose Mountain Lodge, Etna
8. Dexter's Inn and Tennis Club, Sunapee
9. Hickory Stick Farm, Belmont
10. Colby Hill Inn, Henniker
11. Inn at Crotched Mountain, Francestown
12. John Hancock Inn, Hancock
13. Chesterfield Inn, West Chesterfield

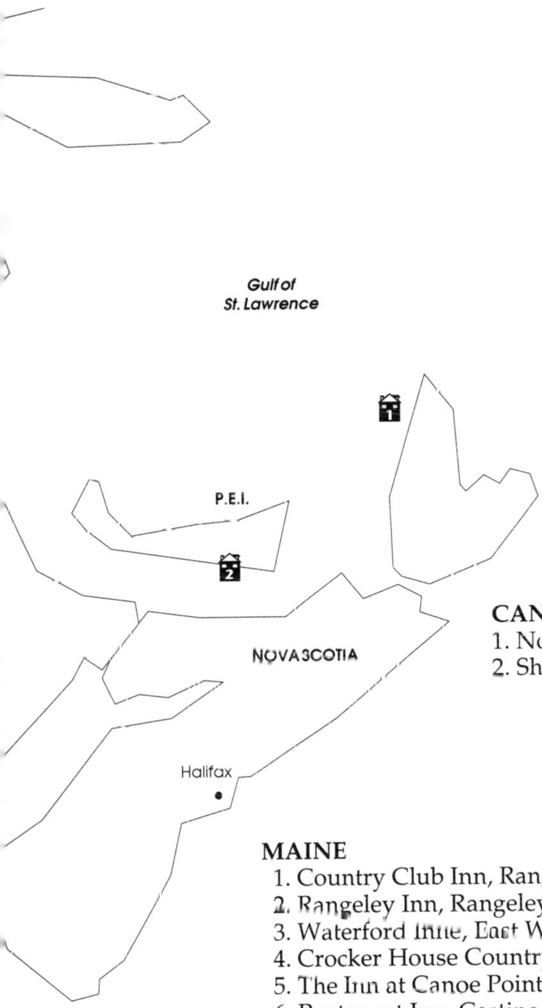

Gulf of
St. Lawrence

P.E.I.

NOVA SCOTIA

Halifax
•

CANADA—MARITIMES

1. Normaway Inn, Margaree Valley
2. Shaw's Hotel, Brackley Beach

MAINE

1. Country Club Inn, Rangeley
2. Rangeley Inn, Rangeley
3. Waterford Inne, East Waterford
4. Crocker House Country Inn, Hancock Point
5. The Inn at Canoe Point, Bar Harbor
6. Pentagoet Inn, Castine
7. Pilgrim's Inn, Deer Isle
8. Claremont Hotel and Cottages, Southwest Harbor
9. Goose Cove Lodge, Sunset
10. Whitehall Inn, Camden
11. Newcastle Inn, Newcastle
12. Squire Tarbox Inn, Wiscasset
13. Black Point Inn, Prouts Neck
14. Captain Lord Mansion, Kennebunkport
15. Old Fort Inn, Kennebunkport
16. Hartwell House, Ogunquit
17. Dockside Guest Quarters, York

Southern New England

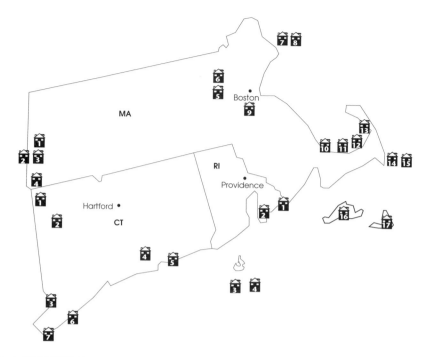

MASSACHUSETTS
1. Village Inn, Lenox
2. Red Lion Inn, Stockbridge
3. Inn at Stockbridge, Stockbridge
4. Weathervane Inn, South Egremont
5. Longfellow's Wayside Inn, South Sudbury
6. Hawthorne Inn, Concord
7. Yankee Clipper Inn, Rockport
8. Ralph Waldo Emerson, Rockport
9. Lenox Hotel, Boston
10. Isaiah Jones Homestead, Sandwich
11. Charles Hinckley House, Barnstable
12. Bramble Inn, Brewster
13. Whalewalk Inn, Eastham
14. The Captain's House Inn, Chatham
15. Queen Anne Inn, Chatham
16. Charlotte Inn, Edgartown,
    Martha's Vineyard Island
17. Jared Coffin House, Nantucket Island

CONNECTICUT
1. Under Mountain Inn, Salisbury
2. Boulders Inn, New Preston
3. West Lane Inn, Ridgefield
4. Griswold Inn, Essex
5. Bee and Thistle Inn, Old Lyme
6. Silvermine Tavern, Norwalk
7. Homestead Inn, Greenwich

RHODE ISLAND
1. The Inntowne, Newport
2. Larchwood Inn, Wakefield
3. Hotel Manisses, Block Island
4. 1661 Inn, Block Island

PENNSYLVANIA
1. Tara, Clark
2. The Tavern, New Wilmington
3. Century Inn, Scenery Hill
4. Gateway Lodge, Cooksburg
5. Crestmont, Eagles Mere
6. Eagles Mere Inn, Eagles Mere
7. Pine Barn Inn, Danville
8. Inn at Starlight Lake, Starlight
9. The Settlers Inn, Hawley
10. Cliff Park, Milford
11. The French Manor, South Sterling
12. Sterling Inn, South Sterling
13. Glasbern, Fogelsville
14. 1740 House, Lumberville
15. Whitehall Inn, New Hope
16. Barley Sheaf Farm, Holicong
17. Smithton Inn, Ephrata
18. Swiss Woods B&B, Lititz
19. Cameron Estate Inn, Mount Joy
20. Hickory Bridge Farm, Orrtanna

Upper Mid-Atlantic

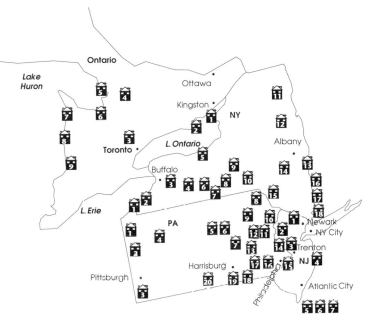

NEW YORK

1. William Seward Inn, Westfield
2. White Inn, Fredonia
3. Asa Ransom House, Clarence
4. The Genesee Country Inn, Mumford
5. Oliver Loud's Inn, Pittsford
6. Morgan-Samuels B&B Inn, Canandaigua
7. Rose Inn, Ithaca
8. Benn Conger Inn, Groton
9. Sherwood Inn, Skaneateles
10. Lincklaen House, Cazenovia
11. Interlaken Inn, Lake Placid
12. Garnet Hill Lodge, North River
13. Sedgwick Inn, Berlin
14. Greenville Arms, Greenville
15. Redcoat's Return, Elka Park
16. Simmon's Way Village Inn, Millerton
17. Beekman Arms, Rhinebeck
18. Bird and Bottle Inn, Garrison

CANADA—ONTARIO

1. Rosemount Inn, Kingston
2. Ste. Anne's, Grafton
3. Elora Mill Inn, Elora
4. Eganridge Inn, Fenelon Falls
5. Sherwood Inn, Port Carling
6. The Briars, Jackson Point
7. Chantry House Inn, Southampton
8. Little Inn of Bayfield, Bayfield
9. Stone Maiden Inn, Stratford

NEW JERSEY

1. Whistling Swan Inn, Stanhope
2. Inn at Millrace Pond, Hope
3. Stockton Inn, Colligan's, Stockton
4. Sea Crest By The Sea, Spring Lake
5. Mainstay Inn & Cottage, Cape May
6. Manor House, Cape May
7. The Queen Victoria, Cape May

Lower Mid-Atlantic

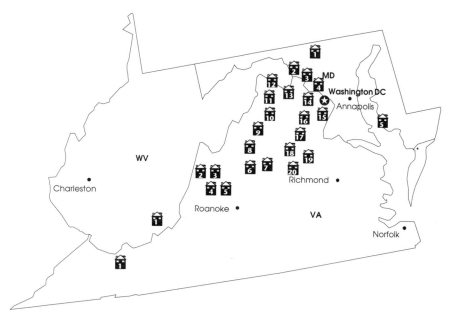

MARYLAND
1. Antrim 1844, Taneytown
2. Antietam Overlook Farm, Keedysville
3. Tyler Spite House, Frederick
4. Inn at Buckeystown, Buckeystown
5. Robert Morris Inn, Oxford

WEST VIRGINA
1. General Lewis Inn, Lewisburg

VIRGINIA
1. The Oaks Bed & Breakfast Inn, Christianburg
2. Inn at Gristmill Square, Warm Springs
3. Meadow Lane Lodge, Warm Springs
4. Alexander Withrow House/McCampbell Inn, Lexington
5. Maple Hall, Lexington
6. Fort Lewis Lodge, Millboro
7. Trillium House, Nellysford
8. The Belle Grae Inn, Staunton
9. Jordan Hollow Farm Inn, Stanley
10. Inn at Little Washington, Washington
11. Inn at Narrow Passage, Woodstock
12. L'Auberge Provencale, White Post
13. Ashby Inn, Paris
14. Red Fox Inn & Tavern, Middleburg
15. The Bailiwick Inn, Fairfax
16. Graves' Mountain Lodge, Syria
17. The Hidden Inn, Orange
18. Silver Thatch Inn, Charlottesville
19. Prospect Hill, Trevilians
20. High Meadows, Scottsville

South Atlantic

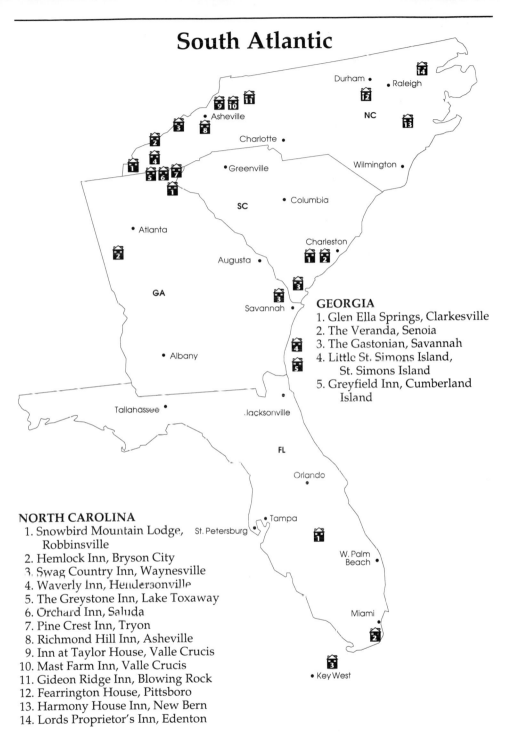

GEORGIA
1. Glen Ella Springs, Clarkesville
2. The Veranda, Senoia
3. The Gastonian, Savannah
4. Little St. Simons Island, St. Simons Island
5. Greyfield Inn, Cumberland Island

NORTH CAROLINA
1. Snowbird Mountain Lodge, Robbinsville
2. Hemlock Inn, Bryson City
3. Swag Country Inn, Waynesville
4. Waverly Inn, Hendersonville
5. The Greystone Inn, Lake Toxaway
6. Orchard Inn, Saluda
7. Pine Crest Inn, Tryon
8. Richmond Hill Inn, Asheville
9. Inn at Taylor House, Valle Crucis
10. Mast Farm Inn, Valle Crucis
11. Gideon Ridge Inn, Blowing Rock
12. Fearrington House, Pittsboro
13. Harmony House Inn, New Bern
14. Lords Proprietor's Inn, Edenton

SOUTH CAROLINA
1. John Rutledge House Inn, Charleston
2. Two Meeting Street, Charleston
3. Rhett House, Beaufort

FLORIDA
1. Chalet Suzanne, Lake Wales
2. Hotel Place St. Michel, Coral Gables
3. The Marquesa Hotel, Key West

West and South

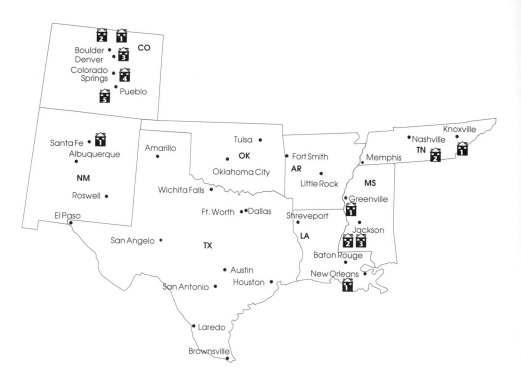

COLORADO
1. River Song, Estes Park
2. The Lovelander Bed & Breakfast Inn, Loveland
3. Castle Marne, Denver
4. Hearthstone Inn, Colorado Springs
5. Abriendo Inn, Pueblo

LOUISIANA
1. Madewood Plantation House, Napoleonville

MISSISSIPPI
1. The Duff Green Mansion, Vicksburg
2. Monmouth Plantation, Natchez
3. The Burn, Natchez

NEW MEXICO
1. Grant Corner Inn, Santa Fe

TENNESSEE
1. Inn at Blackberry Farm, Walland
2. Adams Edgeworth Inn, Monteagle

Midwest

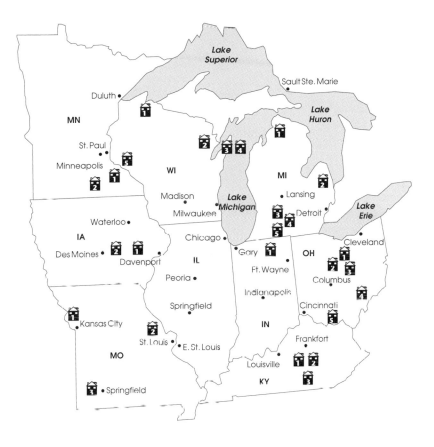

INDIANA
1. The Checkerberry Inn, Goshen

IOWA
1. Die Heimat Inn, Homestead
2. La Corsette Maison Inn, Newton

KENTUCKY
1. Beaumont Inn, Harrodsburg
2. Inn at Pleasant Hill, Harrodsburg
3. Boone Tavern Hotel, Berea

MICHIGAN
1. Stafford's Bay View Inn, Petoskey
2. Montague Inn, Saginaw
3. Dusty's English Inn, Eaton Rapids
4. National House Inn, Marshall
5. Victorian Villa, Union City

MINNESOTA
1. St. James Hotel, Red Wing
2. Schumacher's New Prague Hotel, New Prague

MISSOURI
1. Southmoreland On The Plaza, Kansas City
2. Boone's Lick Trail Inn, St. Charles
3. Walnut Street Inn, Springfield

OHIO
1. Wooster Inn, Wooster
2. Inn at Honey Run, Millersburg
3. White Oak Inn, Danville
4. Inn at Cedar Falls, Logan
5. Murphin Ridge Inn, West Union

WISCONSIN
1. Old Rittenhouse Inn, Bayfield
2. White Gull Inn, Fish Creek
3. Inn at Cedar Crossing, Sturgeon Bay
4. White Lace Inn, Sturgeon Bay
5. The Creamery, Downsville

Far and Northwest

ARIZONA
1. Rancho de Los Caballeros, Wickenburg
2. Lodge on the Desert, Tucson
3. Tanque Verde, Tucson

CALIFORNIA
1. Carter House, Eureka
2. The Gingerbread Mansion, Ferndale
3. Grey Whale Inn, Fort Bragg
4. Harbor House Inn by the Sea, Elk
5. Madrona Manor, Healdsburg
6. Wine Country Inn, St. Helena
7. Groveland Hotel, Groveland
8. The Babbling Brook, Santa Cruz
9. The Inn at Depot Hill, Capitola-by-the-Sea
10. The Martine Inn, Pacific Grove
11. Old Monterrey Inn, Monterrey
12. Sandpiper Inn at-the-Beach, Carmel-by-the-Sea
13. Vagabond's House, Carmel
14. Ballard Inn, Ballard
15. Simpson House, Santa Barbara
16. Seal Beach Inn and Gardens, Seal Beach
17. Villa Royale Inn, Palm Springs

WASHINGTON
1. Turtleback Farm Inn, Eastsound
2. Captain Whidbey Inn, Coupeville
3. Willcox House Country Inn, Bremerton
4. Shelburne Inn, Seaview
5. Birchfield Manor, Yakima

OREGON
1. The Johnson House, Florence
2. Steamboat Inn, Steamboat
3. Tu Tu' Tun Lodge, Gold Beach
4. Jacksonville Inn, Jacksonville
5. The Winchester Country Inn, Ashland

CANADA — BRITISH COLUMBIA
1. Oak Bay Beach Hotel, Victoria
2. Holland House, Victoria
3. Sooke Harbour House, Sooke

The IIA Gift Certificate

A Lovely Gift for Someone Special

The gift of an overnight stay or a weekend at a country inn can be one of the most thoughtful and appreciated gifts you can give your parents or children, dear friends, or valued employees for Christmas, a birthday, an anniversary, or any special occasion. Innkeepers and other employers are discovering this is an excellent way of rewarding their employees, while at the same time giving them some much needed rest and relaxation.

An IIA gift certificate means that you can give the gift of a stay at any one of over 250 member inns from Kennebunkport, Maine to Southern California; from Quebec, Canada to Key West, Florida; from Martha's Vineyard, Massachusetts to Seaview, Washington. We have inns in the Blue Ridge Mountains, on ranches in the western desert, near state parks and forests and nature preserves, in restored villages in historic districts, on lakes and by the sea. Choose your pleasure.

An IIA gift certificate is good for two years and may be purchased through the IIA office by personal check or Mastercard or Visa. With each gift certificate we send along a brand new copy of the *Innkeepers' Register*. For further information call **800-344-5244**.

A five dollar ($5) postage and handling fee will be added to all gift certificate purchases.

Index

The dot indicates those inns that may be booked through your travel agent. Your travel agent should contact the inn directly for specific commission rates and restrictions.

Index

Index

NOTES

NOTES

NOTES

Help us help our members maintain the standards of excellence that the IIA upholds by answering the questions below and mailing the card directly to the IIA office. Your signature below is not necessary; however, we would be pleased to know who you are. Please rate each item on a scale of 1 to 5, with 1 being "least satisfactory" and 5 being "nearly perfect."

Name of the inn: _____

_____ 1) Were you greeted and served with a spirit of hospitality throughout your stay?

_____ 2) Was the guest room equipped with your comfort and safety in mind?

_____ 3) Did the inn evidence high standards of housekeeping and maintenance?

_____ 4) Was the food/service (or the area's food/service) of high quality?

_____ 5) Was the feeling of individuality in the personality or character of the inn aesthetically pleasing and consistent?

_____ 6) Did you receive value for your dollar?

_____ 7) Would you return to this inn?

Additional comments: _____

_____

Name and address of other inns you would like to recommend:

_____

_____

Your name and address (optional) _____

_____

Help us help our members maintain the standards of excellence that the IIA upholds by answering the questions below and mailing the card directly to the IIA office. Your signature below is not necessary; however, we would be pleased to know who you are. Please rate each item on a scale of 1 to 5, with 1 being "least satisfactory" and 5 being "nearly perfect."

Name of the inn: _____

_____ 1) Were you greeted and served with a spirit of hospitality throughout your stay?

_____ 2) Was the guest room equipped with your comfort and safety in mind?

_____ 3) Did the inn evidence high standards of housekeeping and maintenance?

_____ 4) Was the food/service (or the area's food/service) of high quality?

_____ 5) Was the feeling of individuality in the personality or character of the inn aesthetically pleasing and consistent?

_____ 6) Did you receive value for your dollar?

_____ 7) Would you return to this inn?

Additional comments: _____

_____

Name and address of other inns you would like to recommend:

_____

_____

Your name and address (optional) _____

_____

Independent Innkeepers' Association
P.O. Box 150
Marshall, MI 49068

Independent Innkeepers' Association
P.O. Box 150
Marshall, MI 49068